THE CHARLTON STANDARD CATALOGUE OF

CAITHNESS PAPERWEIGHTS

FIRST EDITION

BY
COLIN TERRIS

W. K. CROSS
PUBLISHER

The Charlton Press

TORONTO, ONTARIO * BIRMINGHAM, MICHIGAN

COPYRIGHT NOTICES

Copyright © 1999 Charlton International Inc. All rights reserved
Photographs © Charlton International Inc. 1999

The terms Charlton, Charltons, The Charlton Press and abbreviations thereof are trademarks of Charlton International Inc. and shall not be used without written consent from Charlton International Inc.

No part of this publication, except the various numbering systems, may be reproduced, stored in a retrieval system, or transmitted in any form or by any means, electronic, mechanical, photocopying, recording, or otherwise, without the prior written permission of the copyright owner.

No copyright material may be used without written permission in each instance from Charlton International Inc. Permission is hereby given for brief excerpts to be used in newspapers, magazines, periodicals and bulletins, other than in the advertising of items for sale, provided that the source so used is acknowledged in each instance.

While every care has been taken to ensure accuracy in the compilation of the data in this catalogue, the publisher cannot accept responsibility for typographical errors.

OTHER COPYRIGHTS

Caithness Glass Limited: The words Caithness Glass are a registered trade mark of Royal Doulton (U.K.) Limited and are used herein to express items of collector interest. This book makes reference to various Caithness Glass paperweights. The copyright of which belongs to Royal Doulton (U.K.) Limited.

DISCLAIMER

Products listed or shown were manufactured by Caithness Glass Limited. The publisher has no connection whatsoever with either Caithness Glass Limited or the Caithness Glass Paperweight Collectors Society. Caithness Glass is a registered trade mark and is used in this book with the permission of Royal Doulton (U.K.) Limited. Any opinions expressed are those of the author and are not necessarily endorsed by Royal Doulton (U.K.) Limited.

Canadian Catalogue in Publication Data

The National Library of Canada has catalogued this publication as follows:

Main entry under title:

The Charlton standard catalogue of Caithness Glass paperweights

Biennial
1st ed.-
ISSN 1481-8051
ISBN 0-88968-238-0 (1st edition)

1. Caithness Glass Ltd. Catalogs. 2. Paperweights Scotland Catalogs.

NK5440.P3C4   748.840294411   C99-900175-2

Printed in Canada
in the Province of Ontario

EDITORIAL TEAM

Editor	W. K. Cross
Editorial Assistant	Jean Dale
Graphic Technician	Davina Rowan

ACKNOWLEDGEMENTS

The Charlton Press wishes to thank those who have helped with the first edition of *The Charlton Standard Catalogue of Caithness Glass Paperweights*.

Contributors to the First Edition

Daphne Jones, Peter Jones China, England; Ron Rosenberg; L. H. Selman, U.S.A.

A SPECIAL NOTE TO COLLECTORS

We welcome and appreciate any comments or suggestions in regard to *The Charlton Standard Catalogue of Caithness Glass Paperweights*. If any errors or omissions come to your attention, please write to us, or if you would like to participate in pricing or supply previously unavailable data or information, please contact Jean Dale at (416) 488-1418 or e-mail us at chpress@charltonpress.com.

The Charlton Press

Editorial Office
2040 Yonge Street, Suite 208, Toronto, Canada. M4S 1Z9
Telephone: (416) 488-1418 Fax: (416) 488-4656
Telephone: (800) 442-6042 Fax: (800) 442-1542
url: www.charltonpress.com; e-mail: chpress@charltonpress.com

HOW TO USE THIS GUIDE

THE PURPOSE

This publication has been designed to serve two specific purposes: first, to furnish collectors with accurate and detailed listings that will provide the information needed to build a rich and rewarding collection; second, to provide collectors and dealers with an indication of the current market prices of Caithness Glass paperweights.

THE LISTINGS

The Charlton Standard Catalogue of Caithness Glass Paperweights is divided into two chapters, the first being devoted to the general collection of Caithness Glass weights and the second, to specially commissioned and exclusive weights.

In the first chapter, designs are listed in numerical order. In the second chapter, the companies that commissioned the weights are listed under the country in which they are located, and the weights for these companies are listed in chronological order.

STYLES AND VERSIONS

All listings include the name of the weight, designer, type (i.e. shape), date of issue and edition size, status, series, original issue price and current value. Two points should be noted. First, if only a year is given for the edition, this means that the edition is unlimited. Second, American issue prices do not appear for weights issued prior to 1978, when Caithness began to expand its global distribution and to market its products more intensively in the U.S.

Styles: A change in style occurs when a design is altered or modified by a deliberate change that will result in a new design carrying the same name.

Versions: Versions are modifications in a major style element.

Variations: Variations are modifications in a minor style element. A change in colour is a variation.

THE PRICING

One of the purposes of this catalogue is to give readers the most accurate, up-to-date retail prices for Caithness Glass paperweights in the United States, Canada and the United Kingdom.

To accomplish this, The Charlton Press continues to access an international pricing panel of experts who submit prices based on both dealer and collector retail-price activity, as well as current auction results in the U.S., Canada and the U.K. These market prices are carefully averaged to reflect accurate valuations for paperweights in each of these markets.

Recently issued Caithness Glass paperweights are priced according to the manufacturers suggested retail price in each of the market regions. Please be aware that price or promotional sales discounting is always possible and can result in lower prices than those listed.

One exception, however, occurs in the case of current weights or specially commissioned weights issued in only one of the three markets.

Since such items were priced by Caithness Glass only in the country in which they were to be sold, prices for the other markets are not shown.

A further word on pricing: as mentioned previously, this is a catalogue giving prices for items in the currency of a particular market (for example, U.S. dollars for the American market and pounds sterling for the U.K. market). The bulk of the prices given herein are determined not by currency exchange calculations, but by actual market activity in the market concerned.

In some cases, the number of weights produced is so small that market activity does not exist. There is no price activity on which to base a price. The price in this instance is purely between the buyer and the seller. We have therefore listed the last known auction price for the weight. If the weight were to be offered for sale at a future date, the price might be higher or lower than the auction price listed, depending on the demand for the weight at that time.

When prices are italicized in the pricing tables, this means that the price is only an indication; prices are too volatile to establish a solid market price. Once again, the final price determination must be made between the buyer and the seller. The prices published herein are for weights in mint condition. Collectors are cautioned that a repaired, restored or badly scratched weight may be worth as little as 25 percent of the value of the same weight in mint condition.

THE INTERNET AND PRICING

The Internet is changing the way that business is done in the collectable market. It links millions of collectors around the world to one another, allowing communication to flow freely among them. Chat rooms, antique and collector malls, Internet auctions and producer Web sites all promote the new e-commerce.

The following are three major effects that e-commerce will have on the collectable market:

1. Collectors will deal with collectors. They will also continue with their customer/dealer relationships, but the dealers' margin will come under pressure.

2. Information on new issues, new finds, and new varieties will spread faster — and the bad news will spread even faster. Collectors' wants will be made known instantaneously to a wide universe of dealers and collectors.

3. Prices will be affected on two fronts:

   (A) Price differentials will disappear between global market areas as collectors and delivery services team up to stretch the purchasing power of the collectable dollar/pound.

   (B) As margins come under pressure, overheads being lower in virtual operations, prices of the common to scarce collectable items will adjust downward to compensate. The rare and extremely rare items will move up as a result of their increased exposure.

TABLE OF CONTENTS

COLIN TERRIS

ALASTAIR MACINTOSH

HELEN MACDONALD

INTRODUCTION

HOW CAITHNESS GLASS ENTERED THE PAPERWEIGHT FIELD

In 1961, Robin Sinclair founded Caithness Glass in Wick, in northeastern Scotland. The company's artglass output did not originally include paperweights, but this would change with the arrival in 1962 of Paul Ysart, who was interested in making millefiori paperweights. When Colin Terris joined Caithness in 1968 to establish an engraving studio, he met Paul, the company's training officer, and soon began to experiment with ideas, techniques and designs far removed from the conventional style of paperweight design. In 1969, Colin designed the first modern-style Caithness Glass paperweights, the *Planets* set, which was an instant success.

At the time the first weights were released, the paperweight team consisted of two people working in a corner of the Wick factory. In 1969, Caithness established a second factory in Oban and in 1979 opened the Perth factory. In 1992, new glassworks and visitors centres were opened in both Wick and Oban. By 1993, fourty-four people were involved in the paperweight-production process. Caithness centralized paperweight production in Perth in September 1995.

Over time, Caithness also expanded its roster of designers to include Alastair MacIntosh and Helen MacDonald, among others. This has translated into a diverse range of paperweight designs, from double magnum to miniature weights and from modern to traditional ones, more than 1,700 in total. Caithnesss paperweight output has developed a following among collectors the world over and has brought the company from its small beginnings to its current status as the world's leading producer of fine-quality glass paperweights.

THE DESIGNERS

Colin Terris

Colin Terris was born in Kirkcaldy in the Kingdom of Fife, Scotland, in 1937. A graduate of the Edinburgh College of Art, he specialised in glass design and, in 1960, went to Norway to further his skills in the intricate art of copperwheel glass engraving. He spent a year there, and on his return to Scotland he taught art for eight years before joining Caithness Glass to establish an engraving studio in 1968. Colin met the company's training officer, the legendary Paul Ysart, and was soon experimenting with paperweight design. His *Planets* series weights, the first modern-style Caithness Glass paperweights, were an instant success and marked the creation of a new category of artglass: the modern or contemporary paperweight. His work includes the Colin Terris Designer Collection, launched in 1997; and the Colin Terris Water Lily Collection, produced in 1998; and the Colin Terris Rose Collection, issued in 1999.

Colin was made a Member of the Order of the British Empire (MBE) in 1991 in recognition of his contribution to British glass, and his work can be seen in most major paperweight collections. He is recognized internationally as The Father of Modern Paperweight Design.

Alastair MacIntosh

Alastair MacIntosh was born in Falkirk, Scotland, in 1951. A graduate of the Edinburgh College of Art, he specialized in glass design and was taught by master glassmakers Ken Wainwright and Andrew Scott.

From 1981 to 1987, he ran his own small glassworks, MacIntosh Glass, where he produced and made bowls, vases, perfume bottles and paperweights. He joined Caithness Glass in 1987 and since then has been actively involved in all aspects of product design and development. His first paperweight design for Caithness was *Jamboree*, issued in 1988 in a limited edition of 500. The Alastair MacIntosh Collection, a series of weights that illustrate his distinctive style, was released in 1999.

Helen MacDonald

Helen was born in Caithness, Scotland, in 1958. She joined Caithness Glass in Wick as a trainee glass engraver in 1974 and, by 1979, had attained the highest skill rating in the engraving studios.

In 1985, she transferred to the Perth factory and engraved many prestige presentation pieces, including a number for members of the Royal Family. The year 1991 saw Helens first paperweight designs, and since that time her main design effort has been channelled in this direction. Her biblical theme series, which began with *Covenant* in 1995, is ongoing and is a great favourite with collectors, including those in the U.S., where she has been known mainly for her satin-finished weights and the engraving of the Studio Collection.

Each year, the designers attend a number of paperweight promotions at various locations in the U.K. and the U.S. Collectors have the opportunity to meet the designers and view a large selection of weights from that years collection.

COLLECTING CAITHNESS PAPERWEIGHTS

Production over the years has evolved into three major groups, modern, traditional and Whitefriars. Each group may then be subdivided into limited or unlimited editions depending upon the group. For example, modern weights have always been issued in limited and unlimited editions. Given the range of weights produced, collectors should focus their collections on a particular aspect of Caithnesss output, as the following outline illustrates.

Modern Design

For this collection, designers and glassmakers use new colours, facetting, styles and making techniques to create original designs, often referred to by some as "abstract design."

These innovative weights are issued both in limited and unlimited editions. Caithness Glass, which has produced these weights since 1969, is considered the world leader in the design of modern weights.

Traditional Design

These limited-edition weights are produced in the traditional style of paperweights manufactured. Lampworked designs are first formed and then embedded in glass to form a grerat variety of weights. They will feature designs from the sea and wildlife themes to animals, insects and flowers.

Whitefriars Design

These limited-edition weights in the classical style illustrate floral themes using traditional millefiori and lampwork techniques combined with vibrant colours and new facetting styles. All weights in this collection contain the famous friar or monk signature cane.

FORMING A COLLECTION

A collector may choose to focus on a particular collection, such as Modern, Traditional or Whitefriars and then within these groups to further focus on design charactersitics which may be of interest.

Whatever the method by which a collection is built, the collector will surely find it satisfying to acquire and view these skilfullly crafted works of art.

With the entensive range or weights available it is only sensible to centre on one style of weight. To vary at the early stages can only lead to confusion of tastes, ending later with weights in the "will I buy that" category.

Choose one of three major style groups, modern, traditional or White Friars. Now within these groups you may further subdivide into the minor style groupings, engraved, smooth or facetted, or possibly a little of each.

By Style

A collector may wish to collect only engraved weights, or only smooth or facetted weights, for example.

By Colourway

A collector may concentrate on acquiring weights of a certain colour, such as heather or green.

Again the colourway theme can be carried into similar weights that differ only in colour.

By Shape

Collecting weights in a particular shape is another option. Weights are produced in spherical, domed egg and teardrop shapes, among others.

By Size

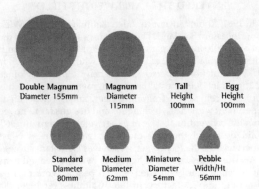

Double Magnum Diameter 155mm   Magnum Diameter 115mm   Tall Height 100mm   Egg Height 100mm

Standard Diameter 80mm   Medium Diameter 62mm   Miniature Diameter 54mm   Pebble Width/Ht 56mm

Acquiring weights of a particular size such as miniature, medium or magnum may appeal to a collector.

Medium and Miniature: This collection of distinctive weights in medium and miniature sizes was introduced in 1985. The weights are available in limited and unlimited editions.

Millefiori Miniatures: These weights in the classical style feature canes surrounding a lampworked design, They are available in limited and unlimited editions.

By Theme

In the Traditional weights, for example, one may collect the sea creatures that are embedded in glass, or possibly insects or the beautiful butterflies. The theme collection favours the lampwork design weight.

By Designer

The work of a particular designer such as Colin Terris, Alastair MacIntosh or Helen MacDonald may interest a collector. Of course you may have the designer within that special group that you have chosen.

THE COLLECTIONS

WHITEFRIARS

No.	Name	No.	Name	No.	Name
CT-256	Snow Crystal	CT-834	Clematis	CT-1244A	Scarlet Pimpernel Perfume Bottle
CT-280	Rings of Roses	CT-835	Edelweiss		
CT-281	Bed of Roses	CT-836	Flag Iris	CT-1244B	Scarlet Pimpernel
CT-282	Spread of Roses	CT-837	Peruvian Lilies	CT-1327	Flame Nasturtium
CT-283	Garland of Roses	CT-889	Dog Rose	CT-1328	Pansy
CT-284	Rose Garden	CT-890	Fuchsia Perfume Bottle	CT-1329	Hosta
CT-285	Star of Roses	CT-891	Honeysuckle	CT-1330	Rock Rose
CT-286	Butterfly	CT-892	Jasmine	CT-1331	Fuchsia
CT-302	Christmas Tree	CT-893	Narcissus	CT-1332	Auricula
CT-323	The Zodiac	CT-894	Nasturtium	CT-1333	Camomile
CT-357	Floral Basket	CT-969	Buttercups and Daisies	CT-1359	Pasque Flower
CT-358	Blue and Pink Posy	CT-970	Cyclamen	CT-1360	Daffodil Spray
CT-359	Blue Flower	CT-971	Harebells	CT-1440	Autumn Gold
CT-360	Fuchsia	CT-972	Poppies Perfume Bottle	CT-1441	Diamond Bouquet
CT-361	Bouquet and Ferns	CT-973	Regal Lily	CT-1442	Festive Delight
CT-362	Amethyst Bouquet	CT-974A	Spring Celebration - One	CT-1443	Trillium
CT-363	Floral Pink	CT-974B	Spring Celebration - Two	CT-1444	Bright New Day
CT-364	White and Pink Spray	CT-975	Summer Flowers	CT-1445	Traditional Tribute
CT-409	Apple Blossom	CT-976	Wild Pansy and Storksbill	CT-1446	Emerald Dancers
CT-410	Pansy	CT-1022	Midnight Orchids	CT-1447	Victorian Memories
CT-411	Primroses	CT-1023A	Summer Celebration - One	CT-1448	Burgundy Bloom
CT-412	Summer Meadow Butterfly	CT-1023B	Summer Celebration - Two	CT-1449	Sweet Sensation Kingfisher
CT-413	Summer MeadowDragonfly	CT-1063	Wood Anemones	CT-1450	Sweet Sensation Cobalt
CT-451	Blue Spray	CT-1064	Lily of the Valley	CT-1515	Eternal Love
CT-495	Nosegay	CT-1065	Christmas Rose	CT-1516	Classical Moment
CT-496	Candida	CT-1066	Magnolia	CT-1517	Spoilt for Choice
CT-497	Rosette	CT-1067A	Autumn Celebration - One	CT-1518	French Fancy
CT-536	Butterfly Duet	CT-1067B	Autumn Celebration - Two	CT-1519	Pretty in Pink
CT-537	Opium Poppy	CT-1068	Pansies	CT-1520	Alpine Glory
CT-538	Blue and White Garland	CT-1069	Periwinkles	CT-1568	Alpine Summer
CT-539	Scarlet Pimpernel	CT-1070	Winter Flowers	CT-1569	Red Rose Bouquet
CT-592	Victorian Bouquet	CT-1071	Cherry Blossom Perfume Bottle	CT-1570	Symphony in Blue
CT-593	Still Life			CT-1571	Fragrant Orchid
CT-594	Sapphire Star	CT-1072A	Carnation Perfume Bottle	CT-1572	Sunny Days Perfume Bottle
CT-59	Midnight Bouquet	CT-1072B	Carnation		
CT-596	Brocade Butterfly	CT-1073	Woodland Glade	CT-1573	Daisy Bouquet
CT-597	Lace	CT-1109	Azalea	CT-1574	Pansy Latticino
CT-598	Floral Whimsy	CT-1110	Azure Bouquet	CT-1575	Spring Florette Cobalt
CT-599	Summer Blue	CT-1111	Butterfly Bouquet	CT-1576	Spring Florette Kingfisher
CT-634	Parrot	CT-1112	Cinquefoil	CT-1577	Amethyst Garland
CT-637	Summer Garden	CT-1113	Hibiscus	CT-1578	Daisy and Forget-Me-Not
CT-638	Hanging Basket	CT-1114	Summer Posy	CT-1579	Buttercups and Butterfly
CT-684	Floriana	CT-1181	Orchid Spray	CT-1580	Hyacinth Bouquet
CT-685	Peacock	CT-1182	Fritillaria	CT-1659	Reticello Rose
CT-686	Royal Blue	CT-1183	Geranium	CT-1660	Golden Awakening
CT-687	Scarlet Bouquet	CT-1184	Marigolds	CT-1661	Valentino
CT-688	Triple Fancy	CT-1185	Pansy Perfume Bottle	CT-1662	Floral Diamond
CT-764	Anemone	CT-1186	Rhododendron	CT-1739	Daisies and Trellis
CT-765	Aquilegia	CT-1187	Iris Bouquet	CT-1740	Diamond Reflections
CT-766	Butterflies	CT-1188	Meconopsis	CT-1741	Burgundy Quartet
CT-767	Daisy Chain	CT-1189	Freesias	CT-1742	Victorian Blossom
CT-768	Delphinium	CT-1190	Cape Primrose	CT-1743	Floral Splendour
CT-769	Fuchsias	CT-1191A	Cosmos Perfume Bottle	CT-1744	Sunflower Celebration
CT-770	Orchids	CT-1191B	Cosmos	CT-1745	Dawn Bouquet
CT-771	Poppies	CT-1239	Dog Tooth Violet	CT-1746	Blue Rhapsody
CT-772	Primula	CT-1240	Rose of Sharon	CT-1747	Two of a Kind
CT-773	Scots Thistle	CT-1241	Mallow	CT-1748	Latticino Posy
CT-774	Spring Flower	CT-1242	Pink Rhododendron	CT-1749	Golden Glory
CT-775	Sweet Pea	CT-1243	Sweet Violet		
CT-833	Alpine Pine				

NATURE STUDY (TRADITIONAL) COLLECTION

No.	Name	No.	Name	No.	Name
CT-1122	Mini Butterly and Orange Flower	CT-1434	Sunset Duet	CT-1505	Wood Violet
CT-1123	Mini Butterfly and Yellow Flower	CT-1435	Fleur Rouge	CT-1506	Ocean Serenade
		CT-1436	Token of Love	CT-1507	Summer Lilies
CT-1124	Orange Butterfly	CT-1504	Compassion	CT-1508	Branching Out
CT-1125	Yellow Butterfly	CT-1320	Emerald Spray	CT-1581	Morning Reflections
CT-1126	Yellow Butterfly-Latticino Base	CT-1322	Poppies	CT-1582	Autumn Hedgerow
CT-1206	Dragonfly - White Flower	CT-1323	White Orchids	CT-1583A	Flowerpot People - One
CT-1207	Dragonfly - Blue Flower	CT-1324	Blue Butterfly - Gold Flower	CT-1583B	Flowerpot People - Two
CT-1208	Dragonfly - Latticino Base	CT-1325	Pink Butterfly - Blue Flower	CT-1584	Bunnies
CT-1209	Mini Dragonfly - Blue Base	CT-1326	Blue Butterfly - Latticino Base	CT-1585	Clematis and Trellis
CT-1210	Mini Dragonfly - Gold Base	CT-1361	Spring Posy	CT-1586	Sunflowers
CT-1254	Butterfly - Purple Flower	CT-1362	Terrarium	CT-1587	Country Posy
CT-1255	Butterfly - Yellow Flower	CT-1363	Tropical Bouquet	CT-1588	Garden Posy
CT-1256	Butterfly - Latticino base	CT-1364	Purple Butterfly - Latticino Base	CT-1663	Diamond Lily
CT-1257	Yellow Butterfly - Miniature			CT-1664	Twilight Mystery
CT-1258	Red Butterfly - Miniature	CT-1365	White Butterfly - Yellow Flower	CT-1665	Heather Corsage
CT-1318	Pink Butterfly - Miniature			CT-1666	Victoriana
CT-1319	Blue Butterfly - Miniature	CT-1366	Gold Butterfly - Pink Flower	CT-1750	Island Dream
		CT-1433	Crab Apple	CT-1752	Celtic Celebration
				CT-1753	Love Token

DESIGNERS' COLLECTIONS

COLIN TERRIS

Introduced in 1997 the Colin Terris Collection has grown from the Designer Collection to include the Rose and Water Lily Collections. Over twenty weights now comprise the series.

Designer Collection

Part One

CT-1464	Carnival Cascade
CT-1465	Cactus Reflection
CT-1466	Blue Lagoon
CT-1467	Emerald Grotto
CT-1468	Chuckie Stane
CT-1469	Coral Garden
CT-1470	Pink Beauty
CT-1471	Camelot II

Part Two

CT-1611	Blue Moon
CT-1612	Cavatina
CT-1613	Opulence
CT-1614	To Boldly Go
CT-1615	Patriot
CT-1616	Secret Garden '98
CT-1617	Faerie Dance
CT-1618	Pagan Ritual
CT-1619	Cosmic Vision

Rose Collection

This collection of limited-edition weights by Colin Terris focuses on rose designs and was produced in 1999.

CT-1718	Jacobean Rose		CT-1721	Radiant Rose
CT-1719	Lunar Rose		CT-1722	Twilight Rose
CT-1720	Fragrant Rose		CT-1723	Golden Rose

Water Lily Collection

These limited-edition weights feature designs by Colin Terris that were inspired by French impressionist painter Claude Monet's waterlily studies. This collection was issued in 1998.

CT-1596	Lily Pool		CT-1600	Tranquil Pond
CT-1597	Morning Flight		CT-1601	Sculptured Pool
CT-1598	Ornamental Pool		CT-1602	Oriental Pool
CT-1599	Water Garden			

ALASTAIR MACINTOSH

At present seven weights make up the Alistair MacIntosh Collection illustrating his distinctive style.

Designer Collection

CT-1724	Deliliah		CT-1728	Solemnity
CT-1725	Dizzy Lizzy		CT-1729	Perplexity
CT-1726	Magic Castle		CT-1730	Over the Hills
CT-1727	Propulsion			

THE MILLENNIUM COLLECTION

This collection of weights was designed to commemorate the new millennium and will be available only in 1999 and the year 2000.

CT-1764	Millennium 2000		CT-1774	Millennium Pebble
CT-1765	Millennium Carnival		CT-1775	Millennium Teddy
CT-1766	Millennium Jewel		CT-1776	Millennium Doves
CT-1767	Millennium Dancer		CT-1777	Millennium Voyager
CT-1768	Capital Celebration Edinburgh		CT-1778	Millennium Fantasy
CT-1769	London Time		CT-1779	Millennium Blossom
CT-1770	Millennium Liberty		CT-1780	Millennium Sands of Time
CT-1771	Millennium Countdown		CT-1781	Millennium Fiesta
CT-1772	Millennium Globe		CT-1782	Millennium Awakening
CT-1773	Millennium Starburst		CT-1783	Millennium Vision

COLLECTORS SOCIETY COLLECTION

First issued in 1977 the Collectors Society Collection has now twenty-two weights in this series.

CT-80	Christmas Weight (1977)		CT-703	Phoenix (1989)
CT-113	Arctic Night (1978)		CT-715	Abseil (1990)
CT-183	Black Gem (1979/80)		CT-805	Floral Illusion (1991)
CT-253	Enigma (1981)		CT-903	Weathervane (1992)
CT-300	Persephone (1982)		CT-941	Fantasy Orchid (1993)
CT-335	Robin and Kettle (1983)		CT-1062	Jubilee Orchid (1994)
CT-373	Solitaire (1984)		CT-1180	Jack-in-the-Box (1995)
CT-435	Moon Orchid (1985)		CT-1304	Tropicana (1996)
CT-498	Domino (1986)		CT-1418	Saladin (1997)
CT-560	Chorale (1987)		CT-1566	Aquamarina (1998)
CT-646	Opus 88 (1988)		CT-1783	Millennium Vision (1999)

DOUBLE MAGNUM COLLECTION

The 155mm giants of the paperweight world. Starting in 1983 and continuing to 1999, Caithness released a double magnum weight each year. These large weights make an outstanding display.

CT-322	Ruby (1983)		CT-905	Double Magnum 92 (1992)
CT-386	Amethyst (1984)		CT-939	Double Magnum 93 (1993)
CT-416	Emerald (1985)		CT-1031	Double Magnum 94 (1994)
CT-472	Violet (1986)		CT-1094	Jubilee 94 (1994)
CT-522	Crimson (1987)		CT-1162	Double Magnum 95 (1995)
CT-615	Sable (1988)		CT-1303	Double Magnum 96 (1996)
CT-691	Azure (1989)		CT-1387	Double Magnum 97 (1997)
CT-780	Jade (1990)		CT-1525	Double Magnum 98 (1998)
CT-846	Magenta (1991)		CT-1677	Double Magnum 99 (1999)

EGG COLLECTION

First launched in 1998 "Collectable Eggs" features intricate patterns and eyecatching colours. Issued in limited editions, over thirty weights are now in the collection.

CT-1603	Arctic Crocus	CT-1654	Eggstravaganza
CT-1604	Turquoise Delight	CT-1655	Wavedancers
CT-1605	Confetti Cascade	CT-1731	Daffodil
CT-1606	From the Flames	CT-1732	Orchid
CT-1607	Amoroso	CT-1733	Violet
CT-1608	Khamsin	CT-1734	Poppy
CT-1609	Effervescence	CT-1735	Crocus
CT-1610	Colour Pool	CT-1736	Katarina
CT-1651	Shambalah	CT-1737	Citron
CT-1652	Anastasia	CT-1738	Sumatra
CT-1653	Azurina		

INK WELL COLLECTION

CT-12	Ink Bottle	CT-1137	Thistle Inkwell
CT-79	Petal Inkwell	CT-1138	Rose Inkwell
CT-997	Balmoral Inkwell	CT-1139	Fuchsia Inkwell
CT-998	Dunvegan Inkwell	CT-1140	Heart Inkwell

PERFUME BOTTLE COLLECTION

CT-96	Ice Petal	CT-575A	Mercury
CT-97	Sea Grass	CT-591	Spring Breeze
CT-98	Quartet	CT-754A	Bezique
CT-119A	Sea Lace	CT-755	Summer Breeze
CT-120	Blue Petal	CT-890	Fuchsia
CT-191A	Blue Rose	CT-910	Mini Butterfly
CT-192A	Black and Gold	CT-911	Mini Heart
CT-217	Zenith	CT-912	Mini Rose
CT-221	Samarkand	CT-968A	Moonlight
CT-222	Aquaflora	CT-972	Poppies
CT-237	Romance	CT-994	Clematis
CT-262A	Curio	CT-995	Fuchsia
CT-264	Enchanté	CT-996	Irish
CT-319A	Sonata	CT-1071	Cherry Blossom
CT-320	Corryvreckan	CT-1072A	Carnation
CT-321	Misty	CT-1185	Pansy
CT-356A	Canata	CT1191A	Cosmos
CT-405	Chantilly	CT-1220	Red Rose
CT-406A	Lilac Time	CT-1244A	Scarlet Pimpernel
CT-414	Bouquet	CT-1271	Glamis Rose
CT-425A	Quintessence	CT-1380	HM Queen Elizabeth 70th Birthday Rose
CT-450	Honeysuckle		
CT-458	Valentine	CT-1474	Royal Golden Wedding
CT-489	Camilla	CT-1572	Sunny Days
CT-571	Poinsetta		

PERFUME FLASK COLLECTION

CT-257	April	CT-966	Milano
CT-258	Bianca	CT-967	Verona
CT-259	Cordella	CT-1155	Siena
CT-260	Danielle	CT1156	Torino
CT-261	Erica	CT-1157	Sorrento
CT-965	Firenze		

ROYALTY COLLECTION

The Royalty Collection began in 1974 with the issue of CT-28 Crown, celebrating the marriage of HRH the Princess Anne to Captain Mark Phillips. Since then over forty-four weights have been released commemorating all manner of Royal events from birthdays to Jubilees to marriages.

Wedding of Princess Anne and Captain Mark Phillips

CT-28	Crown

Silver Jubilee 1977
25th Anniversary of the
Coronation of Elizabeth II

CT-70	Jubilee Moonflower
CT-71	Jubilee Crown Bubble
CT-72	Jubilee Floating Crown
CT-73	Jubilee Millefiori Crown

Coronation

CT-111	Coronation Silver Jubilee

80th Birthday of the
Queen Mother

CT-198	Royal Birthday
CT-199	Queen Mother
CT-200	Royal Arms
CT-201	Thistle and Rose

Wedding of Charles and Diana

CT-238	Royal Wedding
CT-239	Floral Tribute
CT-240	Wedding Bell
CT-241A	Duet - Weight 1
CT-241B	Duet - Weight 2
CT-242	Heart
CT-243	Crown
CT-244	Celebration
CT-245	Garland
CT-246	St. Paul's
CT-247	Royal Portrait
CT-248	Royal Wedding Moonflower
CT-249	Congratulations

Birth of H.R.H. Prince Harry

CT-353	Royal Birthday Tribute
CT-354	Royal Birthday Crown
CT-355	Royal Birthday Moonflower

Wedding of Prince Andrew and Sarah Ferguson

CT-473	Royal Wedding Anchor
CT-474	Royal Wedding Heart
CT-475	Royal Wedding Tribute
CT-476	Royal Wedding Monogram

60th Birthday of Queen Elizabeth II

CT-478	Vivat Regina

90th Birthday of the Queen Mother

CT-776	Royal Birthday Bouquet
CT-777	Royal Birthday Perfume Bottle
CT-778	Royal Birthday Glamis Rose

95th Birthday of the Queen Mother

CT-1271	Glamis Rose Perfume Bottle
CT-1272	Glamis Rose

70th Birthday of Elizabeth II

CT-1377	Birthday Crown Overlay
CT-1378	Birthday Crown
CT-1379	Birthday Rose
CT-1380	Birthday Rose Perfume Bottle

50th Wedding Anniversary of Elizabeth II

CT-1472	Royal Golden Wedding
CT-1473	Royal Golden Wedding Crown
CT-1474	Royal Golden Wedding Perfume Bottle
CT-1475	Royal Golden Wedding Bell

SETS AS COLLECTIONS

Elements

Set One

CT-21A	Earth
CT-21B	Air
CT-21C	Fire
CT-21D	Water

Set Two

CT-653A	Earth
CT-653B	Air
CT-653C	Fire
CT-653D	Water

Four Seasons

Set One

CT-46A	Spring
CT-46B	Summer
CT-46C	Autumn
CT-46D	Winter

Set Two

CT-452	Spring Bouquet
CT-453	Summer Bouquet
CT-454	Autumn Bouquet
CT-455	Winter Bouquet

Set Three

CT-1321A	Spring
CT-1321B	Summer
CT-1321C	Autumn
CT-1321D	Winter

Planets

Series One, Set One

CT-1A	Mars
CT-1B	Mercury
CT-1C	Saturn
CT-1D	Venus

Set Two

CT-4A	Uranus
CT-4B	Jupiter
CT-4C	Nepune
CT-4D	Earth

Set Three

CT-5A	Sun
CT-5B	Moon
CT-5C	Pluto

Series Two, Set One

CT-1158A	Mercury
CT-1158B	Venus
CT-1158C	Saturn
CT-1158D	Mars

Romance

CT-521	Sweetheart
CT-713	Luckenbooth
CT-790	Mini Heart
CT-1217	Eternity
CT-1218	Romance
CT-1219	Red Rose
CT-1220	Red Rose Perfume Bottle

Sea Birds

CT-26	Fulmar
CT-35	Arctic Tern
CT-48	Puffin
CT-49	Cormorant
CT-65	Eider Duck
CT-66	Black-Headed Gull
CT-67	Stormy Petrel
CT-68	Guillemot
CT-82	Kittiwake
CT-83	Skua

Watercolours

CT-458	Valentine
CT-459	Juliet
CT-460	Orchids
CT-461	Butterflies
CT-462	Hearts
CT-468	Iris
CT-489	Camilla Perfume Bottle

Zodiac

CT-1259	Capricorn
CT-1260	Aquarius
CT-1261	Pisces
CT-1262	Aries
CT-1263	Taurus
CT-1264	Gemini
CT-1265	Cancer
CT-1266	Leo
CT-1267	Virgo
CT-1268	Libra
CT-1269	Scorpio
CT-1270	Sagittarius

ROYAL DOULTON COLLECTORS CLUB AND GUILD

Caithness Glass Paperweight Collectors Society

In 1976, the Caithness Glass Paperweight Collectors Society was formed, and the International Society was created in 1995 to serve collectors in countries where there is no national Caithness Glass Society.

The Society is the clearing-house for all information on Caithness paperweights. Members are entitled to receive *Reflections*, the magazine published twice a year by the Society, as well as three newsletters and a personal tour of the Paperweight Studios in Perth, Scotland, if they are ever in the area.

New members receive a free paperweight upon joining, and all members receive advance notice of new or specially commissioned weights and have an opportunity to purchase the Collectors Paperweight for the year, available exclusively to Society members. The Society holds an annual international convention in Scotland in October.

To join the Caithness Glass Paperweight Collectors Society, please contact the Society at one of the addresses or telephone numbers below:

In the U.K. and International:
Caithness Glass Paperweight Collectors Society
Caithness Glass Ltd
Inveralmond, Perth PH1 3TZ, Scotland
Tel: (44) (0) 1738 492329
Fax: (44) (0) 1738 492300

In the U.S.A.:
Caithness Glass Paperweight Collectors Society
Caithness Glass Inc.
141 Lanza Avenue, Building 12
Garfield, N.J. 017026, U.S.A
Tel: (973) 340-3330
Fax: (973) 340-9415

Royal Doulton International Collectors Club

Founded in 1980, the Royal Doulton International Collectors Club provides an information service on all aspects of the company's products, past and present. A club magazine, *Gallery*, is published four times a year with information on new products and current events that will keep the collector up-to-date on the happenings in the world of Royal Doulton. Upon joining the club, each new member will receive a free gift and invitations to special events and exclusive offers throughout the year.

To join the Royal Doulton International Collectors Club, please contact your local stockist, or contact the club directly at the address or telephone numbers below:

Royal Crown Derby Collectors Guild

The Royal Crown Derby Collectors Guild was established in 1994 to facilitate closer contact with Royal Crown Derby collectors. Membership entitles the collector to a yearly subscription to the quarterly *Gallery* magazine, *Royal Crown Derby News*, membership gifts and free admission to the Royal Crown Derby Visitor Centre.

To join the Royal Crown Derby Collectors Guild, please contact the guild at the address or telephone numbers below:

Minton House
London Road, Stoke-on-Trent
Staffordshire, ST4 7QD, England

Telephone:
U.K.: (01782) 292127
U.S.A. and Canada: 1-800-747-3045 (toll-free)
Australia: 011-800-142624 (toll free)
Fax: U.K.: (01782) 292099
Attn: Maria Murtagh

COLLECTORS CLUB CHAPTERS

Chapters of the RDICC have formed across North America and are worthy of consideration in those areas.

Detroit Chapter
Frank Americk, President
1771 Brody, Allen Park, MI 48101

Edmonton Chapter
Mildred's Collectibles
6813 104 Street, Edmonton, AB T6H 2L5

New England Chapter
Charles Wood, President
Charles Briggs, Secretary
21 Walpole Street, Norwood, MA 02062

Northern California Chapter
Donald A. Blubaugh, President
P.O. Box 3665, Walnut Creek, CA 94598
Tel.: (925) 945-1687 Fax: (925) 938-6674
Blubaugh@usa.net

Northwest, Bob Haynes, Chapter
Alan Matthew, President
15202 93rd Place N.E., Bothell, WA 98011
Tel.: (425) 488-9604

Ohio Chapter
Reg Marvis, President
Dick Maschmeier, Treasurer
5556 Whitehaven Avenue
North Olmstead, OH 44070
Tel.: (216) 779-5554

Rochester Chapter
Judith L. Trost, President
103 Garfield Street, Rochester, NY 14611
Tel.: (716) 436-3321

Western Pennsylvania Chapter
John Re, President
9589 Parkedge Drive, Allison Park, PA 15101
Tel.: (412) 366-0201 Fax: (412) 366-2558

CAITHNESS GLASS VISITOR CENTRES

Perth Factory and Visitor Centre

Opened in 1979 in Perth, Scotland, the Visitor Centre is home to the largest public display of Caithness paperweights with over 1,200 designs. There is a resident engraver, and a spacious viewing gallery enables visitors to watch the paperweight-making process from start to finish. In addition, there is a large, well-stocked factory shop with lots of bargains. There is a large restaurant, a childrens play area, and ample free parking.

The Visitor Centre is open seven days a week all year, but the glassmaking section is in operation Monday to Friday all year. Admission to the Visitor Centre is free and no booking is required.

Inveralmond, Perth PH1 3TZ, Scotland
Tel.: (01738) 492320
Fax: (01738) 492300

Wick Factory and Visitor Centre

This centre opened in Wick, Scotland, in 1992. Visitors can watch the glass making process. The Visitor Centre is open all year Monday to Saturday and on Sundays from Easter to December. Glassmaking can be viewed Monday to Friday.

Airport Industrial Estate
Wick KW1 4EP, Scotland
Tel.: (01955) 602286
Fax: (01955) 605200

Oban Factory Shop and Visitor Centre

This centre opened in Oban, Scotland, in 1992. Its small glass studio was replaced in 1995 by an audiovisual and interpretative exhibition that covers the history of Caithness Glass, the designers and early products, as well as the glassmaking process. There is a resident engraver and a well-stocked factory shop with lots of bargains.

The Visitor Centre is open Monday to Saturday throughout the year and on Sundays April to October. Admission to the Visitor Centre is free and no booking is required.

The Waterfront
Railway Pier
Oban PA34 4LW, Scotland
Tel.: (01631) 563386
Fax: (01631) 563386

Caithness Crystal Visitor Centre, Kings Lynn, Norfolk, England

At this centre, visitors can view demonstrations by Creative Glass glassmakers and browse in the well-stocked factory shop. There is also a spacious restaurant.

The factory shop and restaurant are open seven days a week all year. The glassmaking demonstrations can be seen Monday to Friday all year, and Saturday and Sunday from mid-June to mid-September. Admission to the Visitor Centre is free and no booking is required.

Paxman Road
Hardwick Industrial Estate
Kings Lynn, Norfolk, PE30 4NE, England
Tel.: (01553) 765111
Fax: (01553) 767628

Factory Shops

Caithness Glass Visitor Centre
Inveralmond
Perth PH1 3TZ, Scotland
Tel: (01738) 492320

Caithness Glass Visitor Centre
Airport Industrial Estate
Wick KW1 4EP, Scotland
Tel.: (01955) 602286
Fax: (01955) 605200

Caithness Glass Visitor Centre
The Waterfront
Railway Pier
Oban PA34 4LW, Scotland
Tel.: (01631) 563386
Fax: (01631) 563386

Caithness Crystal Visitor Centre
Paxman Road
Hardwick Industrial Estate
Kings Lynn, Norfolk, PE30 4NE, England
Tel.: (01553) 765111
Fax: (01553) 767628

ROYAL DOULTON VISITOR CENTRES

Royal Doulton Visitor Centre

Opened in the summer of 1996, the Royal Doulton Visitor Centre houses the largest collection of Royal Doulton figurines in the world. The centre also is home to the Minton Fine Art Studio, which specializes in hand-painting and gilding. Demonstration areas offer the collector a first-hand insight into how figurines are assembled and decorated. Also at the Visitor Centre is a cinema showing a 20-minute video on the history of Royal Doulton, plus a restaurant, and a retail shop offering both best-quality ware and slight seconds.

Factory tours may be booked Monday to Friday at the Visitor Centre.

Nile Street, Burslem
Stoke-on-Trent, ST6 2AJ, England
Tel.: (01782) 292434
Fax: (01782) 292424
Attn: Yvonne Wood

Royal Doulton John Beswick Studios

Tours of the John Beswick Factory and Museum are available Monday to Thursday by appointment only. Please book in advance.

Gold Street, Longton
Stoke-on-Trent, ST3 2JP, England
Tel.: (01782) 291213
Fax: (01782) 291279

Royal Crown Derby Visitor Centre

Opened in the spring of 1998, the Visitor Centre was created to provide an insight into the tradition, history and skills that go into making Royal Crown Derby collectables. The centre houses the largest collection of Royal Crown Derby seen anywhere in the world, a demonstration area for skilled Royal Crown Derby artists and craftspeople, restaurants, and shops.

Factory tours may be booked Monday to Friday at the centre, with advance bookings suggested.

194 Osmaston Road,
Derby, DE23 8JZ, England
Tel: (01332) 712841
Fax: (01332) 712899
Attn: Stella Birks

Factory Shops

Royal Doulton Visitor Centre
Nile Street, Burslem
Stoke-on-Trent, ST6 2AJ, England
Tel.: (01782) 292451

Royal Doulton Group Factory Shop
Lawley Street, Longton
Stoke-on-Trent, ST3 2PH, England
Tel: (01782) 291172

Royal Doulton Factory Shop
Minton House, London Road
Stoke-on-Trent, ST4 7QD, England
Tel.: (01782) 292121

Royal Doulton Factory Shop
Leek New Road, Baddeley Green
Stoke-on-Trent, ST2 7HS, England
Tel.: (01782) 291700

Royal Doulton Factory Shop
Victoria Road, Fenton
Stoke-on-Trent, ST4 2PJ, England
Tel.: (01782) 291869

Beswick Factory Shop
Barford Street, Longton
Stoke-on-Trent, ST3 2JP, England
Tel.: (01782) 291237

Internet and Customer Enquiries

Sites: www. Caithnessglass.co.uk
www.royal-doulton.com

E-mail:

Clubs: icc@royal-doulton.com
collector@caithnessglass.co.uk
caithglas@aol.com
Visitor Centre:
Visitor@royal-doulton.com

Consumer Enquiries: enquiries@royal-doulton.com
Museum Curator: heritage@royal-doulton.com
Lawleys by Post: lbp@royal-doulton.com

WHERE TO BUY

Discontinued Doulton collectables can be found in antique shops, markets, auctions, shows and fairs. Specialist dealers in Royal Doulton collectables attend many of the events listed below.

For auction happenings, it is necessary to subscribe to auction houses that hold 20th century or Royal Doulton auctions.

UNITED KINGDOM

Auction Houses

BBR Auctions
Elsecar Heritage Centre
Nr. Barnsley
South Yorkshire, S74 8HJ, England
Tel.: (01226) 745156
Fax: (01226) 351561
www.auctions-on-line.com/bbr
Attn: Alan Blakeman

Bonhams
65-69 Lots Road, Chelsea
London, SW10 0RN, England
Tel.: (0171) 393-3900
Fax: (0171) 393-3906
www.bonhams.com
Attn: Neil Grenyer

Christie's South Kensington
85 Old Brompton Road
London, SW7 3LD, England
Tel.: (0171) 581-7611
Fax: (0171) 321-3321
www.christies.com
Attn: Michael Jeffrey

Potteries Specialist Auctions
271 Waterloo Road, Cobridge
Stoke-on-Trent
Staffordshire, ST13 5AJ, England
Tel.: (01782) 286622
Fax: (01782) 213777
www.danielhulme.co.uk/pottery.htm
Attn: Steve Anderson

Louis Taylor
Britannia House
10 Town Road, Hanley
Stoke-on-Trent, ST1 2QG, England
Tel.: (01782) 21411
Fax: (01782) 287874
www.thesaurus.co.uk/louis-taylor
Attn: Clive Hillier

Phillips
101 New Bond Street
London, W1Y 0AS, England
Tel: (0171) 629-6602
Fax: (0171) 629-8876
www.phillips-auctions.com
Attn: Mark Oliver

Sotheby's
34-35 New Bond Street
London, W1A 2AA, England
Tel.: (0171) 293-5000
Fax: (0171) 293-5989
www.sothebys.com
Attn: Christina Donaldson

Sotheby's Sussex
Summers Place
Billingshurst, Sussex, RH14 9AF
England
Tel.: (01403) 833500
Fax: (01403) 833699

Thomson Roddick & Laurie
60 Whitesands
Dumfries, DG1 2RS
Scotland
Tel.: (01387) 255366
Fax: (01387) 266236
Attn: Sybelle Medcalf

Peter Wilson Auctioneers
Victoria Gallery, Market Street
Nantwich, Cheshire, CW5 5DG
England
Tel.: (01270) 623878
Fax: (01270) 610508
Attn: Stella Ashbrook or Robert Stone
eBay U.K.: www.ebay.com/uk/

Antique Fairs

Doulton and Beswick Collectors Fair
National Motorcycle Museum,
Meriden, Birmingham
Usually in March and August.
For information on times and dates:
Doulton and Beswick Dealers Association
(0181) 303-3316

Doulton and Beswick Collectors Fair
The Queensway Hall Civic Centre,
Dunstable,
Bedfordshire. Usually in October.
For information on times and location:
UK Fairs Ltd., 10 Wilford Bridge Spur
Melton, Woodbridge, Suffolk, IP12 1RJ
(01394) 386663

20th Century Fairs
266 Glossop Road, Sheffield, S10 2HS,
England
Usually the last week in May or the
first week in June.
For information on times and dates:
Tel.: (0114) 275-0333
Fax: (0114) 275-4443

International Antique & Collectors Fair
Newark, Nottinghamshire
Usually six fairs annually.
For information on times and dates:
International Antique & Collectors Fair Ltd.
P.O. Box 100, Newark,
Nottinghamshire, NG2 1DJ
(01636) 702326

West London Wade Beswick & Doulton Fair
Brunel University, Kingston Lane
Uxbridge, Middlesex
For information on times and dates:
B & D Fairs, P.O. Box 273, Uxbridge
Middlesex, UB9 4LP
(01895) 834694 or 834357

Yesterdays Doulton Fair
Usually in November.
For information on times and location:
Doulton and Beswick Dealers
Association
Tel.: (0181) 303-3316

London Markets

Alfie's Antique Market
13-25 Church Street, London
Tuesday-Saturday

Camden Passage Market
London
Wednesday and Saturday

New Caledonia Market
Bermondsey Square, London
Friday morning

Portobello Road Market
Portobello Road, London
Saturday

UNITED STATES

Auction Houses

Christie's East
219 East 67th Street
New York, New York 10021
Tel.: (212) 606-0400
www.christies.com
Attn: Timothy Luke

Collectors Sales & Services
P.O. Box 6
Pomfret Center, Connecticut 06259
Tel.: (860) 974-7008
Fax: (860) 974-7010
E-mail: collectors@antiquechina.com
www.antiquechina.com
eBay: www.ebay.com

L. H. Selman Ltd.
123 Locust Street
Santa Cruz, California 95060
Tel.: (831) 427-1177
Fax: (831) 427-0111
E-mail: lselman@paperweight.com
www.selman.com

Skinner, Inc.
The Heritage On The Garden
63 Park Plaza
Boston, Massachusetts 02116
Tel.: (617) 350-5400
Fax: (617) 350-5429
E-mail: info@skinner.com
www.skinnerinc.com

Sotheby's Arcade Auctions
1334 York Avenue
New York, New York 10021
Tel.: (212) 606-7000
Fax: (212) 606-7107
www.sothebys.com
Attn: Andrew Cheney

Collectable Shows

Atlantique City
New Atlantic City Convention Center
Atlantic City, New Jersey
Usually in March and October.
For more information on times and dates:
Brimfield and Associates
P.O. Box 1800, Ocean City,
New Jersey 08226
Tel.: (609) 926-1800
www.atlantiquecity.com

Florida Doulton Convention & Sale
Sheraton Hotel
1825 Griffin Road
Dania, Florida
Usually in mid-January.
For information on times and dates:
Pascoe & Company
932 Ponce De Leon Blvd
Coral Gables, Florida 33134.
Tel.: (305) 445-3229
Charles Dombeck
9720 Ridge Walk Court
Davie, Florida 33328
Tel.: (954) 452-9174

O'Hare National Antiques Show & Sale
Rosemont Convention Centre
Chicago, Illinois
Usually in April, June, August and November.
For information on times and dates:
Manor House Shows Inc.
P.O. Box 7320, Fort Lauderdale, Florida 33338
Tel.: (954) 563-6747

Royal Doulton Convention & Sale
John S. Knight Convention Centre
77 East Mill Street, Akron, Ohio 44308
Usually in August.
For information on times and dates:
Colonial House Productions
182 Front Street, Berea, Ohio 44017
Tel.:(800) 344-9299

CANADA

Auction Houses

Maynards
415 West 2nd Avenue, Vancouver, B.C. V5Y 1E3
Tel.: (604) 876-1311
Fax: (604) 876-2678
E-mail: info@maynards.com
www.maynards.com

Ritchie's
288 King Street East, Toronto, Ontario M5A 1K4
Tel.: (416) 364-1864 Fax: (416) 364-0704
Attn: Caroline Kaiser
eBay Canada
http://www.ebay.com/canada/

Collectables Shows

Canadian Art & Collectibles Show & Sale
Kitchener Memorial Auditorium, Kitchener, Ontario
Usually in early May.
For information on times and location:
George or Jackie Benninger
P.O. Box 130, Durham, Ontario N0G 1R0.
Tel.: (519) 369-6950 Fax: (519) 369-6961

Canadian Doulton & Collectable Fair
Toronto, Ontario
Usually in early September.
For information on times and location:
George or Jackie Benninger
P.O. Box 130, Durham, Ontario N0G 1R0.
Tel.: (519) 369-6950

FURTHER READING

Books

All About Paperweights by Lawrence H. Selman
The Annual Bulletin of the Paperweight Collectors Association published by Collector Books
The Art of the Paperweight by Lawrence H. Selman
The Caithness Collection, 1981 by Glenn S. Johnson
Collectors Guide to Paperweights by Sara Rossi
The Dictionary of Paperweight Signature Canes — Identification and Dating by Andrew H. Dohan
The Encyclopedia of Glass Paperweights by Paul Hollister
The Glass Menagerie — A Study of Silhouette Canes in Antique Paperweights by John D. Hawley
Glass Paperweights, 2nd ed., by Patricia McCawley
Glass Paperweights by James MacKay
Identifying Antique Paperweights — Lampwork by George N. Kulles and Jean Kusy Kulles
Identifying Antique Paperweights — Millefiori by George N. Kulles
Old English Paperweights by Robert G. Hall
Paperweights by Sibylle Jargstorf
Paperweights: The Collector's Guide to Selecting and Enjoying New and Antique Paperweights by Pat Reilly
Paperweights of the World, 2nd ed., by Monika Flemming and Peter Pommerencke
Sotheby's Concise Encyclopedia of Glass by David Battie and Simon Cottle
Sulphides — The Art of Cameo Incrustation by Paul Jokelson

Magazines and Newsletters

Collecting Doulton Magazine, Contact Doug Pinchin, P.O. Box 310, Richmond, Surrey TW9 1FS England
Collect It! Contact subscription department at P.O. Box 3658, Bracknell, Berkshire RG12 7XZ, England.
  Tel.: (1344) 868280 E-mail: collectit@dialpipex.com
Doulton News, published by Thorndon Antiques & Fine China Ltd., edited by David Harcourt
  P.O. Box 12-076 (109 Molesworth Street), Wellington, New Zealand
Glass Collectors Digest, Contact subscription department at P.O. Box 553, Marietta, Ohio 45750, U.S.A.
  Tel.: (800) 533-3433 E-mail: 102552.726@CompuServe.co
Reflections, published by the Caithness Glass Paperweight Collectors Society: Inveralmond, Perth
  PH1 3TZ, Scotland

Videos

Reflections — The Magic of Caithness Glass Paperweights, In the U.S., contact the Secretary of the Caithness Glass
  Paperweight Collectors Society by phone at (973) 340-3330; in the U.K. and international, contact the
  Secretary of the Caithness Glass Paperweight Collectors Society by phone at (44) (0) 1738 492329.

CAITHNESS WEIGHTS

TOPSY-TURVY

Shona Spittal shows us, step-by-step, how to
create four spiraling silvery bubbles, each
rising from its own individual colour thread
from a sparkling crystalline base.

Laying down four colour
pattern

Blocking a large gather of
glass

Re-warming at the glory
hole

Picking up the powdered
glass colours

Paletting to shape (5 & 6).

Piercing a hole through
each colour

Using compressed air to
blow bubbles

Pulling out excess glass

Cutting-in and sealing off
bubbles

Marvering to twist bubbles

Picking up sand for base

Cutting-in at the back of
the paperweight

Applying the punty

Pulling out and cutting off
the punty mark

The final shaping

CT-1A
MARS

Designer:	Colin Terris		
Type:	Weight — Spherical		
Edition:	1969 in a limited edition of 500		
Status:	Fully subscribed		
Series:	Planets, Set One		
Original Issue Price:	£40.00/set		

Name	U.S. $	Can. $	U.K. £
Mars	875.00	1,200.00	625.00
Set	3,500.00	4,800.00	2,500.00

Note: CT-1A, B, C and D were issued and sold as a set.

CT-1B
MERCURY

Designer:	Colin Terris		
Type:	Weight — Spherical		
Edition:	1969 in a limited edition of 500		
Status:	Fully subscribed		
Series:	Planets, Set One		
Original Issue Price:	£40.00/set		

Name	U.S. $	Can. $	U.K. £
Mercury	875.00	1,200.00	625.00

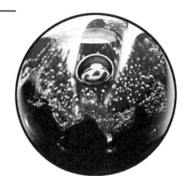

CT-1C
SATURN

Designer:	Colin Terris		
Type:	Weight — Spherical		
Edition:	1969 in a limited edition of 500		
Status:	Fully subscribed		
Series:	Planets, Set One		
Original Issue Price:	£40.00/set		

Name	U.S. $	Can. $	U.K. £
Saturn	875.00	1,200.00	625.00

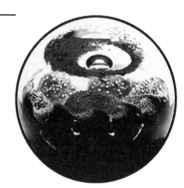

CT-1D
VENUS

Designer:	Colin Terris		
Type:	Weight — Spherical		
Edition:	1969 in a limited edition of 500		
Status:	Fully subscribed		
Series:	Planets, Set One		
Original Issue Price:	£40.00/set		

Name	U.S. $	Can. $	U.K. £
Venus	875.00	1,200.00	625.00

CT-2
MOONFLOWER

Designer:	Colin Terris
Type:	Weight — Spherical
Colour:	Many colour variations
Edition:	1970
Status:	Active
Series:	Unlimited — Modern Design

Original Issue Price: £8.00

Name	U.S. $	Can. $	U.K. £
Moonflower	99.50	175.00	35.00

CT-3
ORBIT

Designer:	Colin Terris
Type:	Weight — Spherical
Edition:	1970 in a limited edition of 500
Status:	Fully subscribed

Original Issue Price: £12.00

Name	U.S. $	Can. $	U.K. £
Orbit	350.00	475.00	275.00

CT-4A
URANUS

Designer:	Colin Terris
Type:	Weight — Spherical
Edition:	1970 in a limited edition of 500
Status:	Fully subscribed
Series:	Planets, Set Two

Original Issue Price: £45.00/set

Name	U.S. $	Can. $	U.K. £
Uranus	550.00	800.00	425.00
Set	2,200.00	3,200.00	1,700.00

Note: CT-4A, B, C and D were issued as a set.

CT-4B
JUPITER

Designer:	Colin Terris
Type:	Weight — Spherical
Edition:	1970 in a limited edition of 500
Status:	Fully subscribed
Series:	Planets, Set Two

Original Issue Price: £45.00/set

Name	U.S. $	Can. $	U.K. £
Jupiter	550.00	800.00	425.00

CT-4C
NEPTUNE

Designer:	Colin Terris
Type:	Weight — Spherical
Edition:	1970 in a limited edition of 500
Status:	Fully subscribed
Series:	Planets, Set Two
Original Issue Price:	£45.00/set

Name	U.S. $	Can. $	U.K. £
Neptune	550.00	800.00	425.00

CT-4D
EARTH

Designer:	Colin Terris
Type:	Weight — Spherical
Edition:	1970 in a limited edition of 500
Status:	Fully subscribed
Series:	Planets, Set Two
Original Issue Price:	£45.00/set

Name	U.S. $	Can. $	U.K. £
Earth	550.00	800.00	425.00

CT-5A
SUN

Designer:	Colin Terris
Type:	Weight — Spherical
Edition:	1971 in a limited edition of 500
Status:	Fully subscribed
Series:	Planets, Set Three
Original Issue Price:	£40.00/set

Name	U.S. $	Can. $	U.K. £
Sun	500.00	750.00	400.00
Set	1,500.00	2,250.00	1,200.00

Note: CT-5A, B and C were issued as a set.

CT-5B
MOON

Designer:	Colin Terris
Type:	Weight — Spherical
Edition:	1971 in a limited edition of 500
Status:	Fully subscribed
Series:	Planets, Set Three
Original Issue Price:	£40.00/set

Name	U.S. $	Can. $	U.K. £
Moon	500.00	750.00	400.00

CT-5C
PLUTO

Designer:	Colin Terris
Type:	Weight — Spherical
Edition:	1971 in a limited edition of 500
Status:	Fully subscribed
Series:	Planets, Set Three
Original Issue Price:	£40.00/set

Name	U.S. $	Can. $	U.K. £
Pluto	500.00	750.00	400.00

CT-6
SPIRAL

Designer:	Colin Terris
Type:	Weight — Spherical
Colour:	See below
Edition:	1971 in a limited edition of 500 for each colourway
Status:	See below
Original Issue Price:	£12.00

Colourways/Status	U.S. $	Can. $	U.K. £
1. Purple and red (Closed at No. 120)	300.00	400.00	200.00
2. Purple and yellow (Closed at No. 150)	300.00	400.00	200.00

CT-7
STARBASE

Designer:	Colin Terris
Type:	Weight — Spherical
Edition:	1971 in a limited edition of 500
Status:	Fully subscribed
Original Issue Price:	£12.00

Name	U.S. $	Can. $	U.K. £
Starbase	650.00	950.00	425.00

CT-8
CORAL

Designer:	Colin Terris
Type:	Weight — Spherical
Colour:	See below
Edition:	1972 in a limited edition of 500 for each colourway
Status:	Fully subscribed
Original Issue Price:	£15.00

Colourways	U.S. $	Can. $	U.K. £
1. Blue	375.00	550.00	250.00
2. Damson	375.00	550.00	250.00
3. Orange	475.00	650.00	300.00

CT-9
CASED CORAL

Designer: Colin Terris
Type: Weight — Spherical
Colour: See below
Edition: 1972 in a limited edition of 100 for each colourway
Status: Fully subscribed
Original Issue Price: £21.00

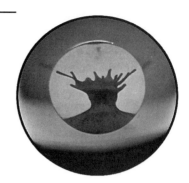

Colourways	U.S. $	Can. $	U.K. £
1. Blue	275.00	375.00	175.00
2. Damson	275.00	375.00	175.00
3. Orange	350.00	475.00	200.00

CT-10
HARLEQUIN SINGLE

Designer: Paul Ysart derivative
Type: Weight — Spherical
Cane: See below
Edition: 1972
Status: Closed
Original Issue Price: 1. £10.00
2. £15.00

Canes	U.S. $	Can. $	U.K. £
1. PH (Peter Holmes) (1972–75)	125.00	150.00	75.00
2. CG (Caithness Glass) (1976)	75.00	100.00	50.00

CT-11
HARLEQUIN DOUBLE

Designer: Paul Ysart derivative
Type: Weight — Domed
Cane: See below
Edition: 1972
Status: Closed
Original Issue Price: 1. £14.00
2. £19.40

Canes	U.S. $	Can. $	U.K. £
1. PH (Peter Holmes) (1972–75)	225.00	300.00	150.00
2. CG (Caithness Glass) (1976)	150.00	225.00	100.00

CT-12
INK BOTTLE

Designer: Peter Holmes
Type: Ink bottle
Cane: See below
Edition: 1972
Status: Closed
Original Issue Price: £19.00

Canes	U.S. $	Can. $	U.K. £
1. PH (Peter Holmes — in stopper) (1972)	325.00	450.00	200.00
2. CG (Caithness Glass — in stopper) (1976)	225.00	325.00	150.00

CT-13
SUNFLOWER

Designer: Colin Terris
Type: Weight — Spherical
Edition: 1972 in a limited edition of 500
Status: Fully subscribed
Original Issue Price: £12.00

Name	U.S. $	Can. $	U.K. £
Sunflower	450.00	600.00	300.00

CT-14
TROPICANA

Designer: Peter Holmes
Type: Weight — Spherical
Colour: See below
Cane: PH (Peter Holmes)
Edition: 1972 in a limited edition of 500 for each colourway
Status: See below
Original Issue Price: £17.00

Colourways/Status	U.S. $	Can. $	U.K. £
1. Pink (Fully subscribed)	225.00	325.00	150.00
2. Purple (Fully subscribed)	225.00	325.00	150.00
3. Yellow (Closed at No. 487)	325.00	450.00	200.00

CT-15
JELLYFISH

Designer: Colin Terris
Type: Weight — Spherical
Colour: See below
Edition: 1972 in a limited edition of 500 for each colourway
Status: See below
Original Issue Price: £9.00

Colourways/Status	U.S. $	Can. $	U.K. £
1. Green (Closed at No. 444)	150.00	200.00	85.00
2. Purple (Fully subscribed)	85.00	125.00	50.00
3. Red (Fully subscribed)	85.00	125.00	50.00

CT-16
SEA URCHIN

Designer: Colin Terris
Type: Weight — Spherical
Edition: 1972 in a limited edition of 500
Status: Fully subscribed
Original Issue Price: £10.00

Name	U.S. $	Can. $	U.K. £
Sea Urchin	125.00	175.00	80.00

CT-17
SHIPWRECK

Designer: Peter Holmes
Type: Weight — Spherical
Edition: 1972 in a limited edition of 50
Status: Fully subscribed
Original Issue Price: £30.00

Name	U.S. $	Can. $	U.K. £
Shipwreck	2,250.00	3,000.00	1,500.00

CT-18
FISH

Designer: Colin Terris
Type: Weight — Spherical, engraved
Edition: 1972 in a limited edition of 500
Status: Fully subscribed
Original Issue Price: £10.00

Name	U.S. $	Can. $	U.K. £
Fish	150.00	200.00	100.00

Note: This was the first engraved paperweight issued by Caithness.

CT-19
ARIEL

Designer: Colin Terris
Type: Weight — Spherical
Edition: 1972 in a limited edition of 500
Status: Fully subscribed
Original Issue Price: £10.00

Name	U.S. $	Can. $	U.K. £
Ariel	150.00	200.00	100.00

CT-20
MAY DANCE

Designer: Colin Terris
Type: Weight — Spherical
Colour: See below
Edition: 1972
Status: Active
Original Issue Price: £8.00

Colourways	U.S. $	Can. $	U.K. £
1. Green	60.00	85.00	35.00
2. Purple	60.00	85.00	35.00
3. Red	60.00	85.00	35.00

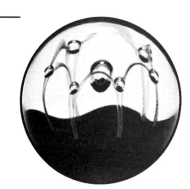

CT-21A
EARTH

Designer: Colin Terris
Type: Weight — Spherical
Edition: 1973 in a limited edition of 1,000
Status: Fully subscribed
Series: Elements, Set One
Original Issue Price: £52.00/set

Name	U.S. $	Can. $	U.K. £
Earth	375.00	500.00	250.00
Set	1,500.00	2,000.00	1,000.00

Note: CT-21A, B, C and D were issued and sold as a set.

CT-21B
AIR

Designer: Colin Terris
Type: Weight — Spherical
Edition: 1973 in a limited edition of 1,000
Status: Fully subscribed
Series: Elements, Set One
Original Issue Price: £52.00/set

Name	U.S. $	Can. $	U.K. £
Air	375.00	500.00	250.00

CT-21C
FIRE

Designer: Colin Terris
Type: Weight — Spherical
Edition: 1973 in a limited edition of 1,000
Status: Fully subscribed
Series: Elements, Set One
Original Issue Price: £52.00/set

Name	U.S. $	Can. $	U.K. £
Fire	375.00	500.00	250.00

CT-21D
WATER

Designer: Colin Terris
Type: Weight — Spherical
Edition: 1973 in a limited edition of 1,000
Status: Fully subscribed
Series: Elements, Set One
Original Issue Price: £52.00/set

Name	U.S. $	Can. $	U.K. £
Water	375.00	500.00	250.00

CT-22
GENESIS

Designer: Colin Terris
Type: Weight — Spherical
Edition: 1973 in a limited edition of 500
Status: Fully subscribed
Original Issue Price: £15.00

Name	U.S. $	Can. $	U.K. £
Genesis	600.00	800.00	400.00

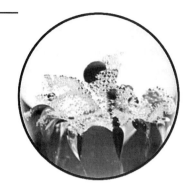

CT-23
SCULPTURE

Designer: Peter Holmes
Type: Weight — Spherical
Edition: 1973 in a limited edition of 500
Status: Fully subscribed
Original Issue Price: £17.00

Name	U.S. $	Can. $	U.K. £
Sculpture	600.00	800.00	400.00

CT-24
STARDUST

Designer: Colin Terris
Type: Weight — Spherical
Edition: 1973 in a limited edition of 500
Status: Fully subscribed
Original Issue Price: £20.00

Name	U.S. $	Can. $	U.K. £
Stardust	500.00	700.00	325.00

CT-25
FIRE DANCE

Designer: Colin Terris
Type: Weight — Spherical
Edition: 1973
Status: Closed
Original Issue Price: £11.00

Name	U.S. $	Can. $	U.K. £
Fire Dance	90.00	125.00	60.00

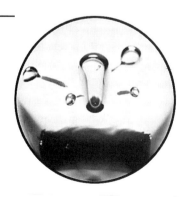

CT-26
FULMAR

Designer:	Colin Terris
Type:	Weight — Spherical, engraved
Edition:	1973 in a limited edition of 500
Status:	Fully subscribed
Series:	Sea Birds
Original Issue Price:	£13.00

Name	U.S. $	Can. $	U.K. £
Fulmar	100.00	125.00	65.00

CT-27
FLOWER IN THE RAIN

Designer:	Jack Allan
Type:	Weight — Spherical
Colour:	See below
Edition:	1974
Status:	Closed
Original Issue Price:	£16.00

Colourways	U.S. $	Can. $	U.K. £
1. Blue	75.00	100.00	50.00
2. Purple	75.00	100.00	50.00
3. Red	75.00	100.00	50.00
4. Yellow	75.00	100.00	50.00

CT-28
CROWN

Designer:	Colin Terris
Type:	Weight — Spherical
Cane:	A & M (Anne and Mark)
Edition:	1974 in a limited edition of 100
Status:	Fully subscribed
Original Issue Price:	£35.00

Name	U.S. $	Can. $	U.K. £
Crown	1,500.00	2,000.00	1,000.00

Note: This paperweight was issued to commemorate the Royal Wedding of Princess Anne and Captain Mark Phillips.

CT-29
SPACE ROSE

Designer:	Colin Terris
Type:	Weight — Spherical
Colour:	See below
Edition:	1974 in a limited edition of 1,000 for each colourway
Status:	See below
Original Issue Price:	£19.50

Colourways/Status	U.S. $	Can. $	U.K. £
1. Ruby (Closed at No. 631)	100.00	125.00	60.00
2. Sienna (Closed at No. 320)	100.00	125.00	60.00
3. White (Closed at No. 273)	150.00	225.00	90.00

CT-30
SEA CRAB

Designer: Colin Terris
Type: Weight — Spherical
Edition: 1974 in a limited edition of 1,500
Status: Fully subscribed
Original Issue Price: £18.00

Name	U.S. $	Can. $	U.K. £
Sea Crab	200.00	250.00	125.00

CT-31
CASCADE

Designer: Peter Holmes
Type: Weight — Domed
Colour: Silver
Cane: See below
Edition: 1974
Status: Closed
Original Issue Price: 1. £17.00
2. £19.50

Canes	U.S. $	Can. $	U.K. £
1. PH (Peter Holmes) (1974/5)	125.00	150.00	80.00
2. CG (Caithness Glass) (1975)	140.00	175.00	90.00

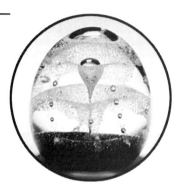

CT-32
CASCADE RAINBOW

Designer: Peter Holmes
Type: Weight — Domed
Colour: Yellow, ruby, blue and green
Cane: See below
Edition: 1974
Status: Closed
Original Issue Price: 1. £17.00
2. £19.50

Canes	U.S. $	Can. $	U.K. £
1. PH (Peter Holmes) (1974/5)	200.00	275.00	125.00
2. CG (Caithness Glass) (1975)	150.00	200.00	90.00

CT-33
BUTTERFLY

Designer: Colin Terris
Type: Weight — Spherical
Cane: CG (Caithness Glass)
Edition: 1974 in a limited edition of 100
Status: Fully subscribed
Original Issue Price: £35.00

Name	U.S. $	Can. $	U.K. £
Butterfly	750.00	1,000.00	500.00

CT-34
BULLSEYE MILLEFIORI

Designer:	Colin Terris
Type:	Weight — Spherical
Cane:	CG (Caithness Glass)
Edition:	1974
Status:	Closed
Original Issue Price:	£25.00

Name	U.S. $	Can. $	U.K. £
Bullseye Millefiori	200.00	300.00	135.00

CT-35
ARCTIC TERN

Designer:	Colin Terris
Type:	Weight — Spherical, engraved
Edition:	1974 in a limited edition of 500
Status:	Fully subscribed
Series:	Sea Birds
Original Issue Price:	£14.00

Name	U.S. $	Can. $	U.K. £
Arctic Tern	75.00	100.00	50.00

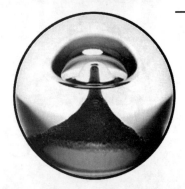

CT-36
SPACE BEACON

Designer:	Colin Terris
Type:	Weight — Spherical
Colour:	See below
Edition:	1975 in a limited edition of 500 for each colourway
Status:	Fully subscribed
Original Issue Price:	£17.00

Colourways	U.S. $	Can. $	U.K. £
1. Damson	150.00	200.00	100.00
2. Green	150.00	200.00	100.00
3. Purple	150.00	200.00	100.00

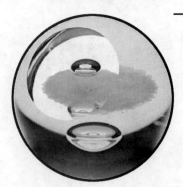

CT-37
REFLECTIONS

Designer:	Colin Terris
Type:	Weight — Spherical
Colour:	See below
Edition:	1975 in a limited edition of 500 for each colourway
Status:	Fully subscribed
Original Issue Price:	£15.00

Colourways	U.S. $	Can. $	U.K. £
1. Blue	125.00	175.00	75.00
2. Damson	125.00	175.00	75.00
3. Green	125.00	175.00	75.00

CT-38
VORTEX

Designer:	Colin Terris
Type:	Weight — Spherical
Colour:	See below
Edition:	1975 in a limited edition of 1,000 for each colourway
Status:	See below
Original Issue Price:	£20.00

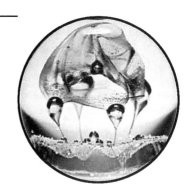

Colourways/Status	U.S. $	Can. $	U.K. £
1. Blue (Fully subscribed)	55.00	80.00	35.00
2. Green (Closed at No. 803)	70.00	95.00	40.00
3. Red (Closed at No. 778)	70.00	95.00	40.00

CT-39
SEA KELP

Designer:	Colin Terris
Type:	Weight — Spherical
Edition:	1975 in a limited edition of 1,500
Status:	Fully subscribed
Original Issue Price:	£16.00

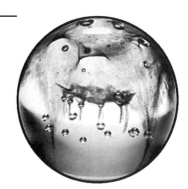

Name	U.S. $	Can. $	U.K. £
Sea Kelp	150.00	200.00	100.00

CT-40
SENTINEL

Designer:	Colin Terris
Type:	Weight — Spherical
Colour:	See below
Edition:	1974
Status:	Closed
Original Issue Price:	£12.00

Colourways	U.S. $	Can. $	U.K. £
1. Green	70.00	95.00	40.00
2. Purple	70.00	95.00	40.00
3. Red	70.00	95.00	40.00

CT-41
DRAGONFLY

Designer:	Colin Terris
Type:	Weight — Spherical
Edition:	1975 in a limited edition of 1,500
Status:	Fully subscribed
Original Issue Price:	£17.00

Name	U.S. $	Can. $	U.K. £
Dragonfly	500.00	700.00	350.00

CT-42
SEABASE

Designer: Colin Terris
Type: Weight — Spherical
Edition: 1976 in a limited edition of 400
Status: Fully subscribed
Original Issue Price: £44.00

Name	U.S. $	Can. $	U.K. £
Seabase	600.00	800.00	400.00

CT-43
SPACE FLOWER

Designer: Colin Terris
Type: Weight — Spherical
Edition: 1976 in a limited edition of 1,000
Status: Fully subscribed
Original Issue Price: £24.00

Name	U.S. $	Can. $	U.K. £
Space Flower	200.00	250.00	125.00

CT-44
SEA ORCHID

Designer: Colin Terris
Type: Weight — Spherical
Edition: 1976 in a limited edition of 1,000
Status: Fully subscribed
Original Issue Price: £24.00

Name	U.S. $	Can. $	U.K. £
Sea Orchid	275.00	350.00	175.00

CT-45
SEA PEARL

Designer: Peter Holmes
Type: Weight — Spherical
Cane: PH (Peter Holmes)
Edition: 1976 in a limited edition of 500
Status: Fully subscribed
Original Issue Price: £30.00

Name	U.S. $	Can. $	U.K. £
Sea Pearl	300.00	400.00	200.00

CT-46A
SPRING

Designer:	Colin Terris
Type:	Weight — Spherical
Cane:	WM (William Manson)
Edition:	1976 in a limited edition of 500
Status:	Closed at No. 473
Series:	Four Seasons
Original Issue Price:	£250.00/set

Name	*U.S. $*	*Can. $*	*U.K. £*
Spring	500.00	675.00	350.00
Set	2,000.00	2,700.00	1,400.00

Note: CT-46A, B, C and D were issued and sold as a set.

CT-46B
SUMMER

Designer:	Colin Terris
Type:	Weight — Spherical
Cane:	WM (William Manson)
Edition:	1976 in a limited edition of 500
Status:	Closed at No. 473
Series:	Four Seasons
Original Issue Price:	£250.00/set

Name	*U.S. $*	*Can. $*	*U.K. £*
Summer	500.00	675.00	350.00

CT-46C
AUTUMN

Designer:	Colin Terris
Type:	Weight — Spherical
Cane:	WM (William Manson)
Edition:	1976 in a limited edition of 500
Status:	Closed at No. 473
Series:	Four Seasons
Original Issue Price:	£250.00/set

Name	*U.S. $*	*Can. $*	*U.K. £*
Autumn	500.00	675.00	350.00

CT-46D
WINTER

Designer:	Colin Terris
Type:	Weight — Spherical
Cane:	WM (William Manson)
Edition:	1976 in a limited edition of 500
Status:	Closed at No. 473
Series:	Four Seasons
Original Issue Price:	£250.00/set

Name	*U.S. $*	*Can. $*	*U.K. £*
Winter	500.00	675.00	350.00

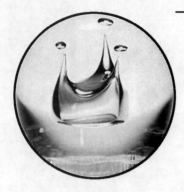

CT-47A
TRIO WEIGHT — ONE

Designer: Colin Terris
Type: Weight — Spherical
Edition: 1976 in a limited edition of 750
Status: Closed at No. 646
Series: Trio Set
Original Issue Price: £70.00/set

Name	U.S. $	Can. $	U.K. £
Trio Weight - One	275.00	375.00	175.00
Set	825.00	1,125.00	525.00

Note: CT-47A, B and C were issued and sold as a set.

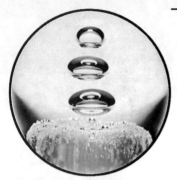

CT-47B
TRIO WEIGHT — TW0

Designer: Colin Terris
Type: Weight — Spherical
Edition: 1976 in a limited edition of 750
Status: Closed at No. 646
Series: Trio Set
Original Issue Price: £70.00/set

Name	U.S. $	Can. $	U.K. £
Trio Weight - Two	275.00	375.00	175.00

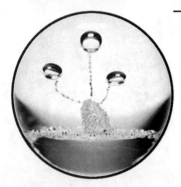

CT-47C
TRIO WEIGHT — THREE

Designer: Colin Terris
Type: Weight — Spherical
Edition: 1976 in a limited edition of 750
Status: Closed at No. 646
Series: Trio Set
Original Issue Price: £70.00/set

Name	U.S. $	Can. $	U.K. £
Trio Weight - Three	275.00	375.00	175.00

CT-48
PUFFIN

Designer: Colin Terris
Type: Weight — Spherical, engraved
Edition: 1976 in a limited edition of 500
Status: Fully subscribed
Series: Sea Birds
Original Issue Price: £17.00

Name	U.S. $	Can. $	U.K. £
Puffin	125.00	175.00	75.00

CT-49
CORMORANT

Designer: Colin Terris
Type: Weight — Spherical, engraved
Edition: 1976 in a limited edition of 500
Status: Fully subscribed
Series: Sea Birds
Original Issue Price: £17.00

Name	U.S. $	Can. $	U.K. £
Cormorant	125.00	175.00	75.00

CT-50
GANNET

Designer: David Gulland
Type: Weight — Spherical, copperwheel engraved
Edition: 1976 in a limited edition of 100
Status: Fully subscribed
Original Issue Price: £60.00

Name	U.S. $	Can. $	U.K. £
Gannet	600.00	800.00	400.00

CT-51
DIVING TERN

Designer: Denis Mann
Type: Weight — Spherical, copperwheel engraved
Edition: 1976 in a limited edition of 100
Status: Fully subscribed
Original Issue Price: £60.00

Name	U.S. $	Can. $	U.K. £
Diving Tern	600.00	800.00	400.00

CT-52
SEAL

Designer: Christine Beaton
Type: Weight — Spherical, copperwheel engraved
Edition: 1976 in a limited edition of 100
Status: Fully subscribed
Original Issue Price: £60.00

Name	U.S. $	Can. $	U.K. £
Seal	600.00	800.00	400.00

CT-53
DOLPHIN

Designer:	David Gulland
Type:	Weight — Spherical, copperwheel engraved
Edition:	1976 in a limited edition of 100
Status:	Fully subscribed
Original Issue Price:	£60.00

Name	U.S. $	Can. $	U.K. £
Dolphin	600.00	800.00	400.00

CT-54
SPECTRE

Designer:	Colin Terris
Type:	Weight — Spherical
Edition:	1976 in a limited edition of 1,000
Status:	Fully subscribed
Original Issue Price:	£17.00

Name	U.S. $	Can. $	U.K. £
Spectre	150.00	200.00	100.00

CT-55
SUN DANCE

Designer:	Colin Terris
Type:	Weight — Spherical
Edition:	1976 in a limited edition of 3,000
Status:	Fully subscribed
Original Issue Price:	£19.50

Name	U.S. $	Can. $	U.K. £
Sun Dance	200.00	275.00	125.00

CT-56
ALIEN

Designer:	Peter Holmes
Type:	Weight — Spherical
Cane:	CG (Caithness Glass)
Edition:	1976 in a limited edition of 2,000
Status:	Fully subscribed
Original Issue Price:	£20.50

Name	U.S. $	Can. $	U.K. £
Alien	100.00	125.00	75.00

CT-57
FIRST QUARTER

Designer:	Peter Holmes
Type:	Weight — Spherical
Cane:	PH (Peter Holmes)
Edition:	1976 in a limited edition of 1,500
Status:	Fully subscribed
Original Issue Price:	£20.50

Name	U.S. $	Can. $	U.K. £
First Quarter	150.00	200.00	100.00

CT-58
RHAPSODY

Designer:	Colin Terris
Type:	Weight — Spherical
Edition:	1976 in a limited edition of 400
Status:	Closed at No. 378
Original Issue Price:	£30.00

Name	U.S. $	Can. $	U.K. £
Rhapsody	150.00	200.00	100.00

CT-59
MILLEFIORI REFLECTIONS

Designer:	William Manson
Type:	Weight — Spherical
Cane:	CG (Caithness Glass)
Edition:	1976
Status:	Closed
Original Issue Price:	£20.00

Name	U.S. $	Can. $	U.K. £
Millefiori Reflections	100.00	125.00	75.00

CT-60
LATTICINO

Designer:	William Manson
Type:	Weight — Spherical
Cane:	CG (Caithness Glass)
Edition:	1976
Status:	Closed
Original Issue Price:	£24.00

Name	U.S. $	Can. $	U.K. £
Latticino	100.00	125.00	75.00

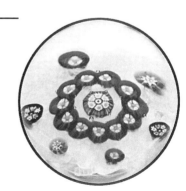

CT-62
POLAR BEAR

Designer:	Christine Beaton
Type:	Weight — Spherical, copperwheel engraved
Edition:	1976 in a limited edition of 100
Status:	Closed at No. 46
Original Issue Price:	£74.40

Name	U.S. $	Can. $	U.K. £
Polar Bear	600.00	800.00	400.00

CT-63
OTTER

Designer:	Denis Mann
Type:	Weight — Spherical, copperwheel engraved
Edition:	1976 in a limited edition of 100
Status:	Fully subscribed
Original Issue Price:	£74.40

Name	U.S. $	Can. $	U.K. £
Otter	475.00	600.00	300.00

CT-64
OSPREY

Designer:	Denis Mann
Type:	Weight — Spherical, copperwheel engraved
Edition:	1976 in a limited edition of 100
Status:	Fully subscribed
Original Issue Price:	£74.40

Name	U.S. $	Can. $	U.K. £
Osprey	475.00	600.00	300.00

CT-65
EIDER DUCK

Designer:	Denis Mann
Type:	Weight — Spherical, engraved
Edition:	1976 in a limited edition of 500
Status:	Fully subscribed
Series:	Sea Birds
Original Issue Price:	£19.50

Name	U.S. $	Can. $	U.K. £
Eider Duck	100.00	150.00	65.00

CT-66
BLACK HEADED GULL

Designer:	Denis Mann
Type:	Weight — Spherical, engraved
Edition:	1976 in a limited edition of 500
Status:	Fully subscribed
Series:	Sea Birds
Original Issue Price:	£19.50

Name	U.S. $	Can. $	U.K. £
Black Headed Gull	95.00	135.00	60.00

CT-67
STORMY PETREL

Designer:	Denis Mann
Type:	Weight — Spherical, engraved
Edition:	1977 in a limited edition of 500
Status:	Fully subscribed
Series:	Sea Birds
Original Issue Price:	£21.40

Name	U.S. $	Can. $	U.K. £
Stormy Petrel	95.00	135.00	60.00

CT-68
GUILLEMOT

Designer:	Denis Mann
Type:	Weight — Spherical, engraved
Edition:	1977 in a limited edition of 500
Status:	Fully subscribed
Series:	Sea Birds
Original Issue Price:	£21.40

Name	U.S. $	Can. $	U.K. £
Guillemot	95.00	135.00	60.00

CT-69
LOBSTER

Designer:	Colin Terris
Type:	Weight — Spherical
Edition:	1977 in a limited edition of 1,500
Status:	Closed at No. 1,245
Original Issue Price:	£25.00

Name	U.S. $	Can. $	U.K. £
Lobster	95.00	135.00	60.00

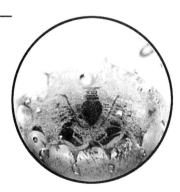

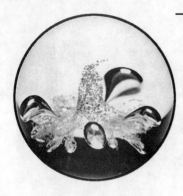

CT-70
JUBILEE MOONFLOWER

Designer:	Colin Terris
Type:	Weight — Spherical
Colour:	Silver
Edition:	1977 in a limited edition of 3,000
Status:	Fully subscribed
Series:	HM Queen Elizabeth II Silver Jubilee Collection

Original Issue Price: £15.00

Name	U.S. $	Can. $	U.K. £
Jubilee Moonflower	125.00	150.00	75.00

Note: CT-70 and the following three weights were issued to commemorate the 25th anniversary of the coronation of Queen Elizabeth II.

CT-71
JUBILEE CROWN BUBBLE

Designer:	Colin Terris
Type:	Weight — Spherical
Edition:	1977 in a limited edition of 3,000
Status:	Fully subscribed
Series:	HM Queen Elizabeth II Silver Jubilee Collection

Original Issue Price: £17.00

Name	U.S. $	Can. $	U.K. £
Jubilee Crown Bubble	100.00	125.00	65.00

CT-72
JUBILEE FLOATING CROWN

Designer:	Colin Terris
Type:	Weight — Spherical
Edition:	1977 in a limited edition of 1,000
Status:	Fully subscribed
Series:	HM Queen Elizabeth II Silver Jubilee Collection

Original Issue Price: £45.00

Name	U.S. $	Can. $	U.K. £
Jubilee Floating Crown	250.00	325.00	175.00

CT-73
JUBILEE MILLEFIORI CROWN

Designer:	Colin Terris
Type:	Weight — Spherical
Cane:	EIIR (Queen Elizabeth II)
Edition:	1977 in a limited edition of 500
Status:	Fully subscribed
Series:	HM Queen Elizabeth II Silver Jubilee Collection

Original Issue Price: £70.00

Name	U.S. $	Can. $	U.K. £
Jubilee Millefiori Crown	450.00	600.00	300.00

CT-75
COMET

Designer:	Colin Terris		
Type:	Weight — Spherical		
Edition:	1977 in a limited edition of 3,000		
Status:	Fully subscribed		
Original Issue Price:	£25.00		

Name	U.S. $	Can. $	U.K. £
Comet	125.00	175.00	75.00

CT-76
PLOUGH

Designer:	Colin Terris		
Type:	Weight — Spherical		
Edition:	1977 in a limited edition of 3,000		
Status:	Closed at No. 2,332		
Original Issue Price:	£25.40		

Name	U.S. $	Can. $	U.K. £
Plough	90.00	125.00	60.00

Note: This is the constellation known in North America as the Big Dipper.

CT-77
INTRUDER

Designer:	Colin Terris		
Type:	Weight — Spherical		
Edition:	1977 in a limited edition of 2,000		
Status:	Closed at No. 904		
Original Issue Price:	£26.00		

Name	U.S. $	Can. $	U.K. £
Intruder	150.00	200.00	125.00

CT-78
ZEPHYR

Designer:	Colin Terris		
Type:	Weight — Spherical		
Edition:	1977 in a limited edition of 400		
Status:	Fully subscribed		
Original Issue Price:	£35.00		

Name	U.S. $	Can. $	U.K. £
Zephyr	275.00	375.00	175.00

CT-79
PETAL INKWELL

Designer:	Colin Terris
Type:	Inkwell
Edition:	1977
Status:	Closed
Original Issue Price:	£50.00

Name	U.S. $	Can. $	U.K. £
Petal Inkwell	250.00	325.00	175.00

CT-80
CHRISTMAS WEIGHT

Designer:	Colin Terris
Type:	Weight — Spherical
Edition:	1977 in a limited edition of 500
Status:	Fully subscribed
Original Issue Price:	£50.00

Name	U.S. $	Can. $	U.K. £
Christmas Weight	700.00	950.00	475.00

Note: This is the first Collectors' Club Weight.

CT-81
ANGEL FISH

Designer:	Jennie Robertson
Type:	Weight — Spherical, engraved
Edition:	1978 in a limited edition of 1,500
Status:	Closed at No. 1,347
Series:	Exotic Fishes
Original Issue Price:	£25.00

Name	U.S. $	Can. $	U.K. £
Angel Fish	95.00	125.00	60.00

CT-82
KITTIWAKE

Designer:	Denis Mann
Type:	Weight — Spherical, engraved
Edition:	1978 in a limited edition of 500
Status:	Closed at No. 473
Series:	Sea Birds
Original Issue Price:	£23.50

Name	U.S. $	Can. $	U.K. £
Kittiwake	95.00	125.00	60.00

CT-83
SKUA

Designer:	Denis Mann
Type:	Weight — Spherical, engraved
Edition:	1978 in a limited edition of 500
Status:	Closed at No. 460
Series:	Sea Birds
Original Issue Price:	£23.50

Name	U.S. $	Can. $	U.K. £
Skua	95.00	125.00	60.00

CT-84
EIDER DUCK

Designer:	Denis Mann
Type:	Weight — Spherical, copperwheel engraved
Edition:	1978 in a limited edition of 100
Status:	Fully subscribed
Original Issue Price:	£80.00

Name	U.S. $	Can. $	U.K. £
Eider Duck	500.00	675.00	375.00

CT-85
MERMAID

Designer:	Ann Robertson
Type:	Weight — Spherical, copperwheel engraved
Edition:	1978 in a limited edition of 100
Status:	Fully subscribed
Original Issue Price:	£80.00

Name	U.S. $	Can. $	U.K. £
Mermaid	500.00	675.00	375.00

CT-86
AQUILA

Designer:	Colin Terris
Type:	Weight — Spherical
Edition:	1978 in a limited edition of 3,000
Status:	Closed at No. 1,029
Series:	Stars and Constellations
Original Issue Price:	£25.50

Name	U.S. $	Can. $	U.K. £
Aquila	80.00	100.00	65.00

CT-87
SAGITTARIUS

Designer:	Colin Terris
Type:	Weight — Spherical
Edition:	1978 in a limited edition of 3,000
Status:	Closed at No. 1,949
Series:	Stars and Constellations
Original Issue Price:	£25.50

Name	U.S. $	Can. $	U.K. £
Sagittarius	90.00	125.00	65.00

CT-88
ASTEROID

Designer:	Colin Terris
Type:	Weight — Spherical
Edition:	1978 in a limited edition of 3,000
Status:	Closed at No. 995
Original Issue Price:	£25.00

Name	U.S. $	Can. $	U.K. £
Asteroid	90.00	125.00	65.00

CT-89
SPINDRIFT

Designer:	Colin Terris
Type:	Weight — Spherical
Edition:	1978 in a limited edition of 3,000
Status:	Fully subscribed
Original Issue Price:	£19.00

Name	U.S. $	Can. $	U.K. £
Spindrift	135.00	175.00	90.00

CT-90
SUNFLARE

Designer:	Colin Terris
Type:	Weight — Spherical
Edition:	1978 in a limited edition of 3,000
Status:	Closed at No. 1,387
Original Issue Price:	£27.00

Name	U.S. $	Can. $	U.K. £
Sunflare	90.00	125.00	65.00

CT-91
MYRIAD

Designer: Oban Studios
Type: Weight — Spherical
Colour: See below
Edition: 1978
Status: Closed
Series: Unlimited — Modern Design
Original Issue Price: £11.00, U.S. $50.00

Colourways	U.S. $	Can. $	U.K. £
1. Blue	60.00	85.00	35.00
2. Green	60.00	85.00	35.00
3. Purple	60.00	85.00	35.00
4. Red	60.00	85.00	35.00

CT-92
MORNING DEW

Designer: Colin Terris
Type: Weight — Spherical
Colour: See below
Edition: 1978
Status: Closed
Original Issue Price: £13.00, U.S. $50.00

Colourways	U.S. $	Can. $	U.K. £
1. Blue	65.00	90.00	40.00
2. Green	65.00	90.00	40.00
3. Orange	65.00	90.00	40.00
4. Red	65.00	90.00	40.00
5. Silver	65.00	90.00	40.00
6. Yellow	65.00	90.00	40.00

CT-93
MAROONED

Designer: Colin Terris
Type: Weight — Spherical
Edition: 1978 in a limited edition of 3,000
Status: Closed at No. 1,454
Series: Limited — Modern Design
Original Issue Price: £27.50, U.S. $95.00

Name	U.S. $	Can. $	U.K. £
Marooned	100.00	135.00	65.00

CT-94
PEGASUS

Designer: Colin Terris
Type: Weight — Spherical
Edition: 1978 in a limited edition of 1,500
Status: Closed at No. 655
Series: Limited — Modern Design
Original Issue Price: £27.00, U.S. $125.00

Name	U.S. $	Can. $	U.K. £
Pegasus	125.00	150.00	75.00

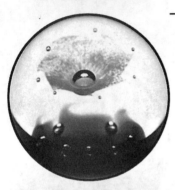

CT-95
SPACE PEARL

Designer: Colin Terris
Type: Weight — Spherical
Edition: 1978 in a limited edition of 3,000
Status: Closed at No. 1,648
Series: Limited — Modern Design
Original Issue Price: £27.00, U.S. $125.00

Name	U.S. $	Can. $	U.K. £
Space Pearl	125.00	180.00	60.00

CT-96
ICE PETAL PERFUME BOTTLE

Designer: Colin Terris
Type: Perfume bottle
Edition: 1978
Status: Closed
Series: Limited — Modern Design
Original Issue Price: £55.00, U.S. $235.00

Name	U.S. $	Can. $	U.K. £
Ice Petal Perfume Bottle	235.00	325.00	150.00

CT-97
SEA GRASS PERFUME BOTTLE

Designer: Colin Terris
Type: Perfume bottle
Edition: 1978
Status: Closed
Series: Unlimited — Modern Design
Original Issue Price: £55.00, U.S. $235.00

Name	U.S. $	Can. $	U.K. £
Sea Grass Perfume Bottle	235.00	325.00	150.00

CT-98
QUARTET PERFUME BOTTLE

Designer:	Colin Terris
Type:	Perfume bottle
Edition:	1978
Status:	Closed
Series:	Limited — Modern Design
Original Issue Price:	£55.00, U.S. $235.00

Name	U.S. $	Can. $	U.K. £
Quartet Perfume Bottle	235.00	325.00	150.00

CT-99
SNOWFLOWER

Designer:	Colin Terris
Type:	Weight — Spherical
Edition:	1978 in a limited edition of 3,000
Status:	Fully subscribed
Original Issue Price:	£30.00, U.S. $135.00

Name	U.S. $	Can. $	U.K. £
Snowflower	150.00	200.00	100.00

CT-100
COBRA

Designer:	Colin Terris and William Manson
Type:	Weight — Spherical
Cane:	78 (in base)
Edition:	1978 in a limited edition of 50
Status:	Fully subscribed
Original Issue Price:	£200.00, U.S. $850.00

Name	U.S. $	Can. $	U.K. £
Cobra	1,250.00	1,650.00	700.00

Note: See CT-135 for the 1979 issue and CT-190 for the 1980 issue.

CT-101
SALAMANDER

Designer:	Colin Terris and William Manson
Type:	Weight — Spherical
Cane:	78 (in base)
Edition:	1978 in a limited edition of 50
Status:	Fully subscribed
Original Issue Price:	£200.00, U.S. $850.00

Name	U.S. $	Can. $	U.K. £
Salamander	1,250.00	1,650.00	700.00

Note: See CT-136 for the 1979 issue and CT-187 for the 1980 issue.

CT-102
OCTOPUS

Designer:	William Manson
Type:	Weight — Spherical
Cane:	78 (in base)
Edition:	1978 in a limited edition of 50
Status:	Fully subscribed
Original Issue Price:	£200.00, U.S. $850.00

Name	U.S. $	Can. $	U.K. £
Octopus	1,250.00	1,650.00	700.00

Note: See CT-138 for the 1979 issue.

CT-103
MANTA RAY

Designer:	Colin Terris and William Manson
Type:	Weight — Spherical
Cane:	78 (in base)
Edition:	1978 in a limited edition of 50
Status:	Fully subscribed
Original Issue Price:	£200.00, U.S. $850.00

Name	U.S. $	Can. $	U.K. £
Manta Ray	1,250.00	1,650.00	700.00

Note: See CT-137 for the 1979 issue and CT-189 for the 1980 issue.

CT-104
EL DORADO

Designer:	Colin Terris and William Manson
Type:	Weight — Spherical
Cane:	78 (in base)
Edition:	1978 in a limited edition of 100
Status:	Fully subscribed
Original Issue Price:	£100.00, U.S. $450.00

Name	U.S. $	Can. $	U.K. £
El Dorado	600.00	900.00	375.00

CT-105
LADYBIRD

Designer:	Colin Terris
Type:	Weight — Spherical
Cane:	78 (in base)
Edition:	1978 in a limited edition of 100
Status:	Fully subscribed
Original Issue Price:	£100.00, U.S. $450.00

Name	U.S. $	Can. $	U.K. £
Ladybird	450.00	650.00	275.00

Note: See CT-139 for the 1979 issue.

CT-106
SWAN

Designer:	Colin Terris and William Manson
Type:	Weight — Spherical
Cane:	78 (in base)
Edition:	1978 in a limited edition of 100
Status:	Fully subscribed
Original Issue Price:	£100.00, U.S. $450.00

Name	*U.S. $*	*Can. $*	*U.K. £*
Swan	650.00	850.00	250.00

Note: See CT-144 for the 1979 issue.

CT-107
BUTTERFLY and FLOWER

Designer:	Colin Terris
Type:	Weight — Spherical
Cane:	78 (in base)
Edition:	1978 in a limited edition of 250
Status:	Fully subscribed
Original Issue Price:	£130.00, U.S. $565.00

Name	*U.S. $*	*Can. $*	*U.K. £*
Butterfly and Flower	565.00	800.00	300.00

Note: See CT-140 for the 1979 issue.

CT-108
SILVER LIZARD

Designer:	Colin Terris and David Hodge
Type:	Weight — Spherical
Edition:	1978 in a limited edition of 50
Status:	Closed at No. 45
Original Issue Price:	£200.00

Name	*U.S. $*	*Can. $*	*U.K. £*
Silver Lizard	1,500.00	2,000.00	1,000.00

Note: This paperweight was not issued in the U.S.

CT-109
MISTLETOE

Designer:	Colin Terris
Type:	Weight — Spherical
Edition:	1978 in a limited edition of 500
Status:	Fully subscribed
Original Issue Price:	£75.00

Name	*U.S. $*	*Can. $*	*U.K. £*
Mistletoe	375.00	500.00	200.00

Note: This paperweight was not issued in the U.S.

CT-110
JOURNEY OF THE WISE MEN

Designer: Helen MacDonald
Type: Weight — Spherical, engraved
Edition: 1978 in a limited edition of 2,000
Status: Closed at No. 1,583
Series: Nativity
Original Issue Price: £50.00, U.S. $195.00

Name	U.S. $	Can. $	U.K. £
Journey of the Wise Men	195.00	275.00	100.00

CT-111
CORONATION SILVER JUBILEE

Designer: Colin Terris
Type: Weight — Spherical
Edition: 1978 in a limited edition of 1,000
Status: Closed at No. 156
Series: Limited — Modern Design
Original Issue Price: £25.00

Name	U.S. $	Can. $	U.K. £
Coronation Silver Jubilee	175.00	225.00	125.00

Note: This paperweight was issued to commemorate the 25th anniversary of the coronation of Queen Elizabeth II. It was not issued in the U.S.

CT-113
ARCTIC NIGHT

Designer: Colin Terris
Type: Weight — Spherical
Edition: 1978 in a limited edition of 1,500
Status: Closed at No. 839
Original Issue Price: £30.00

Name	U.S. $	Can. $	U.K. £
Arctic Night	100.00	125.00	50.00

Note: The 1978 Collectors' Weight was offered to U.K. Club members only.

CT-114
KING NEPTUNE

Designer: Ann Robertson
Type: Weight — Spherical, copperwheel engraved
Edition: 1979 in a limited edition of 100
Status: Fully subscribed
Original Issue Price: £80.00, U.S. $400.00

Name	U.S. $	Can. $	U.K. £
King Neptune	475.00	600.00	200.00

CT-115
VEIL TAIL

Designer: Colin Terris
Type: Weight — Spherical, engraved
Edition: 1979 in a limited edition of 1,500
Status: Closed at No. 1,145
Original Issue Price: £26.00, U.S. $130.00

Name	U.S. $	Can. $	U.K. £
Veil Tail	130.00	180.00	50.00

CT-116
HUMMING BIRD

Designer: Colin Terris
Type: Weight — Spherical, engraved
Edition: 1979 in a limited edition of 1,000
Status: Fully subscribed
Series: Exotic Birds
Original Issue Price: £35.00, U.S. $120.00

Name	U.S. $	Can. $	U.K. £
Humming Bird	120.00	170.00	60.00

CT-117
LIBRA

Designer: Colin Terris
Type: Weight — Spherical
Edition: 1979 in a limited edition of 1,500
Status: Closed at No. 450
Original Issue Price: £25.00, U.S. $125.00

Name	U.S. $	Can. $	U.K. £
Libra	125.00	180.00	50.00

CT-118
ARIES

Designer: Colin Terris
Type: Weight — Spherical
Edition: 1979 in a limited edition of 1,500
Status: Closed at No. 447
Original Issue Price: £25.00, U.S. $125.00

Name	U.S. $	Can. $	U.K. £
Aries	125.00	180.00	50.00

CT-119A
SEA LACE PERFUME BOTTLE

Designer: Colin Terris
Type: Perfume bottle
Edition: 1979 in a limited edition of 100
Status: Fully subscribed
Original Issue Price: £90.00/set, U.S. $450.00/set

Name	U.S. $	Can. $	U.K. £
Sea Lace Perfume Bottle	600.00	800.00	400.00
Set	900.00	1,200..00	600.00

Note: CT-119A and B were issued and sold as a set.

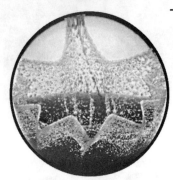

CT-119B
SEA LACE

Designer: Colin Terris
Type: Weight — Spherical
Edition: 1979 in a limited edition of 100
Status: Fully subscribed
Original Issue Price: £90.00/set, U.S. $450.00/set

Name	U.S. $	Can. $	U.K. £
Sea Lace	300.00	400.00	200.00

CT-120
BLUE PETAL PERFUME BOTTLE

Designer: Colin Terris
Type: Perfume bottle
Edition: 1979
Status: Closed
Series: Unlimited — Modern Design
Original Issue Price: £55.00, U.S. $265.00

Name	U.S. $	Can. $	U.K. £
Blue Petal Perfume Bottle	265.00	375.00	125.00

CT-121
SILVER SENTINEL

Designer: Colin Terris
Type: Weight — Spherical
Edition: 1979
Status: Closed
Original Issue Price: £15.00, U.S. $75.00

Name	U.S. $	Can. $	U.K. £
Silver Sentinel	75.00	100.00	35.00

CT-122A
DAWN

Designer:	Colin Terris
Type:	Weight — Spherical
Edition:	1979 in a limited edition of 750
Status:	Fully subscribed
Original Issue Price:	£60.00/set, U.S. $295.00/set

Name	U.S. $	Can. $	U.K. £
Dawn	225.00	300.00	150.00
Set	450.00	600.00	300.00

Note: CT-122A and B were issued and sold as a set.

CT-122B
DUSK

Designer:	Colin Terris
Type:	Weight — Spherical
Edition:	1979 in a limited edition of 750
Status:	Fully subscribed
Original Issue Price:	£60.00/set, U.S. $295.00/set

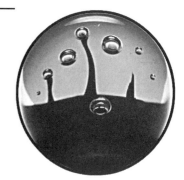

Name	U.S. $	Can. $	U.K. £
Dusk	225.00	300.00	150.00

CT-123
ICE FLAME

Designer:	Colin Terris
Type:	Weight — Spherical
Edition:	1979 in a limited edition of 1,000
Status:	Closed at No. 905
Series:	Limited — Modern Design
Original Issue Price:	£27.00, U.S. $135.00

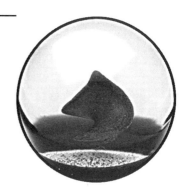

Name	U.S. $	Can. $	U.K. £
Ice Flame	150.00	200.00	65.00

CT-124
STAR FLOWER

Designer:	Colin Terris
Type:	Weight — Spherical
Edition:	1979 in a limited edition of 1,000
Status:	Fully subscribed
Series:	Limited — Modern Design
Original Issue Price:	£27.00, U.S. $135.00

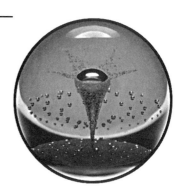

Name	U.S. $	Can. $	U.K. £
Star Flower	150.00	200.00	70.00

CT-125
NOMAD

Designer:	Colin Terris
Type:	Weight — Spherical
Edition:	1979 in a limited edition of 1,000
Status:	Fully subscribed
Series:	Limited — Modern Design
Original Issue Price:	£27.00, U.S. $135.00

Name	U.S. $	Can. $	U.K. £
Nomad	135.00	175.00	90.00

CT-126
TRIAD

Designer:	Colin Terris
Type:	Weight — Spherical
Edition:	1979 in a limited edition of 1,500
Status:	Closed at No. 815
Series:	Limited — Modern Design
Original Issue Price:	£25.00, U.S. $125.00

Name	U.S. $	Can. $	U.K. £
Triad	125.00	180.00	50.00

CT-127
CAROUSEL

Designer:	Colin Terris
Type:	Weight — Spherical
Edition:	1979 in a limited edition of 1,000
Status:	Fully subscribed
Series:	Limited — Modern Design
Original Issue Price:	£27.00, U.S. $135.00

Name	U.S. $	Can. $	U.K. £
Carousel	135.00	190.00	60.00

CT-128
ICE FOUNTAIN

Designer:	Colin Terris
Type:	Weight — Spherical
Edition:	1979 in a limited edition of 1,500
Status:	Fully subscribed
Series:	Limited — Modern Design
Original Issue Price:	£25.00, U.S. $125.00

Name	U.S. $	Can. $	U.K. £
Ice Fountain	125.00	180.00	50.00

CT-129
FLOWER FORM

Designer: Colin Terris
Type: Weight — Spherical
Edition: 1979 in a limited edition of 1,500
Status: Closed at No. 1,484
Series: Limited — Modern Design
Original Issue Price: £25.00, U.S. $125.00

Name	U.S. $	Can. $	U.K. £
Flower Form	125.00	180.00	60.00

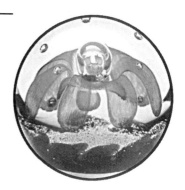

CT-130
ICE BLOSSOM

Designer: Colin Terris
Type: Weight — Spherical
Edition: 1979 in a limited edition of 1,000
Status: Closed at No. 854
Series: Limited — Modern Design
Original Issue Price: £30.00, U.S. $150.00

Name	U.S. $	Can. $	U.K. £
Ice Blossom	150.00	200.00	85.00

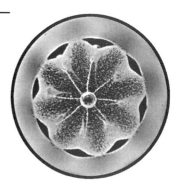

CT-131
ATLANTIS

Designer: Colin Terris
Type: Weight — Spherical
Edition: 1979 in a limited edition of 1,500
Status: Fully subscribed
Series: Limited — Modern Design
Original Issue Price: £25.00, U.S. $125.00

Name	U.S. $	Can. $	U.K. £
Atlantis	175.00	225.00	135.00

CT-132
OCTET

Designer: Colin Terris
Type: Weight — Spherical
Edition: 1979 in a limited edition of 500
Status: Fully subscribed
Series: Limited — Modern Design
Original Issue Price: £37.00, U.S. $185.00

Name	U.S. $	Can. $	U.K. £
Octet	185.00	250.00	100.00

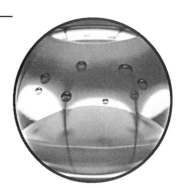

CT-133
ILLUSION

Designer:	Colin Terris
Type:	Weight — Spherical
Edition:	1979 in a limited edition of 1,000
Status:	Fully subscribed
Series:	Limited — Modern Design
Original Issue Price:	£27.00, U.S. $135.00

Name	U.S. $	Can. $	U.K. £
Illusion	135.00	175.00	85.00

CT-134
MYSTIQUE

Designer:	Colin Terris
Type:	Weight — Spherical
Edition:	1979 in a limited edition of 750
Status:	Closed at No. 630
Series:	Limited — Modern Design
Original Issue Price:	£45.00, U.S. $225.00

Name	U.S. $	Can. $	U.K. £
Mystique	225.00	325.00	100.00

CT-135
COBRA

Designer:	Colin Terris and William Manson
Type:	Weight — Spherical
Cane:	79 (in base)
Edition:	1979 in a limited edition of 50
Status:	Fully subscribed
Original Issue Price:	£215.00, U.S. $950.00

Name	U.S. $	Can. $	U.K. £
Cobra	1,175.00	1,550.00	500.00

Note: See CT-100 for the 1978 issue and CT-190 for the 1980 issue.

CT-136
SALAMANDER

Designer:	Colin Terris and William Manson
Type:	Weight — Spherical
Cane:	79 (in base)
Edition:	1979 in a limited edition of 50
Status:	Fully subscribed
Original Issue Price:	£215.00, U.S. $950.00

Name	U.S. $	Can. $	U.K. £
Salamander	1,175.00	1,550.00	500.00

Note: See CT-101 for the 1978 issue and CT-187 for the 1980 issue.

CT-137
MANTA RAY

Designer:	Colin Terris and William Manson
Type:	Weight — Spherical
Cane:	79 (in base)
Edition:	1979 in a limited edition of 50
Status:	Fully subscribed
Original Issue Price:	£215.00, U.S. $950.00

Name	U.S. $	Can. $	U.K. £
Manta Ray	1,150.00	1,550.00	500.00

Note: See CT-103 for the 1978 issue and CT-189 for the 1980 issue.

CT-138
OCTOPUS

Designer:	William Manson
Type:	Weight — Spherical
Cane:	79 (in base)
Edition:	1979 in a limited edition of 50
Status:	Fully subscribed
Original Issue Price:	£215.00, U.S. $950.00

Name	U.S. $	Can. $	U.K. £
Octopus	1,150.00	1,550.00	500.00

Note: See CT-102 for the 1978 issue.

CT-139
LADYBIRD

Designer:	Colin Terris
Type:	Weight — Spherical
Cane:	79 (in base)
Edition:	1979 in a limited edition of 100
Status:	Closed at No. 51
Original Issue Price:	£100.00, U.S. $495.00

Name	U.S. $	Can. $	U.K. £
Ladybird	550.00	750.00	300.00

Note: See CT-105 for the 1978 issue.

CT-140
BUTTERFLY and FLOWER

Designer:	Colin Terris
Type:	Weight — Spherical
Cane:	79 (in base)
Edition:	1979 in a limited edition of 250
Status:	Closed at No. 104
Original Issue Price:	£130.00, U.S. $220.00

Name	U.S. $	Can. $	U.K. £
Butterfly and Flower	500.00	750.00	300.00

Note: See CT-107 for the 1978 issue.

CT-141
HEATHER BELL

Designer:	William Manson
Type:	Weight — Spherical
Edition:	1979 in a limited edition of 100
Status:	Closed at No. 91
Original Issue Price:	£100.00, U.S. $465.00

Name	U.S. $	Can. $	U.K. £
Heather Bell	600.00	800.00	300.00

CT-142
ROSEBUD

Designer:	William Manson
Type:	Weight — Spherical
Cane:	79 (in base)
Edition:	1979 in a limited edition of 50
Status:	Fully subscribed
Original Issue Price:	£200.00, U.S. $950.00

Name	U.S. $	Can. $	U.K. £
Rosebud	1,200.00	1,500.00	500.00

Note: See CT-188 for the 1980 issue.

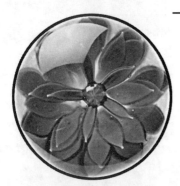

CT-143
FLORAL FOUNTAIN

Designer:	Colin Terris
Type:	Weight — Spherical
Colour:	Red
Cane:	CG (Caithness Glass)
Edition:	1979 in a limited edition of 750
Status:	Closed at No. 636
Original Issue Price:	£45.00, U.S. $225.00

Name	U.S. $	Can. $	U.K. £
Floral Fountain	250.00	300.00	125.00

CT-144
SWAN

Designer:	Colin Terris and William Manson
Type:	Weight — Spherical
Cane:	79 (in base)
Edition:	1979 in a limited edition of 100
Status:	Fully subscribed
Original Issue Price:	£100.00, U.S. $495.00

Name	U.S. $	Can. $	U.K. £
Swan	600.00	800.00	300.00

CT-145
HOLLY WREATH

Designer: Colin Terris
Type: Weight — Spherical
Edition: 1979 in a limited edition of 500
Status: Closed at No. 495
Original Issue Price: £89.00, U.S. $395.00

Name	U.S. $	Can. $	U.K. £
Holly Wreath	400.00	550.00	155.00

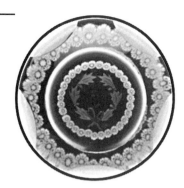

CT-146
SHEPHERDS

Designer: Helen MacDonald
Type: Weight — Spherical, engraved
Edition: 1979 in a limited edition of 2,000
Status: Closed at No. 864
Series: Nativity
Original Issue Price: £55.00, U.S. $195.00

Name	U.S. $	Can. $	U.K. £
Shepherds	200.00	275.00	100.00

CT-147
CHRISTMAS ROSE

Designer: Colin Terris
Type: Weight — Spherical, sulphide and lampwork
Edition: 1979 in a limited edition of 1,000
Status: Closed at No. 507
Original Issue Price: £70.00, U.S. $375.00

Name	U.S. $	Can. $	U.K. £
Christmas Rose	375.00	525.00	125.00

CT-148
HENRY VIII

Designer: Colin Terris
Type: Weight — Spherical, sulphide
Edition: 1979 in a limited edition of 1,000
Status: Closed at No. 502
Original Issue Price: £70.00, U.S. $375.00

Name	U.S. $	Can. $	U.K. £
Henry VIII	375.00	525.00	125.00

CT-149
KALEIDOSCOPE

Designer:	Colin Terris		
Type:	Weight — Spherical		
Edition:	1979		
Status:	Closed		
Original Issue Price:	£10.00, U.S. $15.00		

Name	*U.S. $*	*Can. $*	*U.K. £*
Kaleidoscope	75.00	100.00	40.00

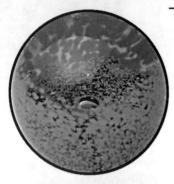

CT-150
NUCLEUS

Designer:	Colin Terris
Type:	Weight — Spherical
Edition:	1979 in a limited edition of 1,500
Status:	Closed at No. 383
Series:	Limited — Modern Design
Original Issue Price:	£30.90, U.S. $135.00

Name	*U.S. $*	*Can. $*	*U.K. £*
Nucleus	135.00	190.00	45.00

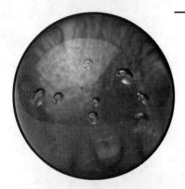

CT-151
OCEAN SPRING

Designer:	Colin Terris
Type:	Weight — Spherical
Edition:	1979 in a limited edition of 1,500
Status:	Closed at No. 630
Series:	Limited — Modern Design
Original Issue Price:	£30.90, U.S. $135.00

Name	*U.S. $*	*Can. $*	*U.K. £*
Ocean Spring	135.00	190.00	60.00

CT-152
EMBRYO

Designer:	Colin Terris
Type:	Weight — Spherical
Edition:	1979 in a limited edition of 1,500
Status:	Closed at No. 649
Series:	Limited — Modern Design
Original Issue Price:	£30.90, U.S. $135.00

Name	*U.S. $*	*Can. $*	*U.K. £*
Embryo	135.00	190.00	50.00

CT-157
DREAM FLOWER

Designer:	Colin Terris
Type:	Weight — Spherical
Edition:	1980 in a limited edition of 750
Status:	Fully subscribed
Series:	Limited — Modern Design
Original Issue Price:	£41.55, U.S. $185.00

Name	U.S. $	Can. $	U.K. £
Dream Flower	200.00	275.00	90.00

CT-158
NIGHT VENTURE

Designer:	Colin Terris
Type:	Weight — Spherical
Edition:	1980 in a limited edition of 1,500
Status:	Closed at No. 827
Series:	Limited — Modern Design
Original Issue Price:	£30.90, U.S. $135.00

Name	U.S. $	Can. $	U.K. £
Night Venture	135.00	190.00	50.00

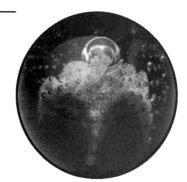

CT-159
SPACE ORCHID

Designer:	Colin Terris
Type:	Weight — Spherical
Edition:	1980 in a limited edition of 1,000
Status:	Fully subscribed
Series:	Limited — Modern Design
Original Issue Price:	£35.00, U.S. $155.00

Name	U.S. $	Can. $	U.K. £
Space Orchid	155.00	200.00	80.00

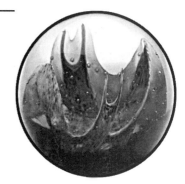

CT-160
SPACE TRAVELLER

Designer:	Colin Terris
Type:	Weight — Spherical
Edition:	1980 in a limited edition of 1,000
Status:	Closed at No. 571
Series:	Limited — Modern Design
Original Issue Price:	£35.15, U.S. $155.00

Name	U.S. $	Can. $	U.K. £
Space Traveller	155.00	200.00	50.00

CT-161
COSMIC RAIN

Designer:	Colin Terris
Type:	Weight — Spherical
Edition:	1980 in a limited edition of 750
Status:	Closed at No. 394
Series:	Limited — Modern Design
Original Issue Price:	£55.40, U.S. $250.00

Name	U.S. $	Can. $	U.K. £
Cosmic Rain	250.00	350.00	100.00

CT-162
BLUE FLORAL FOUNTAIN

Designer:	Colin Terris
Type:	Weight — Spherical
Edition:	1980 in a limited edition of 750
Status:	Fully subscribed
Original Issue Price:	£58.60, U.S. $265.00

Name	U.S. $	Can. $	U.K. £
Blue Floral Fountain	275.00	375.00	100.00

CT-163
BAUBLE, BANGLE and BEADS

Designer:	Colin Terris
Type:	Weight — Spherical
Edition:	1980 in a limited edition of 1,500
Status:	Closed at No. 1,054
Series:	Limited — Modern Design
Original Issue Price:	£30.90, U.S. $135.00

Name	U.S. $	Can. $	U.K. £
Bauble, Bangle and Beads	135.00	190.00	45.00

CT-164
BLUE SPIRAL

Designer:	Colin Terris
Type:	Weight — Spherical
Edition:	1980 in a limited edition of 750
Status:	Closed at No. 724
Series:	Limited — Modern Design
Original Issue Price:	£39.40, U.S. $175.00

Name	U.S. $	Can. $	U.K. £
Blue Spiral	175.00	250.00	75.00

CT-165
MOONPROBE

Designer:	Colin Terris
Type:	Weight — Spherical
Edition:	1980 in a limited edition of 1,000
Status:	Closed at No. 398
Series:	Limited — Modern Design
Original Issue Price:	£33.55, U.S. $150.00

Name	U.S. $	Can. $	U.K. £
Moonprobe	150.00	200.00	65.00

CT-166
VERTIGO

Designer:	Colin Terris
Type:	Weight — Spherical
Edition:	1980 in a limited edition of 1,500
Status:	Closed at No. 571
Series:	Limited — Modern Design
Original Issue Price:	£30.90, U.S. $135.00

Name	U.S. $	Can. $	U.K. £
Vertigo	135.00	190.00	55.00

CT-167
DOUBLE SPIRAL

Designer:	Colin Terris
Type:	Weight — Spherical
Edition:	1980 in a limited edition of 1,000
Status:	Closed at No. 643
Series:	Limited — Modern Design
Original Issue Price:	£33.55, U.S. $150.00

Name	U.S. $	Can. $	U.K. £
Double Spiral	150.00	200.00	50.00

CT-168
SANCTUARY

Designer:	Colin Terris
Type:	Weight — Spherical
Edition:	1980 in a limited edition of 500
Status:	Fully subscribed
Series:	Limited — Modern Design
Original Issue Price:	£55.45, U.S. $250.00

Name	U.S. $	Can. $	U.K. £
Sanctuary	250.00	350.00	150.00

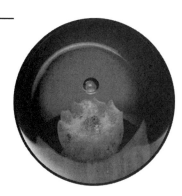

CT-169
NIGHT FLOWER

Designer:	Colin Terris
Type:	Weight — Spherical
Edition:	1980 in a limited edition of 1,500
Status:	Fully subscribed
Series:	Limited — Modern Design
Original Issue Price:	£30.90, U.S. $135.00

Name	U.S. $	Can. $	U.K. £
Night Flower	135.00	190.00	75.00

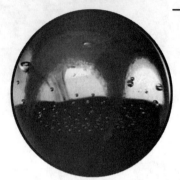

CT-170
FIRE FLOWER

Designer:	Colin Terris
Type:	Weight — Spherical
Edition:	1980 in a limited edition of 1,500
Status:	Closed at No. 406
Series:	Limited — Modern Design
Original Issue Price:	£30.90, U.S. $135.00

Name	U.S. $	Can. $	U.K. £
Fire Flower	135.00	190.00	45.00

CT-171
SATELLITE

Designer:	Colin Terris
Type:	Weight — Spherical
Edition:	1980 in a limited edition of 1,000
Status:	Closed at No. 948
Series:	Limited — Modern Design
Original Issue Price:	£35.15, U.S. $165.00

Name	U.S. $	Can. $	U.K. £
Satellite	165.00	225.00	70.00

CT-172
TIME ZONE

Designer:	Colin Terris
Type:	Weight — Spherical
Edition:	1980 in a limited edition of 1,500
Status:	Closed at No. 426
Series:	Limited — Modern Design
Original Issue Price:	£30.90, U.S. $135.00

Name	U.S. $	Can. $	U.K. £
Time Zone	135.00	190.00	60.00

CT-173
CONTRAST

Designer: Colin Terris
Type: Weight — Spherical
Edition: 1980 in a limited edition of 1,500
Status: Closed at No. 769
Series: Limited — Modern Design
Original Issue Price: £30.90, U.S. $135.00

Name	U.S. $	Can. $	U.K. £
Contrast	135.00	190.00	50.00

CT-174
FIREWORKS

Designer: Colin Terris
Type: Weight — Spherical
Edition: 1980 in a limited edition of 1,000
Status: Fully subscribed
Series: Limited — Modern Design
Original Issue Price: £30.90, U.S. $165.00

Name	U.S. $	Can. $	U.K. £
Fireworks	175.00	225.00	115.00

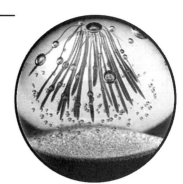

CT-175
PARASOL

Designer: Colin Terris
Type: Weight — Spherical
Edition: 1980 in a limited edition of 1,000
Status: Closed at No. 956
Series: Limited — Modern Design
Original Issue Price: £35.15, U.S. $165.00

Name	U.S. $	Can. $	U.K. £
Parasol	165.00	225.00	60.00

CT-176
TWILIGHT

Designer: Colin Terris
Type: Weight — Spherical
Edition: 1980 in a limited edition of 750
Status: Closed at No. 539
Series: Limited — Modern Design
Original Issue Price: £39.40, U.S. $175.00

Name	U.S. $	Can. $	U.K. £
Twilight	175.00	250.00	60.00

CT-177
FLAMENCO

Designer:	Alistair Ross
Type:	Weight — Spherical
Edition:	1980
Status:	Closed
Series:	Unlimited — Modern Design
Original Issue Price:	£23.95, U.S. $115.00

Name	U.S. $	Can. $	U.K. £
Flamenco	115.00	160.00	45.00

CT-178
METEOR

Designer:	Colin Terris
Type:	Weight — Spherical
Edition:	1980 in a limited edition of 1,000
Status:	Closed at No. 518
Series:	Limited — Modern Design
Original Issue Price:	£31.95, U.S. $145.00

Name	U.S. $	Can. $	U.K. £
Meteor	145.00	200.00	50.00

CT-179
SUNSET

Designer:	Colin Terris
Type:	Weight — Spherical
Edition:	1980 in a limited edition of 1,000
Status:	Closed at No. 434
Series:	Limited — Modern Design
Original Issue Price:	£31.95, U.S. $145.00

Name	U.S. $	Can. $	U.K. £
Sunset	145.00	200.00	50.00

CT-180
WINTER MOON

Designer:	Colin Terris
Type:	Weight — Spherical
Edition:	1980 in a limited edition of 1,000
Status:	Closed at No. 418
Series:	Limited — Modern Design
Original Issue Price:	£31.95, U.S. $145.00

Name	U.S. $	Can. $	U.K. £
Winter Moon	145.00	200.00	55.00

CT-181
SKYLINE

Designer:	Colin Terris
Type:	Weight — Spherical
Edition:	1980 in a limited edition of 1,000
Status:	Closed at No. 404
Series:	Limited — Modern Design
Original Issue Price:	£31.95, U.S. $145.00

Name	U.S. $	Can. $	U.K. £
Skyline	145.00	200.00	50.00

CT-182
SPACEPORT

Designer:	Colin Terris
Type:	Weight — Spherical
Edition:	1980 in a limited edition of 1,500
Status:	Closed at No. 723
Series:	Limited — Modern Design
Original Issue Price:	£30.90, U.S. $135.00

Name	U.S. $	Can. $	U.K. £
Spaceport	135.00	190.00	50.00

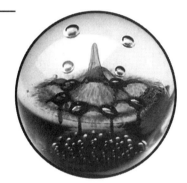

CT-183
BLACK GEM

Designer:	Colin Terris
Type:	Weight — Spherical
Edition:	1980 in a limited edition of 1,000
Status:	Closed at No. 857
Original Issue Price:	£27.50

Name	U.S. $	Can. $	U.K. £
Black Gem	90.00	125.00	60.00

Note: The 1979/80 Collectors' Weight was not issued in the U.S.

CT-184
NATIVITY

Designer:	Helen MacDonald
Type:	Weight — Spherical, engraved
Edition:	1980 in a limited edition of 2,000
	(1,000 in the U.K. and 1,000 in the U.S.)
Status:	Closed at No. 557
Series:	Nativity
Original Issue Price:	£63.90, U.S. $275.00

Name	U.S. $	Can. $	U.K. £
Nativity	275.00	375.00	95.00

CT-185
SIAMESE FIGHTING FISH

Designer:	Jennie Robertson
Type:	Weight — Spherical, engraved
Edition:	1980 in a limited edition of 1,500
Status:	Closed at No. 367
Series:	Exotic Fishes
Original Issue Price:	£31.95, U.S. $145.00

Name	U.S. $	Can. $	U.K. £
Siamese Fighting Fish	145.00	200.00	55.00

CT-186
SEAL

Designer:	Ray Gannon
Type:	Weight — Spherical
Edition:	1980 in a limited edition of 50
Status:	Closed at No. 27
Original Issue Price:	£215.00

Name	U.S. $	Can. $	U.K. £
Seal	1,000.00	1,500.00	600.00

Note: This paperweight was not issued in the U.S.

CT-187
SALAMANDER

Designer:	Caithness Paperweight Studio
Type:	Weight — Spherical
Cane:	80 (in base)
Edition:	1980 in a limited edition of 50
Status:	Closed at No. 39
Original Issue Price:	£215.00, U.S. $950.00

Name	U.S. $	Can. $	U.K. £
Salamander	950.00	1,350.00	350.00

Note: See CT-101 for the 1978 issue and CT-136 for the 1979 issue.

CT-188
ROSEBUD

Designer:	Caithness Paperweight Studio
Type:	Weight — Spherical
Edition:	1980 in a limited edition of 50
Status:	Fully subscribed
Original Issue Price:	£215.00, U.S. $950.00

Name	U.S. $	Can. $	U.K. £
Rosebud	950.00	1,350.00	300.00

Note: See CT-142 for the 1979 issue.

CT-189
MANTA RAY

Designer:	Caithness Paperweight Studio		
Type:	Weight — Spherical		
Cane:	80 (in base)		
Edition:	1980 in a limited edition of 50		
Status:	Closed at No. 30		
Original Issue Price:	£215.00, U.S. $950.00		

Name	U.S. $	Can. $	U.K. £
Manta Ray	950.00	1,350.00	250.00

Note: See CT-103 for the 1978 issue and CT-137 for the 1979 issue.

CT-190
COBRA

Designer:	Caithness Paperweight Studio		
Type:	Weight — Spherical		
Cane:	80 (in base)		
Edition:	1980 in a limited edition of 50		
Status:	Closed at No. 27		
Original Issue Price:	£215.00, U.S. $950.00		

Name	U.S. $	Can. $	U.K. £
Cobra	950.00	1,350.00	275.00

Note: See CT-100 for the 1978 issue and CT-135 for the 1979 issue.

CT-191A
BLUE ROSE PERFUME BOTTLE

Designer:	Colin Terris		
Type:	Perfume bottle		
Edition:	1980 in a limited edition of 100		
Status:	Fully subscribed		
Original Issue Price:	£124.60/set, U.S. $550.00/set		

Name	U.S. $	Can. $	U.K. £
Blue Rose Perfume Bottle	600.00	800.00	400.00
Set	900.00	1,200.00	600.00

Note: CT-191A and B were issued and sold as a set.

CT-191B
BLUE ROSE

Designer:	Colin Terris		
Type:	Weight — Spherical		
Edition:	1980 in a limited edition of 100		
Status:	Fully subscribed		
Original Issue Price:	£124.60/set, U.S. $550.00/set		

Name	U.S. $	Can. $	U.K. £
Blue Rose	300.00	400.00	200.00

CT-192A
BLACK and GOLD PERFUME BOTTLE

Designer: James MacBeath
Type: Perfume bottle
Edition: 1980 in a limited edition of 100
Status: Fully subscribed
Original Issue Price: £124.60/set, U.S. $550.00/set

Name	U.S. $	Can. $	U.K. £
Black and Gold Perfume Bottle	600.00	800.00	400.00
Set	900.00	1,200.00	600.00

Note: CT-192A and B were issued and sold as a set.

CT-192B
BLACK and GOLD

Designer: James MacBeath
Type: Weight — Spherical
Edition: 1980 in a limited edition of 100
Status: Fully subscribed
Original Issue Price: £124.60/set, U.S. $550.00/set

Name	U.S. $	Can. $	U.K. £
Black and Gold	300.00	400.00	200.00

CT-195
GOLD THROAT

Designer: Colin Terris
Type: Weight — Spherical, engraved
Edition: 1980 in a limited edition of 1,000
Status: Closed at No. 545
Series: Exotic Birds
Original Issue Price: £42.60, U.S. $195.00

Name	U.S. $	Can. $	U.K. £
Gold Throat	195.00	275.00	70.00

CT-196
SILENT WATCHER

Designer: Ray Gannon
Type: Weight — Domed
Edition: 1980 in a limited edition of 50
Status: Closed at No. 23
Original Issue Price: £225.60

Name	U.S. $	Can. $	U.K. £
Silent Watcher	750.00	1,000.00	450.00

Note: This paperweight was not issued in the U.S.

CT-197
QUEEN ELIZABETH I

Designer: Colin Terris
Type: Weight — Spherical, sulphide
Edition: 1980 in a limited edition of 1,000
Status: Closed at No. 390
Original Issue Price: £81.75, U.S. $395.00

Name	U.S. $	Can. $	U.K. £
Queen Elizabeth I	395.00	550.00	150.00

CT-198
ROYAL BIRTHDAY

Designer: Colin Terris
Type: Weight — Spherical, engraved
Edition: 1980 in a limited edition of 1,000
Status: Closed at No. 188
Original Issue Price: £30.00

Name	U.S. $	Can. $	U.K. £
Royal Birthday	150.00	225.00	50.00

Note: Weights CT-198, 199, 200 and 201 were issued to commemorate the 80th birthday of HM Queen Elizabeth The Queen Mother. They were not issued in the U.S.

CT-199
QUEEN MOTHER

Designer: Colin Terris
Type: Weight — Spherical, sulphide
Cane: 1980
Edition: 1980 in a limited edition of 1,000
Status: Closed at No. 310
Original Issue Price: £85.00

Name	U.S. $	Can. $	U.K. £
Queen Mother	200.00	275.00	125.00

CT-200
ROYAL ARMS

Designer: Jennie Robertson
Type: Weight — Spherical, engraved
Edition: 1980 in a limited edition of 80
Status: Fully subscribed
Original Issue Price: £99.00

Name	U.S. $	Can. $	U.K. £
Royal Arms	350.00	500.00	200.00

CT-201
THISTLE AND ROSE

Designer: Helen MacDonald
Type: Weight — Spherical
Edition: 1980 in a limited edition of 1,000
Status: Closed at No. 796
Original Issue Price: £39.50

Name	U.S. $	Can. $	U.K. £
Thistle and Rose	90.00	125.00	60.00

Note: This paperweight was not issued in the U.S.

CT-202
PIROUETTE

Designer: Colin Terris
Type: Weight — Spherical
Edition: 1980 in a limited edition of 1,000
Status: Closed at No. 527
Original Issue Price: £35.00

Name	U.S. $	Can. $	U.K. £
Pirouette	135.00	175.00	85.00

Note: The 1980 Collectors' Weight was offered to U.K. Club members only.

CT-203
SPRINGTIME

Designer: Andrew Lawson
Type: Weight — Spherical
Edition: 1981 in a limited edition of 750
Status: Fully subscribed
Series: Limited — Modern Design
Original Issue Price: £44.75, U.S. $195.00

Name	U.S. $	Can. $	U.K. £
Springtime	195.00	275.00	75.00

CT-204
ELEGANCE

Designer: Colin Terris
Type: Weight — Spherical
Edition: 1981 in a limited edition of 250
Status: Fully subscribed
Series: Limited — Modern Design
Original Issue Price: £63.00, U.S. $295.00

Name	U.S. $	Can. $	U.K. £
Elegance	295.00	425.00	175.00

CT-205
PEACH FLORAL FOUNTAIN

Designer:	Colin Terris
Type:	Weight — Spherical
Edition:	1981 in a limited edition of 750
Status:	Fully subscribed
Original Issue Price:	£63.00, U.S. $265.00

Name	U.S. $	Can. $	U.K. £
Peach Floral Fountain	265.00	375.00	120.00

CT-206
FANTASIA

Designer:	Colin Terris
Type:	Weight — Spherical
Edition:	1981 in a limited edition of 750
Status:	Closed at No. 592
Original Issue Price:	£50.00, U.S. $225.00

Name	U.S. $	Can. $	U.K. £
Fantasia	225.00	325.00	70.00

CT-207
TRISTAR

Designer:	Colin Terris
Type:	Weight — Spherical
Edition:	1981 in a limited edition of 750
Status:	Closed at No. 711
Original Issue Price:	£50.00, U.S. $225.00

Name	U.S. $	Can. $	U.K. £
Tristar	225.00	325.00	70.00

CT-208
SPACE SHUTTLE

Designer:	Colin Terris
Type:	Weight — Spherical
Edition:	1981 in a limited edition of 1,000
Status:	Fully subscribed
Series:	Limited — Modern Design
Original Issue Price:	£32.00, U.S. $135.00

Name	U.S. $	Can. $	U.K. £
Space Shuttle	135.00	190.00	55.00

CT-209
TOUCHDOWN

Designer: Colin Terris
Type: Weight — Spherical
Edition: 1981 in a limited edition of 1,000
Status: Closed at No. 988
Original Issue Price: £32.00, U.S. $135.00

Name	U.S. $	Can. $	U.K. £
Touchdown	135.00	190.00	85.00

CT-210
LUNAR III

Designer: Colin Terris
Type: Weight — Spherical
Edition: 1981 in a limited edition of 750
Status: Fully subscribed
Original Issue Price: £41.00, U.S. $175.00

Name	U.S. $	Can. $	U.K. £
Lunar III	175.00	250.00	100.00

CT-211
STAR PAVILION

Designer: Colin Terris
Type: Weight — Spherical
Edition: 1981 in a limited edition of 750
Status: Closed at No. 246
Series: Limited — Modern Design
Original Issue Price: £41.50, U.S. $175.00

Name	U.S. $	Can. $	U.K. £
Star Pavilion	175.00	250.00	55.00

CT-212
JESTER

Designer: Caithness Paperweight Studios
Type: Weight — Spherical
Edition: 1981 in a limited edition of 1,000
Status: Closed at No. 961
Series: Limited — Modern Design
Original Issue Price: £32.00, U.S. $135.00

Name	U.S. $	Can. $	U.K. £
Jester	135.00	190.00	50.00

CT-213
CORONET

Designer: Colin Terris
Type: Weight — Spherical
Edition: 1981 in a limited edition of 750
Status: Closed at No. 120
Series: Limited — Modern Design
Original Issue Price: £41.50, U.S. $175.00

Name	U.S. $	Can. $	U.K. £
Coronet	175.00	250.00	50.00

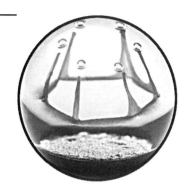

CT-214
GAZEBO

Designer: Caithness Paperweight Studios
Type: Weight — Spherical
Edition: 1981 in a limited edition of 1,000
Status: Fully subscribed
Series: Limited — Modern Design
Original Issue Price: £32.00, U.S. $135.00

Name	U.S. $	Can. $	U.K. £
Gazebo	135.00	190.00	50.00

CT-215
VIKING FLAME

Designer: Colin Terris
Type: Weight — Spherical
Edition: 1981 in a limited edition of 750
Status: Closed at No. 390
Series: Limited — Modern Design
Original Issue Price: £41.50, U.S. $175.00

Name	U.S. $	Can. $	U.K. £
Viking Flame	175.00	250.00	50.00

CT-216
MIDAS

Designer: Colin Terris
Type: Weight — Spherical
Edition: 1981 in a limited edition of 750
Status: Closed at No. 738
Series: Limited — Modern Design
Original Issue Price: £41.50, U.S. $175.00

Name	U.S. $	Can. $	U.K. £
Midas	175.00	250.00	60.00

CT-217
ZENITH PERFUME BOTTLE

Designer: Colin Terris
Type: Perfume bottle
Edition: 1981 in a limited edition of 150
Status: Closed at No. 125
Original Issue Price: £85.00, U.S. $375.00

Name	U.S. $	Can. $	U.K. £
Zenith Perfume Bottle	450.00	650.00	250.00

CT-218A
FAITH

Designer: Colin Terris
Type: Weight — Spherical
Edition: 1981 in a limited edition of 250
Status: Closed at No. 237
Series: Limited — Modern Design
Original Issue Price: £127.50/set, U.S. $575.00/set

Name	U.S. $	Can. $	U.K. £
Faith	250.00	350.00	150.00
Set	750.00	1,050.00	450.00

Note: CT-218A, B and C were issued and sold as a set.

CT-218B
HOPE

Designer: Colin Terris
Type: Weight — Spherical
Edition: 1981 in a limited edition of 250
Status: Closed at No. 237
Series: Limited — Modern Design
Original Issue Price: £127.50/set, U.S. $575.00/set

Name	U.S. $	Can. $	U.K. £
Hope	250.00	350.00	150.00

CT-218C
CHARITY

Designer: Colin Terris
Type: Weight — Spherical
Edition: 1981 in a limited edition of 250
Status: Closed at No. 237
Series: Limited — Modern Design
Original Issue Price: £127.50/set, U.S. $575.00/set

Name	U.S. $	Can. $	U.K. £
Charity	250.00	350.00	150.00

CT-219
SAND SPRITE

Designer:	Colin Terris
Type:	Weight — Spherical
Edition:	1981 in a limited edition of 750
Status:	Closed at No. 743
Series:	Limited — Modern Design
Original Issue Price:	£41.50, U.S. $175.00

Name	U.S. $	Can. $	U.K. £
Sand Sprite	175.00	250.00	75.00

CT-220
ETERNA

Designer:	Colin Terris
Type:	Weight — Spherical
Edition:	1981 in a limited edition of 500
Status:	Closed at No. 334
Series:	Limited — Modern Design
Original Issue Price:	£59.50, U.S. $275.00

Name	U.S. $	Can. $	U.K. £
Eterna	275.00	375.00	125.00

CT-221
SAMARKAND PERFUME BOTTLE

Designer:	Colin Terris
Type:	Perfume bottle
Edition:	1981 in a limited edition of 150
Status:	Fully subscribed
Series:	Limited — Modern Design
Original Issue Price:	£85.00, U.S. $375.00

Name	U.S. $	Can. $	U.K. £
Samarkand Perfume Bottle	450.00	650.00	200.00

CT-222
AQUAFLORA PERFUME BOTTLE

Designer:	Colin Terris
Type:	Perfume bottle
Edition:	1981
Status:	Closed
Original Issue Price:	£55.00, U.S. $245.00

Name	U.S. $	Can. $	U.K. £
Aquaflora Perfume Bottle	250.00	350.00	75.00

CT-223
ENCHANTED FOREST

Designer:	Colin Terris
Type:	Weight — Spherical
Edition:	1981 in a limited edition of 1,000
Status:	Closed at No. 227
Original Issue Price:	£28.75, U.S. $125.00

Name	U.S. $	Can. $	U.K. £
Enchanted Forest	125.00	180.00	40.00

CT-224
COQUETTE

Designer:	Douglas Cowie
Type:	Weight — Spherical, engraved
Edition:	1981 in a limited edition of 1,000
Status:	Closed at No. 254
Series:	Exotic Birds
Original Issue Price:	£45.75, U.S. $195.00

Name	U.S. $	Can. $	U.K. £
Coquette	195.00	275.00	60.00

CT-225
WHIRLYGIG

Designer:	Colin Terris
Type:	Weight — Spherical
Colour:	Silver
Edition:	1981
Status:	Closed
Series:	Unlimited — Modern Design
Original Issue Price:	£12.75, U.S. $57.50

Name	U.S. $	Can. $	U.K. £
Whirlygig	60.00	85.00	20.00

CT-226
NOVA

Designer:	Colin Terris
Type:	Weight — Conical
Colour:	Many colour variations
Edition:	1981
Status:	Closed
Series:	Unlimited — Modern Design
Original Issue Price:	£10.75, U.S. $49.50

Name	U.S. $	Can. $	U.K. £
Nova	50.00	75.00	20.00

CT-227
POLKA

Designer: Colin Terris
Type: Weight — Spherical
Colour: Many colour variations
Edition: 1981
Status: Closed
Series: Unlimited — Modern Design
Original Issue Price: £13.75, U.S. $62.50

Name	U.S. $	Can. $	U.K. £
Polka	65.00	95.00	25.00

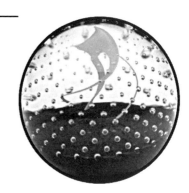

CT-228
TIGER

Designer: Douglas Cowie
Type: Weight — Spherical, engraved
Edition: 1981 in a limited edition of 1,500
Status: Closed at No. 105
Original Issue Price: £28.75, U.S. $125.00

Name	U.S. $	Can. $	U.K. £
Tiger	135.00	175.00	75.00

CT-229
WHITE RHINO

Designer: Caithness Engraving Studios
Type: Weight — Spherical, engraved
Edition: 1981 in a limited edition of 1,500
Status: Closed at No. 138
Original Issue Price: £28.75, U.S. $125.00

Name	U.S. $	Can. $	U.K. £
White Rhino	135.00	175.00	65.00

CT-230
PANDA

Designer: Douglas Cowie
Type: Weight — Spherical, engraved
Edition: 1981 in a limited edition of 1,500
Status: Closed at No. 185
Original Issue Price: £28.75, U.S. $125.00

Name	U.S. $	Can. $	U.K. £
Panda	135.00	175.00	50.00

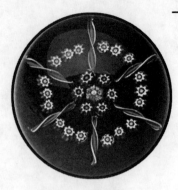

CT-231
SHIP'S WHEEL

Designer:	Colin Terris
Type:	Weight — Spherical
Edition:	1981 in a limited edition of 1,000
Status:	Closed at No. 891
Original Issue Price:	£35.00, U.S. $135.00

Name	U.S. $	Can. $	U.K. £
Ship's Wheel	135.00	190.00	50.00

CT-232
REGENCY STRIPE

Designer:	Colin Terris
Type:	Weight — Spherical
Edition:	1981 in a limited edition of 1,000
Status:	Closed at No. 749
Original Issue Price:	£35.00, U.S. $135.00

Name	U.S. $	Can. $	U.K. £
Regency Stripe	135.00	190.00	50.00

CT-233
INITIAL

Designer:	Colin Terris
Type:	Weight — Spherical
Cane:	Initial
Edition:	1981
Status:	Closed
Original Issue Price:	£33.20, U.S. $125.00

Name	U.S. $	Can. $	U.K. £
Initial	125.00	180.00	40.00

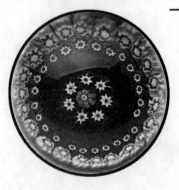

CT-234
AMETHYST LACE

Designer:	Colin Terris
Type:	Weight — Spherical
Cane:	CG (Caithness Glass)
Edition:	1981 in a limited edition of 1,000
Status:	Closed at No. 831
Original Issue Price:	£35.00, U.S. $135.00

Name	U.S. $	Can. $	U.K. £
Amethyst Lace	135.00	190.00	50.00

CT-235
THE GLASSMAKER

Designer:	Colin Terris
Type:	Weight — Spherical
Cane:	CG (Caithness Glass — in base)
Edition:	1981 in a limited edition of 1,000
Status:	Closed at No. 995
Original Issue Price:	£35.00, U.S. $135.00

Name	U.S. $	Can. $	U.K. £
The Glassmaker	135.00	190.00	60.00

CT-236
HEART

Designer:	Colin Terris
Type:	Weight — Spherical
Cane:	CG (Caithness Glass)
Edition:	1981 in a limited edition of 1,000
Status:	Closed at No. 998
Original Issue Price:	£35.00, U.S. $135.00

Name	U.S. $	Can. $	U.K. £
Heart	135.00	190.00	45.00

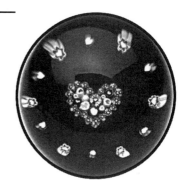

CT-237
ROMANCE PERFUME BOTTLE

Designer:	Colin Terris
Type:	Perfume bottle
Edition:	1981
Status:	Closed
Series:	Unlimited — Modern Design
Original Issue Price:	£63.00, U.S. $295.00

Name	U.S. $	Can. $	U.K. £
Romance Perfume Bottle	295.00	425.00	100.00

CT-238
ROYAL WEDDING

Designer:	Colin Terris
Type:	Weight — Spherical, sulphide
Edition:	1981 in a limited edition of 750
Status:	Closed at No. 131
Series:	Royal Wedding Collection
Original Issue Price:	£81.75

Name	U.S. $	Can. $	U.K. £
Royal Wedding	300.00	400.00	200.00

Note: This paperweight and the following twelve paperweights were issued to commemorate the wedding of Prince Charles and Lady Diana Spencer. This paperweight was not issued in the U.S.

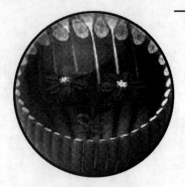

CT-239
FLORAL TRIBUTE

Designer:	Colin Terris
Type:	Weight — Spherical
Canes:	C & D (Charles and Diana)
Edition:	1981 in a limited edition of 100
Status:	Fully subscribed
Series:	Royal Wedding Collection
Original Issue Price:	£150.00

Name	U.S. $	Can. $	U.K. £
Floral Tribute	750.00	1,000.00	500.00

Note: This paperweight was not issued in the U.S.

CT-240
WEDDING BELL

Designer:	Colin Terris
Type:	Weight — Spherical
Cane:	C & D (Charles and Diana)
Edition:	1981 in a limited edition of 250
Status:	Fully subscribed
Series:	Royal Wedding Collection
Original Issue Price:	£96.00, U.S. $450.00

Name	U.S. $	Can. $	U.K. £
Wedding Bell	450.00	650.00	140.00

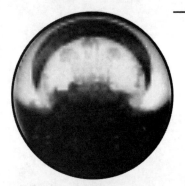

CT-241A
DUET — ONE

Designer:	Caithness Engraving Studios
Type:	Weight — Spherical, engraved
Edition:	1981 in a limited edition of 500
Status:	Fully subscribed
Series:	Royal Wedding Collection
Original Issue Price:	£75.00/set, U.S. $350.00/set

Name	U.S. $	Can. $	U.K. £
Duet - One	175.00	250.00	65.00
Set	350.00	500.00	130.00

Note: This paperweight forms a set with CT-241B, Duet Weight 2.

CT-241B
DUET — TWO

Designer:	Caithness Engraving Studios
Type:	Weight — Spherical, engraved
Edition:	1981 in a limited edition of 500
Status:	Fully subscribed
Series:	Royal Wedding Collection
Original Issue Price:	£75.00/set, U.S. $350.00/set

Name	U.S. $	Can. $	U.K. £
Duet - Two	175.00	250.00	65.00

CT-242
HEART

Designer:	Colin Terris
Type:	Weight — Spherical
Cane:	C & D (Charles and Diana)
Edition:	1981 in a limited edition of 250
Status:	Fully subscribed
Series:	Royal Wedding Collection
Original Issue Price:	£75.00, U.S. $375.00

Name	U.S. $	Can. $	U.K. £
Heart	375.00	525.00	120.00

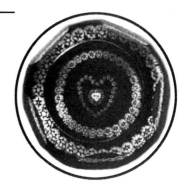

CT-243
CROWN

Designer:	Colin Terris
Type:	Weight — Spherical
Cane:	C & D (Charles and Diana)
Edition:	1981 in a limited edition of 250
Status:	Fully subscribed
Series:	Royal Wedding Collection
Original Issue Price:	£58.50, U.S. $295.00

Name	U.S. $	Can. $	U.K. £
Crown	295.00	425.00	100.00

CT-244
CELEBRATION

Designer:	Colin Terris
Type:	Weight — Spherical
Cane:	C & D (Charles and Diana)
Edition:	1981 in a limited edition of 750
Status:	Closed at No. 425
Series:	Royal Wedding Collection
Original Issue Price:	£50.00, U.S. $235.00

Name	U.S. $	Can. $	U.K. £
Celebration	235.00	325.00	70.00

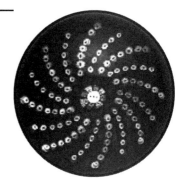

CT-245
GARLAND

Designer:	Colin Terris
Type:	Weight — Spherical
Cane:	C & D (Charles and Diana)
Edition:	1981 in a limited edition of 750
Status:	Closed at No. 420
Series:	Royal Wedding Collection
Original Issue Price:	£44.75, U.S. $210.00

Name	U.S. $	Can. $	U.K. £
Garland	210.00	300.00	60.00

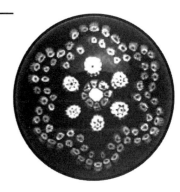

CT-246
ST. PAUL'S

Designer:	Caithness Engraving Studios
Type:	Weight — Spherical, engraved
Edition:	1981 in a limited edition of 750
Status:	Fully subscribed
Series:	Royal Wedding Collection

Original Issue Price: £39.50, U.S. $185.00

Name	U.S. $	Can. $	U.K. £
St. Paul's	185.00	250.00	50.00

CT-247
ROYAL PORTRAIT

Designer:	Caithness Engraving Studios
Type:	Weight — Spherical, engraved
Edition:	1981 in a limited edition of 750
Status:	Closed at No. 734
Series:	Royal Wedding Collection

Original Issue Price: £39.50, U.S. $185.00

Name	U.S. $	Can. $	U.K. £
Royal Portrait	185.00	250.00	50.00

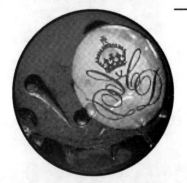

CT-248
ROYAL WEDDING MOONFLOWER

Designer:	Colin Terris
Type:	Weight — Spherical
Edition:	1981 in a limited edition of 1,500
Status:	Fully subscribed
Series:	Royal Wedding Collection

Original Issue Price: £30.00, U.S. $135.00

Name	U.S. $	Can. $	U.K. £
Royal Wedding Moonflower	135.00	190.00	50.00

CT-249
CONGRATULATIONS

Designer:	Colin Terris
Type:	Weight — Spherical
Edition:	1981
Status:	Closed
Series:	Royal Wedding Collection

Original Issue Price: £20.00, U.S. $95.00

Name	U.S. $	Can. $	U.K. £
Congratulations	95.00	130.00	30.00

CT-252
I SAW THREE SHIPS

Designer:	John Taylor	
Type:	Weight — Spherical, engraved	
Edition:	1981 in a limited edition of 500	
Status:	Closed at No. 263	
Series:	Limited — Modern Design	
Original Issue Price:	£50.00, U.S. $195.00	

Name	U.S. $	Can. $	U.K. £
I Saw Three Ships	195.00	275.00	80.00

CT-253
ENIGMA

Designer:	Colin Terris
Type:	Weight — Spherical
Edition:	1981 in a limited edition of 1,000
Status:	Closed at No. 558
Original Issue Price:	£35.00

Name	U.S. $	Can. $	U.K. £
Enigma	100.00	130.00	70.00

Note: The 1981 Collectors' Weight was offered to U.K. Club members only.

CT-254
ROBIN

Designer:	Colin Terris and William Manson
Type:	Weight — Spherical
Edition:	1981 in a limited edition of 500
Status:	Closed at No. 489
Original Issue Price:	£96.00, U.S. $395.00

Name	U.S. $	Can. $	U.K. £
Robin	400.00	550.00	150.00

CT-255
SNOWFLAKE CROWN

Designer:	Colin Terris
Type:	Weight — Spherical
Edition:	1981 in a limited edition of 250
Status:	Fully subscribed
Series:	Traditional Collection
Original Issue Price:	£63.95, U.S. $275.00

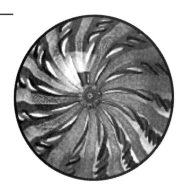

Name	U.S. $	Can. $	U.K. £
Snowflake Crown	275.00	375.00	150.00

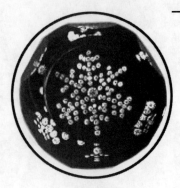

CT-256
SNOW CRYSTAL

Designer: Colin Terris
Type: Weight — Spherical
Edition: 1981 in a limited edition of 1,000
Status: Closed at No. 280
Series: Whitefriars Collection
Original Issue Price: £63.00, U.S. $250.00

Name	U.S. $	Can. $	U.K. £
Snow Crystal	250.00	350.00	110.00

CT-257
APRIL PERFUME FLASK

Designer: Colin Terris
Type: Perfume flask
Edition: 1982
Status: Closed
Original Issue Price: £44.75

Name	U.S. $	Can. $	U.K. £
April Perfume Flask	150.00	200.00	55.00

Note: This perfume flask was not issued in the U.S.

CT-258
BIANCA PERFUME FLASK

Designer: Colin Terris
Type: Perfume flask
Edition: 1982
Status: Closed
Original Issue Price: £50.00

Name	U.S. $	Can. $	U.K. £
Bianca Perfume Flask	150.00	200.00	55.00

Note: This perfume flask was not issued in the U.S.

CT-259
CORDELIA PERFUME FLASK

Designer: Colin Terris
Type: Perfume flask
Edition: 1982
Status: Closed
Original Issue Price: £44.75

Name	U.S. $	Can. $	U.K. £
Cordelia Perfume Flask	150.00	200.00	50.00

Note: This perfume flask was not issued in the U.S.

CT-260
DANIELLE PERFUME FLASK

Designer: Colin Terris
Type: Perfume flask
Edition: 1982
Status: Closed
Original Issue Price: £55.00

Name	U.S. $	Can. $	U.K. £
Danielle Perfume Flask	150.00	200.00	100.00

Note: This perfume flask was not issued in the U.S.

CT-261
ERICA PERFUME FLASK

Designer: Colin Terris
Type: Perfume flask
Edition: 1982
Status: Closed
Original Issue Price: £39.95

Name	U.S. $	Can. $	U.K. £
Erica Perfume Flask	150.00	200.00	100.00

Note: This perfume flask was not issued in the U.S.

CT-262A
CURIO PERFUME BOTTLE

Designer: Colin Terris
Type: Perfume bottle
Edition: 1982 in a limited edition of 150
Status: Closed at No. 124
Original Issue Price: £150.00/set, U.S. $625.00/set

Name	U.S. $	Can. $	U.K. £
Curio Perfume Bottle	450.00	750.00	300.00
Set	700.00	1,100.00	450.00

Note: CT-262A and B were issued and sold as a set.

CT-262B
CURIO

Designer: Colin Terris
Type: Weight — Spherical
Edition: 1982 in a limited edition of 150
Status: Closed at No. 124
Original Issue Price: £150.00/set, U.S. $625.00/set

Name	U.S. $	Can. $	U.K. £
Curio	250.00	350.00	150.00

CT-263A
FROST

Designer: Colin Terris
Type: Weight — Spherical
Edition: 1982 in a limited edition of 150
Status: Fully subscribed
Series: Limited — Modern Design
Original Issue Price: £115.00/set, U.S. $475.00/set

Name	U.S. $	Can. $	U.K. £
Frost	275.00	375.00	175.00
Set	550.00	750.00	350.00

Note: CT-263A and B were issued and sold as a set.

CT-263B
FIRE

Designer: Colin Terris
Type: Weight — Spherical
Edition: 1982 in a limited edition of 150
Status: Fully subscribed
Series: Limited — Modern Design
Original Issue Price: £115.00/set, U.S. $475.00/set

Name	U.S. $	Can. $	U.K. £
Fire	275.00	375.00	175.00

CT-264
ENCHANTÉ PERFUME BOTTLE

Designer: Colin Terris
Type: Perfume bottle
Edition: 1982 in a limited edition of 250
Status: Fully subscribed
Original Issue Price: £75.00, U.S. $315.00

Name	U.S. $	Can. $	U.K. £
Enchanté Perfume Bottle	315.00	450.00	100.00

CT-265
SPLASHDOWN

Designer: Colin Terris
Type: Weight — Spherical
Edition: 1982
Status: Active
Series: Unlimited — Modern Design
Original Issue Price: £15.95, U.S. $67.50

Name	U.S. $	Can. $	U.K. £
Splashdown	99.50	150.00	20.00

Note: This paperweight is active only in the U.S.

CT-266
WHIRLYGIG AMETHYST

Designer:	Colin Terris
Type:	Weight — Spherical
Edition:	1982
Status:	Closed
Series:	Unlimited — Modern Design
Original Issue Price:	£13.85, U.S. $57.50

Name	U.S. $	Can. $	U.K. £
Whirlygig Amethyst	60.00	80.00	25.00

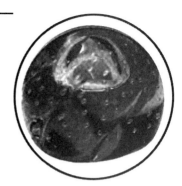

CT-267
VERMILION

Designer:	Colin Terris
Type:	Weight — Spherical
Edition:	1982 in a limited edition of 500
Status:	Closed at No. 178
Series:	Limited — Modern Design
Original Issue Price:	£37.50, U.S. $165.00

Name	U.S. $	Can. $	U.K. £
Vermilion	165.00	225.00	85.00

CT-268
TERRA NOVA

Designer:	Colin Terris
Type:	Weight — Spherical
Edition:	1982 in a limited edition of 1,000
Status:	Closed at No. 862
Series:	Limited — Modern Design
Original Issue Price:	£36.75, U.S. $165.00

Name	U.S. $	Can. $	U.K. £
Terra Nova	165.00	225.00	55.00

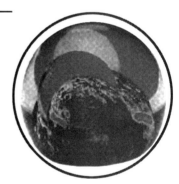

CT-269
HARMONY

Designer:	Colin Terris
Type:	Weight — Spherical
Edition:	1982 in a limited edition of 1,000
Status:	Fully subscribed
Series:	Limited — Modern Design
Original Issue Price:	£35.00, U.S. $145.00

Name	U.S. $	Can. $	U.K. £
Harmony	145.00	200.00	70.00

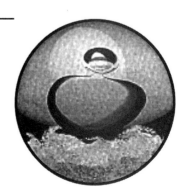

CT-270
NOCTURNE

Designer: Colin Terris
Type: Weight — Spherical
Edition: 1982 in a limited edition of 1,000
Status: Closed at No. 260
Series: Limited — Modern Design
Original Issue Price: £35.00, U.S. $145.00

Name	U.S. $	Can. $	U.K. £
Nocturne	145.00	200.00	40.00

CT-271
POPPIES

Designer: Colin Terris
Type: Weight — Spherical
Edition: 1982 in a limited edition of 750
Status: Closed at No. 423
Series: Limited — Modern Design
Original Issue Price: £36.75, U.S. $150.00

Name	U.S. $	Can. $	U.K. £
Poppies	150.00	200.00	50.00

CT-272
DAMSON FLORAL FOUNTAIN

Designer: Colin Terris
Type: Weight — Spherical
Edition: 1982 in a limited edition of 750
Status: Closed at No. 228
Original Issue Price: £63.00, U.S. $265.00

Name	U.S. $	Can. $	U.K. £
Damson Floral Fountain	265.00	375.00	125.00

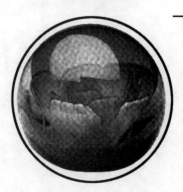

CT-273
FRAGRANCE

Designer: Colin Terris
Type: Weight — Spherical
Edition: 1982 in a limited edition of 250
Status: Fully subscribed
Series: Limited — Modern Design
Original Issue Price: £63.00, U.S. $265.00

Name	U.S. $	Can. $	U.K. £
Fragrance	265.00	375.00	125.00

CT-274
CHERRIES

Designer:	William Manson
Type:	Weight — Spherical
Edition:	1982 in a limited edition of 150
Status:	Fully subscribed
Series:	Traditional Collection
Original Issue Price:	£110.00, U.S. $350.00

Name	U.S. $	Can. $	U.K. £
Cherries	350.00	500.00	140.00

CT-275
WHITE ROSE

Designer:	William Manson
Type:	Weight — Spherical
Edition:	1982 in a limited edition of 150
Status:	Closed at No. 108
Original Issue Price:	£125.00, U.S. $525.00

Name	U.S. $	Can. $	U.K. £
White Rose	525.00	750.00	140.00

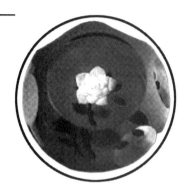

CT-276
DRAGONFLY AND FLOWERS

Designer:	William Manson
Type:	Weight — Spherical
Edition:	1982 in a limited edition of 500
Status:	Closed at No. 436
Series:	Traditional Collection
Original Issue Price:	£90.00, U.S. $295.00

Name	U.S. $	Can. $	U.K. £
Dragonfly and Flowers	295.00	425.00	125.00

CT-277
FIONA

Designer:	Caithness Paperweight Studios
Type:	Weight — Spherical
Edition:	1982 in a limited edition of 500
Status:	Closed at No. 151
Original Issue Price:	£75.00, U.S. $295.00

Name	U.S. $	Can. $	U.K. £
Fiona	295.00	425.00	90.00

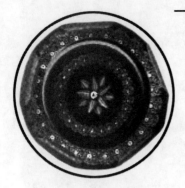

CT-278
HEATHER

Designer:	Caithness Paperweight Studios
Type:	Weight — Spherical
Edition:	1982 in a limited edition of 500
Status:	Closed at No. 126
Series:	Traditional Collection
Original Issue Price:	£75.00, U.S. $250.00

Name	U.S. $	Can. $	U.K. £
Heather	250.00	350.00	80.00

CT-279
RONA

Designer:	Caithness Paperweight Studios
Type:	Weight — Spherical
Edition:	1982 in a limited edition of 500
Status:	Closed at No. 163
Original Issue Price:	£75.00, U.S. $295.00

Name	U.S. $	Can. $	U.K. £
Rona	295.00	425.00	80.00

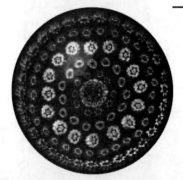

CT-280
RINGS OF ROSES

Designer:	Colin Terris
Type:	Weight — Spherical
Edition:	1982
Status:	Closed
Series:	Whitefriars Collection
Original Issue Price:	£39.50, U.S. $150.00

Name	U.S. $	Can. $	U.K. £
Rings of Roses	150.00	200.00	60.00

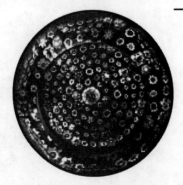

CT-281
BED OF ROSES

Designer:	Colin Terris
Type:	Weight — Spherical
Cane:	82
Edition:	1982 in a limited edition of 750
Status:	Closed at No. 246
Series:	Whitefriars Collection
Original Issue Price:	£55.00, U.S. $195.00

Name	U.S. $	Can. $	U.K. £
Bed of Roses	195.00	275.00	65.00

CT-282
SPREAD OF ROSES

Designer:	Colin Terris
Type:	Weight — Spherical
Edition:	1982 in a limited edition of 750
Status:	Closed at No. 275
Series:	Whitefriars Collection

Original Issue Price: £55.00, U.S. $195.00

Name	U.S. $	Can. $	U.K. £
Spread of Roses	195.00	275.00	75.00

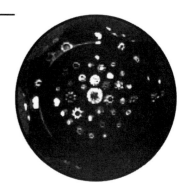

CT-283
GARLAND OF ROSES

Designer:	Colin Terris
Type:	Weight — Spherical
Edition:	1982 in a limited edition of 750
Status:	Closed at No. 217
Series:	Whitefriars Collection

Original Issue Price: £55.00, U.S. $195.00

Name	U.S. $	Can. $	U.K. £
Garland of Roses	195.00	275.00	75.00

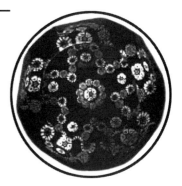

CT-284
ROSE GARDEN

Designer:	Colin Terris
Type:	Weight — Spherical, double overlay
Edition:	1982 in a limited edition of 100
Status:	Fully subscribed
Series:	Whitefriars Collection

Original Issue Price: £150.00, U.S. $595.00

Name	U.S. $	Can. $	U.K. £
Rose Garden	595.00	850.00	200.00

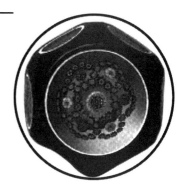

CT-285
STAR OF ROSES

Designer:	Colin Terris
Type:	Weight — Spherical, double overlay
Edition:	1982 in a limited edition of 100
Status:	Closed at No. 83
Series:	Whitefriars Collection

Original Issue Price: £150.00, U.S. $650.00

Name	U.S. $	Can. $	U.K. £
Star of Roses	650.00	925.00	200.00

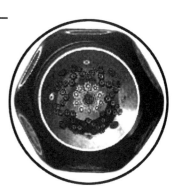

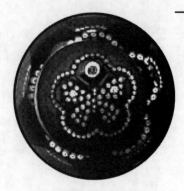

CT-286
BUTTERFLY

Designer: Colin Terris
Type: Weight — Spherical
Edition: 1982 in a limited edition of 750
Status: Closed at No. 312
Series: Whitefriars Collection
Original Issue Price: £55.00, U.S. $195.00

Name	U.S. $	Can. $	U.K. £
Butterfly	195.00	275.00	75.00

CT-287
ROYAL BIRTHDAY TRIBUTE

Designer: Colin Terris
Type: Weight — Spherical
Edition: 1982 in a limited edition of 100
Status: Fully subscribed
Original Issue Price: £150.00, U.S. $550.00

Name	U.S. $	Can. $	U.K. £
Royal Birthday Tribute	700.00	1,000.00	225.00

Note: CT-287, 288 and 289 were issued to commemorate the birth of HRH Prince William on June 21, 1982.

CT-288
ROYAL BIRTHDAY MOONFLOWER

Designer: Colin Terris
Type: Weight — Spherical
Edition: 1982 in a limited edition of 750
Status: Fully subscribed
Original Issue Price: £29.95, U.S. $135.00

Name	U.S. $	Can. $	U.K. £
Royal Birthday Moonflower	135.00	190.00	45.00

CT-289
ROYAL BIRTHDAY CROWN

Designer: Colin Terris
Type: Weight — Spherical
Edition: 1982 in a limited edition of 250
Status: Fully subscribed
Original Issue Price: £75.00

Name	U.S. $	Can. $	U.K. £
Royal Birthday Crown	225.00	300.00	150.00

Note: This paperweight was not issued in the U.S.

CT-290
CAULDRON AQUA

Designer: Innes Burns
Type: Weight — Spherical
Edition: 1982
Status: Active
Series: Unlimited — Modern Design
Original Issue Price: £14.95, U.S. $49.50

Name	U.S. $	Can. $	U.K. £
Cauldron Aqua	95.00	125.00	30.00

CT-291
CAULDRON RUBY

Designer: Innes Burns
Type: Weight — Spherical
Edition: 1982
Status: Active
Series: Unlimited — Modern Design
Original Issue Price: £14.95, U.S. $49.50

Name	U.S. $	Can. $	U.K. £
Cauldron Ruby	95.00	125.00	30.00

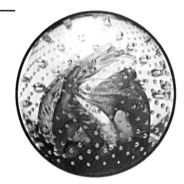

CT-292
MAGIC CIRCLE

Designer: Colin Terris
Type: Weight — Spherical
Edition: 1982
Status: Closed
Series: Unlimited — Modern Design
Original Issue Price: £14.95, U.S. $49.50

Name	U.S. $	Can. $	U.K. £
Magic Circle	60.00	80.00	30.00

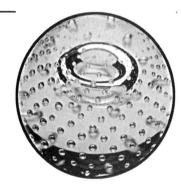

CT-293
CREATION

Designer: Colin Terris
Type: Weight — Spherical, iridescent overlay
Edition: 1982 in a limited edition of 500
Status: Fully subscribed
Series: Limited — Modern Design
Original Issue Price: £39.95, U.S. $135.00

Name	U.S. $	Can. $	U.K. £
Creation	135.00	190.00	70.00

CT-294
STARBURST

Designer:	Colin Terris
Type:	Weight — Spherical
Edition:	1982 in a limited edition of 500
Status:	Fully subscribed
Original Issue Price:	£35.00, U.S. $115.00

Name	U.S. $	Can. $	U.K. £
Starburst	115.00	165.00	60.00

CT-295
SEAFORM

Designer:	Innes Burns
Type:	Weight — Spherical
Edition:	1982
Status:	Closed
Series:	Unlimited — Modern Design
Original Issue Price:	£15.95, U.S. $57.50

Name	U.S. $	Can. $	U.K. £
Seaform	60.00	80.00	25.00

CT-296
SPACE COURIER

Designer:	Colin Terris
Type:	Weight — Spherical
Edition:	1982 in a limited edition of 750
Status:	Closed at No. 500
Series:	Limited — Modern Design
Original Issue Price:	£29.75, U.S. $97.50

Name	U.S. $	Can. $	U.K. £
Space Courier	135.00	195.00	50.00

CT-297
SPACE TRAIL

Designer:	Colin Terris
Type:	Weight — Spherical
Edition:	1982
Status:	Closed
Series:	Unlimited — Modern Design
Original Issue Price:	£16.95, U.S. $49.50

Name	U.S. $	Can. $	U.K. £
Space Trail	50.00	70.00	30.00

CT-298
SPACE VISTA

Designer: Colin Terris
Type: Weight — Spherical, iridescent overlay
Edition: 1982 in a limited edition of 500
Status: Closed at No. 333
Series: Limited — Modern Design
Original Issue Price: £39.95, U.S. $135.00

Name	U.S. $	Can. $	U.K. £
Space Vista	135.00	190.00	70.00

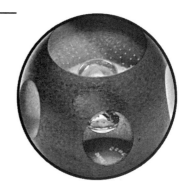

CT-300
PERSEPHONE

Designer: David Green
Type: Weight — Spherical
Edition: 1982 in a limited edition of 1,000
Status: Closed at No. 474
Series: Limited — Modern Design
Original Issue Price: £35.00

Name	U.S. $	Can. $	U.K. £
Persephone	95.00	130.00	65.00

Note: The winning entry in a design competition run by the Collectors' Club, this was the 1982 Collectors' Weight. It was not issued in the U.S.

CT-301
CHRISTMAS ROSE

Designer: Colin Terris
Type: Weight — Spherical
Edition: 1982 in a limited edition of 500
Status: Closed at No. 307
Original Issue Price: £75.00, U.S. $345.00

Name	U.S. $	Can. $	U.K. £
Christmas Rose	345.00	500.00	110.00

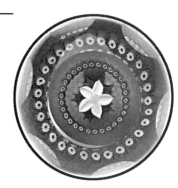

CT-302
CHRISTMAS TREE

Designer: Colin Terris
Type: Weight — Spherical
Edition: 1982 in a limited edition of 1,000
Status: Closed at No. 310
Series: Whitefriars Collection
Original Issue Price: £58.75, U.S. $250.00

Name	U.S. $	Can. $	U.K. £
Christmas Tree	250.00	350.00	90.00

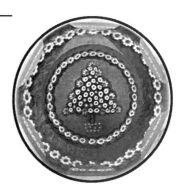

CT-303
ANTENNAE

Designer:	Colin Terris
Type:	Weight — Spherical
Edition:	1983 in a limited edition of 750
Status:	Fully subscribed
Series:	Limited — Modern Design
Original Issue Price:	£41.50, U.S. $150.00

Name	U.S. $	Can. $	U.K. £
Antennae	150.00	200.00	85.00

CT-304
HELTER SKELTER

Designer:	Colin Terris
Type:	Weight — Spherical
Edition:	1983
Status:	Closed
Series:	Unlimited — Modern Design
Original Issue Price:	£19.75, U.S. $75.00

Name	U.S. $	Can. $	U.K. £
Helter Skelter	75.00	100.00	35.00

CT-305
FIREBALL

Designer:	Colin Terris
Type:	Weight — Spherical
Edition:	1983
Status:	Closed
Series:	Unlimited — Modern Design
Original Issue Price:	£15.95, U.S. $72.50

Name	U.S. $	Can. $	U.K. £
Fireball	110.00	175.00	30.00

CT-306
ANDROMEDA

Designer:	Colin Terris
Type:	Weight — Spherical
Edition:	1983 in a limited edition of 500
Status:	Fully subscribed
Series:	Limited — Modern Design
Original Issue Price:	£45.75, U.S. $175.00

Name	U.S. $	Can. $	U.K. £
Andromeda	175.00	250.00	95.00

CT-307
CAMELOT

Designer: Colin Terris
Type: Weight — Spherical
Edition: 1983 in a limited edition of 750
Status: Fully subscribed
Series: Limited — Modern Design
Original Issue Price: £35.00, U.S. $135.00

Name	U.S. $	Can. $	U.K. £
Camelot	300.00	225.00	120.00

CT-308
MOONSCAPE

Designer: Colin Terris
Type: Weight — Spherical
Edition: 1983 in a limited edition of 750
Status: Fully subscribed
Series: Limited — Modern Design
Original Issue Price: £35.00, U.S. $135.00

Name	U.S. $	Can. $	U.K. £
Moonscape	200.00	215.00	95.00

CT-309
HONESTY

Designer: Colin Terris
Type: Weight — Spherical
Edition: 1983 in a limited edition of 250
Status: Fully subscribed
Series: Limited — Modern Design
Original Issue Price: £50.00, U.S. $195.00

Name	U.S. $	Can. $	U.K. £
Honesty	225.00	275.00	150.00

CT-310
FUGUE

Designer: Colin Terris
Type: Weight — Spherical
Colour: Orange, ruby, green and blue
Edition: 1983 in a limited edition of 750
Status: Fully subscribed
Series: Limited — Modern Design
Original Issue Price: £39.95, U.S. $175.00

Name	U.S. $	Can. $	U.K. £
Fugue	175.00	250.00	70.00

CT-311
WHIRLWIND

Designer:	Colin Terris
Type:	Weight — Spherical
Edition:	1983
Status:	Closed
Series:	Unlimited — Modern Design
Original Issue Price:	£13.85, U.S. $55.00

Name	U.S. $	Can. $	U.K. £
Whirlwind	55.00	75.00	25.00

CT-312
SYMPHONY

Designer:	Andrew Lawson
Type:	Weight — Spherical
Edition:	1983 in a limited edition of 750
Status:	Fully subscribed
Series:	Limited — Modern Design
Original Issue Price:	£47.95, U.S. $195.00

Name	U.S. $	Can. $	U.K. £
Symphony	195.00	275.00	75.00

CT-313
JOURNEY'S END

Designer:	Colin Terris
Type:	Weight — Spherical
Edition:	1983 in a limited edition of 750
Status:	Fully subscribed
Series:	Limited — Modern Design
Original Issue Price:	£33.50, U.S. $125.00

Name	U.S. $	Can. $	U.K. £
Journey's End	125.00	180.00	50.00

CT-314
CAPRICE

Designer:	Colin Terris
Type:	Weight — Spherical
Edition:	1983 in a limited edition of 750
Status:	Fully subscribed
Series:	Limited — Modern Design
Original Issue Price:	£39.95, U.S. $150.00

Name	U.S. $	Can. $	U.K. £
Caprice	150.00	200.00	60.00

CT-315
HENRY VIII

Designer: Colin Terris
Type: Weight — Spherical, sulphide
Edition: 1983 in a limited edition of 250
Status: Closed at No. 51
Original Issue Price: £50.00, U.S. $175.00

Name	U.S. $	Can. $	U.K. £
Henry VIII	225.00	300.00	50.00

Note: The miniature sulphide is set in a millefiori cane circle.

CT-316
ELIZABETH I

Designer: Colin Terris
Type: Weight — Spherical, sulphide
Edition: 1983 in a limited edition of 250
Status: Closed at No. 69
Original Issue Price: £50.00, U.S. $175.00

Name	U.S. $	Can. $	U.K. £
Elizabeth I	225.00	300.00	50.00

Note: The miniature sulphide is set in a millefiori cane circle.

CT-317
ROYAL WEDDING

Designer: Colin Terris
Type: Weight — Spherical, sulphide
Edition: 1983 in a limited edition of 500
Status: Closed at No. 69
Original Issue Price: £50.00, U.S. $175.00

Name	U.S. $	Can. $	U.K. £
Royal Wedding	225.00	300.00	150.00

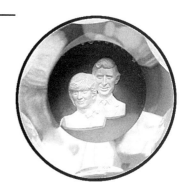

Note: The miniature sulphide is set in a millefiori cane circle.

CT-318
FLOWER IN THE SNOW

Designer: Colin Terris
Type: Weight — Spherical
Edition: 1983
Status: Closed
Series: Unlimited — Modern Design
Original Issue Price: £29.75, U.S. $99.50

Name	U.S. $	Can. $	U.K. £
Flower in the Snow	100.00	140.00	40.00

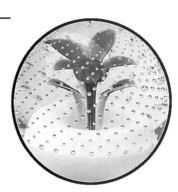

CT-319A
SONATA PERFUME BOTTLE

Designer:	Colin Terris
Type:	Perfume bottle
Edition:	1983 in a limited edition of 150
Status:	Closed at No. 120
Series:	Limited — Modern Design
Original Issue Price:	£125.00/set, U.S. $495.00/set

Name	U.S. $	Can. $	U.K. £
Sonata Perfume Bottle	325.00	450.00	200.00
Set	500.00	700.00	300.00

Note: CT-319A and B were issued and sold as a set.

CT-319B
SONATA

Designer:	Colin Terris
Type:	Weight — Spherical
Edition:	1983 in a limited edition of 150
Status:	Closed at No. 120
Series:	Limited — Modern Design
Original Issue Price:	£125.00/set, U.S. $495.00/set

Name	U.S. $	Can. $	U.K. £
Sonata	175.00	250.00	100.00

CT-320
CORRYVRECKAN PERFUME BOTTLE

Designer:	Colin Terris
Type:	Perfume bottle
Edition:	1983
Status:	Closed
Series:	Unlimited — Modern Design
Original Issue Price:	£39.95, U.S. $135.00

Name	U.S. $	Can. $	U.K. £
Corryvreckan Perfume Bottle	135.00	190.00	50.00

CT-321
MISTY PERFUME BOTTLE

Designer:	Colin Terris
Type:	Perfume bottle
Edition:	1983
Status:	Closed
Series:	Unlimited — Modern Design
Original Issue Price:	£39.95, U.S. $135.00

Name	U.S. $	Can. $	U.K. £
Misty Perfume Bottle	135.00	190.00	50.00

CT-322
DOUBLE MAGNUM RUBY

Designer: Colin Terris
Type: Weight — Spherical, double magnum
Edition: 1983
Status: Closed
Series: Unlimited — Modern Design
Original Issue Price: £125.00, U.S. $450.00

Name	U.S. $	Can. $	U.K. £
Double Magnum Ruby	450.00	650.00	200.00

CT-323
THE ZODIAC

Designer: Colin Terris
Type: Weight — Spherical
Edition: 1983 in a limited edition of 250
Status: Closed at No. 155
Series: Whitefriars Collection
Original Issue Price: £96.00, U.S. $350.00

Name	U.S. $	Can. $	U.K. £
The Zodiac	350.00	475.00	200.00

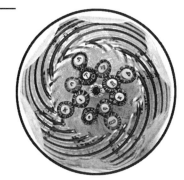

CT-324
WINTER FLOWER

Designer: William Manson
Type: Weight — Spherical
Edition: 1983 in a limited edition of 500
Status: Closed at No. 415
Series: Traditional Collection
Original Issue Price: £56.50, U.S. $225.00

Name	U.S. $	Can. $	U.K. £
Winter Flower	225.00	325.00	60.00

CT-325
MARGUERITE

Designer: William Manson
Type: Weight — Spherical
Edition: 1983 in a limited edition of 500
Status: Closed at No. 474
Series: Traditional Collection
Original Issue Price: £50.00, U.S. $195.00

Name	U.S. $	Can. $	U.K. £
Marguerite	195.00	275.00	60.00

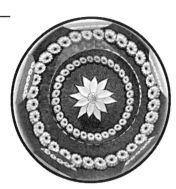

CT-326
CROCUS

Designer:	William Manson
Type:	Weight — Spherical
Edition:	1983 in a limited edition of 500
Status:	Closed at No. 450
Series:	Traditional Collection
Original Issue Price:	£50.00, U.S. $195.00

Name	U.S. $	Can. $	U.K. £
Crocus	195.00	275.00	60.00

CT-327
HIGHLAND FLING

Designer:	William Manson
Type:	Weight — Spherical
Edition:	1983 in a limited edition of 250
Status:	Fully subscribed
Series:	Traditional Collection
Original Issue Price:	£69.50, U.S. $275.00

Name	U.S. $	Can. $	U.K. £
Highland Fling	275.00	375.00	125.00

CT-328
PARTRIDGE IN A PEAR TREE

Designer:	William Manson
Type:	Weight — Spherical
Edition:	1983 in a limited edition of 500
Status:	Closed at No. 382
Series:	Traditional Collection
Original Issue Price:	£69.50, U.S. $250.00

Name	U.S. $	Can. $	U.K. £
Partridge in a Pear Tree	250.00	350.00	85.00

CT-329
FLORA

Designer:	William Manson
Type:	Weight — Spherical
Edition:	1983 in a limited edition of 500
Status:	Closed at No. 165
Series:	Traditional Collection
Original Issue Price:	£50.00, U.S. $185.00

Name	U.S. $	Can. $	U.K. £
Flora	185.00	250.00	60.00

CT-330
BLUE CORAL

Designer: Colin Terris
Type: Weight — Domed
Edition: 1983 in a limited edition of 250
Status: Fully subscribed
Series: Limited — Modern Design
Original Issue Price: £52.95, U.S. $175.00

Name	U.S. $	Can. $	U.K. £
Blue Coral	200.00	275.00	135.00

CT-331
DARK ISLAND

Designer: Colin Terris
Type: Weight — Spherical
Edition: 1983 in a limited edition of 500
Status: Fully subscribed
Series: Limited — Modern Design
Original Issue Price: £48.00, U.S. $175.00

Name	U.S. $	Can. $	U.K. £
Dark Island	175.00	250.00	90.00

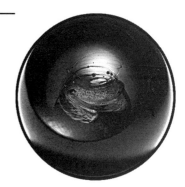

CT-332
FREE SPIRIT

Designer: Colin Terris
Type: Weight — Spherical
Edition: 1983 in a limited edition of 750
Status: Fully subscribed
Series: Limited — Modern Design
Original Issue Price: £36.95, U.S. $135.00

Name	U.S. $	Can. $	U.K. £
Free Spirit	135.00	190.00	60.00

CT-333
OCTAVIA

Designer: Colin Terris
Type: Weight — Spherical
Colour: Fuchsia
Edition: 1983 in a limited edition of 500
Status: Fully subscribed
Series: Limited — Modern Design
Original Issue Price: £41.95, U.S. $175.00

Name	U.S. $	Can. $	U.K. £
Octavia	175.00	250.00	60.00

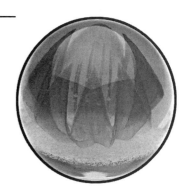

CT-334
RICHARD III

Designer:	Colin Terris
Type:	Weight — Spherical, sulphide
Edition:	1983 in a limited edition of 500
Status:	Closed at No. 81
Original Issue Price:	£50.00, U.S. $175.00

Name	U.S. $	Can. $	U.K. £
Richard III	200.00	275.00	75.00

Note: The sulphide is set in a millefiori cane circle. This paperweight, while originally created exclusively for the Richard III Society, was later offered on general release within the U.K. only.

CT-335
ROBIN and KETTLE

Designer:	Colin Terris
Type:	Weight — Spherical
Edition:	1983 in a limited edition of 1,000
Status:	Closed at No. 536
Series:	Traditional Collection
Original Issue Price:	£55.00, U.S. $200.00

Name	U.S. $	Can. $	U.K. £
Robin and Kettle	200.00	275.00	75.00

Note: This is the 1983 Collectors' Weight.

CT-336
WHITE FUGUE

Designer:	Colin Terris
Type:	Weight — Spherical
Edition:	1983 in a limited edition of 500
Status:	Fully subscribed
Series:	Limited — Modern Design
Original Issue Price:	U.S. $175.00

Name	U.S. $	Can. $	U.K. £
White Fugue	225.00	325.00	150.00

Note: This paperweight was first issued by Gump's; see page 477.

CT-337
SEA DANCE

Designer:	Colin Terris
Type:	Weight — Spherical
Colour:	Gold
Edition:	1983
Status:	Active
Series:	Unlimited — Modern Design
Original Issue Price:	£23.50, U.S. $85.00

Name	U.S. $	Can. $	U.K. £
Sea Dance	125.00	165.00	38.00

CT-338
SPINAWAY

Designer:	Colin Terris
Type:	Weight — Spherical
Edition:	1983
Status:	Closed
Series:	Unlimited — Modern Design
Original Issue Price:	£16.95, U.S. $62.50

Name	U.S. $	Can. $	U.K. £
Spinaway	65.00	90.00	25.00

CT-339
BLUE OCTAVIA

Designer:	Colin Terris
Type:	Weight — Spherical
Edition:	1984 in a limited edition of 500
Status:	Fully subscribed
Series:	Limited — Modern Design
Original Issue Price:	£43.95, U.S. $150.00

Name	U.S. $	Can. $	U.K. £
Blue Octavia	150.00	200.00	65.00

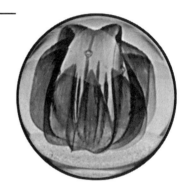

CT-340
CHANTILLY

Designer:	Jeneo Lewis
Type:	Weight — Spherical
Edition:	1984 in a limited edition of 500
Status:	Fully subscribed
Series:	Limited — Modern Design
Original Issue Price:	£43.95, U.S. $150.00

Name	U.S. $	Can. $	U.K. £
Chantilly	150.00	200.00	85.00

CT-341
DILEMMA

Designer:	Colin Terris
Type:	Weight — Spherical
Edition:	1984 in a limited edition of 750
Status:	Fully subscribed
Series:	Limited — Modern Design
Original Issue Price:	£39.95, U.S. $150.00

Name	U.S. $	Can. $	U.K. £
Dilemma	150.00	200.00	65.00

CT-342
GRACE

Designer:	Colin Terris
Type:	Weight — Domed
Edition:	1984 in a limited edition of 500
Status:	Fully subscribed
Series:	Limited — Modern Design
Original Issue Price:	£60.00, U.S. $225.00

Name	U.S. $	Can. $	U.K. £
Grace	225.00	325.00	100.00

CT-343
MOUNTAINS OF MARS

Designer:	Colin Terris
Type:	Weight — Spherical
Edition:	1984 in a limited edition of 750
Status:	Fully subscribed
Series:	Limited — Modern Design
Original Issue Price:	£39.95, U.S. $150.00

Name	U.S. $	Can. $	U.K. £
Mountains of Mars	150.00	200.00	90.00

CT-344
NAUTILUS

Designer:	Colin Terris
Type:	Weight — Domed
Edition:	1984 in a limited edition of 500
Status:	Fully subscribed
Series:	Limited — Modern Design
Original Issue Price:	£60.00, U.S. $225.00

Name	U.S. $	Can. $	U.K. £
Nautilus	225.00	325.00	95.00

CT-345
THREE WITCHES

Designer:	Colin Terris
Type:	Weight — Spherical
Edition:	1984 in a limited edition of 500
Status:	Fully subscribed
Series:	Limited — Modern Design
Original Issue Price:	£43.95, U.S. $150.00

Name	U.S. $	Can. $	U.K. £
Three Witches	150.00	200.00	75.00

CT-346
BLUEBIRDS

Designer:	William Manson
Type:	Weight — Spherical
Edition:	1984 in a limited edition of 250
Status:	Fully subscribed
Series:	Traditional Collection

Original Issue Price: £85.00, U.S. $325.00

Name	U.S. $	Can. $	U.K. £
Bluebirds	325.00	450.00	100.00

CT-347
DOLPHIN

Designer:	William Manson
Type:	Weight — Spherical
Edition:	1984 in a limited edition of 100
Status:	Fully subscribed
Series:	Traditional Collection

Original Issue Price: £125.00, U.S. $450.00

Name	U.S. $	Can. $	U.K. £
Dolphin	500.00	700.00	150.00

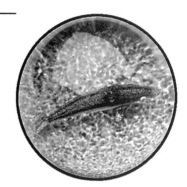

CT-348
FIRE LIZARD

Designer:	William Manson
Type:	Weight — Spherical
Edition:	1984 in a limited edition of 100
Status:	Fully subscribed
Series:	Traditional Collection

Original Issue Price: £200.00, U.S. $750.00

Name	U.S. $	Can. $	U.K. £
Fire Lizard	800.00	1,100.00	275.00

CT-349
MANTA RAY and CORAL

Designer:	William Manson
Type:	Weight — Spherical
Edition:	1984 in a limited edition of 100
Status:	Fully subscribed
Series:	Traditional Collection

Original Issue Price: £125.00, U.S. $450.00

Name	U.S. $	Can. $	U.K. £
Manta Ray and Coral	500.00	700.00	150.00

CT-350
TROUT and MAYFLY

Designer:	William Manson
Type:	Weight — Spherical
Edition:	1984 in a limited edition of 100
Status:	Fully subscribed
Series:	Traditional Collection
Original Issue Price:	£250.00, U.S. $900.00

Name	U.S. $	Can. $	U.K. £
Trout and Mayfly	1,000.00	1,350.00	350.00

CT-351
TROUT

Designer:	William Manson
Type:	Weight — Spherical
Edition:	1984 in a limited edition of 100
Status:	Fully subscribed
Series:	Traditional Collection
Original Issue Price:	£125.00, U.S. $450.00

Name	U.S. $	Can. $	U.K. £
Trout	500.00	700.00	150.00

CT-352
TWO SALMON

Designer:	William Manson
Type:	Weight — Spherical
Edition:	1984 in a limited edition of 100
Status:	Closed at No. 86
Series:	Traditional Collection
Original Issue Price:	£200.00, U.S. $750.00

Name	U.S. $	Can. $	U.K. £
Two Salmon	800.00	1,100.00	275.00

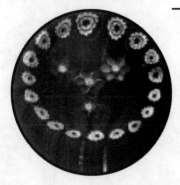

CT-353
ROYAL BIRTHDAY TRIBUTE

Designer:	Colin Terris
Type:	Weight — Spherical
Edition:	1984 in a limited edition of 100
Status:	Fully subscribed
Original Issue Price:	£175.00, U.S. $600.00

Name	U.S. $	Can. $	U.K. £
Royal Birthday Tribute	600.00	850.00	300.00

Note: Weights CT-353, 354 and 355 were issued to commemorate the birth of HRH Prince Harry.

CT-354
ROYAL BIRTHDAY CROWN

Designer: Colin Terris
Type: Weight — Spherical
Edition: 1984 in a limited edition of 250
Status: Fully subscribed
Original Issue Price: £85.00, U.S. $300.00

Name	U.S. $	Can. $	U.K. £
Royal Birthday Crown	300.00	425.00	135.00

CT-355
ROYAL BIRTHDAY MOONFLOWER

Designer: Colin Terris
Type: Weight — Spherical
Edition: 1984 in a limited edition of 750
Status: Fully subscribed
Original Issue Price: £43.95, U.S. $165.00

Name	U.S. $	Can. $	U.K. £
Royal Birthday Moonflower	165.00	225.00	50.00

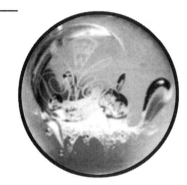

CT-356A
CANTATA PERFUME BOTTLE

Designer: Colin Terris
Type: Perfume bottle
Edition: 1984 in a limited edition of 150
Status: Closed at No. 123
Original Issue Price: £137.50/set, U.S. $495.00/set

Name	U.S. $	Can. $	U.K. £
Cantata Perfume Bottle	325.00	475.00	200.00
Set	500.00	725.00	300.00

Note: CT-356A and B were issued and sold as a set.

CT-356B
CANTATA

Designer: Colin Terris
Type: Weight — Spherical
Edition: 1984 in a limited edition of 150
Status: Closed at No. 123
Original Issue Price: £137.50/set, U.S. $495.00/set

Name	U.S. $	Can. $	U.K. £
Cantata	175.00	250.00	100.00

CT-357
FLORAL BASKET

Designer:	Colin Terris
Type:	Weight — Domed
Edition:	1984
Status:	Closed
Series:	Whitefriars Collection
Original Issue Price:	£39.50, U.S. $145.00

Name	U.S. $	Can. $	U.K. £
Floral Basket	145.00	200.00	75.00

CT-358
BLUE and PINK POSY

Designer:	Allan Scott
Type:	Weight — Spherical
Edition:	1984 in a limited edition of 250
Status:	Fully subscribed
Series:	Whitefriars Collection
Original Issue Price:	£59.50, U.S. $235.00

Name	U.S. $	Can. $	U.K. £
Blue and Pink Posy	235.00	325.00	75.00

CT-359
BLUE FLOWER

Designer:	Allan Scott
Type:	Weight — Spherical
Edition:	1984 in a limited edition of 250
Status:	Closed at No. 117
Series:	Whitefriars Collection
Original Issue Price:	£47.50, U.S. $150.00

Name	U.S. $	Can. $	U.K. £
Blue Flower	165.00	225.00	75.00

CT-360
FUCHSIA

Designer:	Allan Scott
Type:	Weight — Spherical
Edition:	1984 in a limited edition of 250
Status:	Fully subscribed
Series:	Whitefriars Collection
Original Issue Price:	£59.50, U.S. $195.00

Name	U.S. $	Can. $	U.K. £
Fuchsia	195.00	275.00	85.00

CT-361
BOUQUET and FERNS

Designer:	Allan Scott
Type:	Weight — Spherical
Edition:	1984 in a limited edition of 150
Status:	Fully subscribed
Series:	Whitefriars Collection
Original Issue Price:	£150.00, U.S. $595.00

Name	U.S. $	Can. $	U.K. £
Bouquet and Ferns	595.00	850.00	150.00

CT-362
AMETHYST BOUQUET

Designer:	Allan Scott
Type:	Weight — Spherical
Edition:	1984 in a limited edition of 150
Status:	Fully subscribed
Series:	Whitefriars Collection
Original Issue Price:	£125.00, U.S. $475.00

Name	U.S. $	Can. $	U.K. £
Amethyst Bouquet	475.00	675.00	125.00

CT-363
FLORAL PINK

Designer:	Allan Scott
Type:	Weight — Spherical
Edition:	1984 in a limited edition of 250
Status:	Fully subscribed
Series:	Whitefriars Collection
Original Issue Price:	£75.00, U.S. $275.00

Name	U.S. $	Can. $	U.K. £
Floral Pink	275.00	375.00	75.00

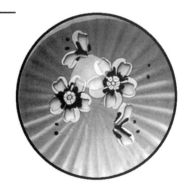

CT-364
WHITE and PINK SPRAY

Designer:	Allan Scott
Type:	Weight — Spherical
Edition:	1984 in a limited edition of 250
Status:	Fully subscribed
Series:	Whitefriars Collection
Original Issue Price:	£69.50, U.S. $265.00

Name	U.S. $	Can. $	U.K. £
White and Pink Spray	265.00	375.00	70.00

CT-365
SEA DANCE BLUE

Designer:	Colin Terris
Type:	Weight — Spherical
Edition:	1984
Status:	Closed
Series:	Unlimited — Modern Design
Original Issue Price:	£24.95, U.S. $85.00

Name	U.S. $	Can. $	U.K. £
Sea Dance Blue	85.00	120.00	40.00

CT-366
BOLERO

Designer:	Colin Terris
Type:	Weight — Spherical
Edition:	1984 in a limited edition of 750
Status:	Fully subscribed
Series:	Limited — Modern Design
Original Issue Price:	£35.95, U.S. $125.00

Name	U.S. $	Can. $	U.K. £
Bolero	125.00	180.00	65.00

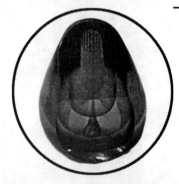

CT-367
CITADEL

Designer:	Colin Terris
Type:	Weight — Domed
Edition:	1984 in a limited edition of 500
Status:	Fully subscribed
Series:	Limited — Modern Design
Original Issue Price:	£60.00, U.S. $225.00

Name	U.S. $	Can. $	U.K. £
Citadel	225.00	325.00	75.00

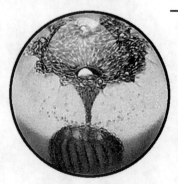

CT-368
EVERGREEN

Designer:	Colin Terris
Type:	Weight — Spherical
Edition:	1984 in a limited edition of 750
Status:	Closed at No. 500
Series:	Limited — Modern Design
Original Issue Price:	£35.95, U.S. $135.00

Name	U.S. $	Can. $	U.K. £
Evergreen	135.00	190.00	40.00

CT-369
GYRO

Designer:	Colin Terris
Type:	Weight — Spherical
Edition:	1984 in a limited edition of 750
Status:	Fully subscribed
Series:	Limited — Modern Design
Original Issue Price:	£35.95, U.S. $135.00

Name	U.S. $	Can. $	U.K. £
Gyro	135.00	190.00	40.00

CT-370
LIFE FORCE

Designer:	Colin Terris
Type:	Weight — Spherical
Edition:	1984 in a limited edition of 750
Status:	Fully subscribed
Series:	Limited — Modern Design
Original Issue Price:	£37.95, U.S. $135.00

Name	U.S. $	Can. $	U.K. £
Life Force	135.00	190.00	50.00

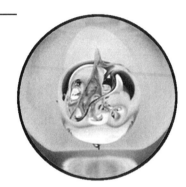

CT-371
MARINER 2

Designer:	Colin Terris
Type:	Weight — Spherical
Edition:	1984 in a limited edition of 750
Status:	Fully subscribed
Original Issue Price:	£39.95, U.S. $125.00

Name	U.S. $	Can. $	U.K. £
Mariner 2	125.00	180.00	60.00

CT-372
NINETEEN EIGHTY-FOUR

Designer:	Colin Terris
Type:	Weight — Spherical
Edition:	1984 in a limited edition of 750
Status:	Fully subscribed
Series:	Limited — Modern Design
Original Issue Price:	£42.25, U.S. $135.00

Name	U.S. $	Can. $	U.K. £
Nineteen Eighty-Four	135.00	190.00	75.00

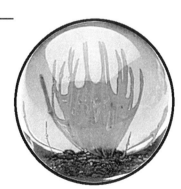

CT-373
SOLITAIRE

Designer: Colin Terris
Type: Weight — Spherical
Edition: 1984 in a limited edition of 1,000
Status: Closed at No. 461
Original Issue Price: £39.95, U.S. $175.00

Name	U.S. $	Can. $	U.K. £
Solitaire	175.00	250.00	75.00

Note: This is the 1984 Collectors' Weight.

CT-374
PAGODA

Designer: Colin Terris
Type: Weight — Domed
Edition: 1984 in a limited edition of 500
Status: Fully subscribed
Series: Limited — Modern Design
Original Issue Price: £60.00, U.S. $195.00

Name	U.S. $	Can. $	U.K. £
Pagoda	195.00	275.00	100.00

CT-375
SPECTRUM

Designer: Colin Terris
Type: Weight — Spherical
Edition: 1984 in a limited edition of 750
Status: Fully subscribed
Series: Limited — Modern Design
Original Issue Price: £37.95, U.S. $125.00

Name	U.S. $	Can. $	U.K. £
Spectrum	125.00	180.00	45.00

CT-376
STAR BEACON

Designer: Colin Terris
Type: Weight — Spherical
Edition: 1984 in a limited edition of 750
Status: Fully subscribed
Series: Limited — Modern Design
Original Issue Price: £39.95, U.S. $150.00

Name	U.S. $	Can. $	U.K. £
Star Beacon	150.00	200.00	45.00

CT-377
TRANQUILLITY

Designer: Colin Terris
Type: Weight — Spherical
Edition: 1984 in a limited edition of 750
Status: Fully subscribed
Series: Limited — Modern Design
Original Issue Price: £49.95, U.S. $175.00

Name	U.S. $	Can. $	U.K. £
Tranquillity	175.00	250.00	65.00

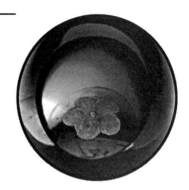

CT-378
WHISPERS

Designer: Colin Terris
Type: Weight — Spherical
Edition: 1984 in a limited edition of 500
Status: Fully subscribed
Series: Limited — Modern Design
Original Issue Price: £49.95, U.S. $175.00

Name	U.S. $	Can. $	U.K. £
Whispers	175.00	250.00	75.00

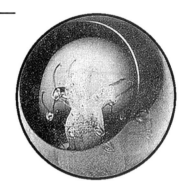

CT-379
SAFFRON

Designer: Colin Terris
Type: Weight — Spherical
Edition: 1984
Status: Closed
Series: Unlimited — Modern Design
Original Issue Price: £16.95, U.S. $65.00

Name	U.S. $	Can. $	U.K. £
Saffron	65.00	90.00	30.00

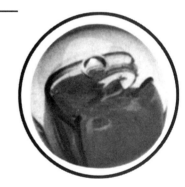

CT-380
CHRISTMAS CANDLE

Designer: Colin Terris
Type: Weight — Spherical
Edition: 1984 in a limited edition of 500
Status: Closed at No. 268
Series: Traditional Collection
Original Issue Price: £75.00, U.S. $265.00

Name	U.S. $	Can. $	U.K. £
Christmas Candle	265.00	375.00	80.00

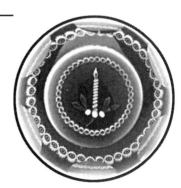

CT-381
BLACK SALAMANDER

Designer:	William Manson
Type:	Weight — Spherical
Edition:	1984 in a limited edition of 100
Status:	Fully subscribed
Series:	Traditional Collection
Original Issue Price:	£200.00, U.S. $750.00

Name	U.S. $	Can. $	U.K. £
Black Salamander	750.00	1,000.00	250.00

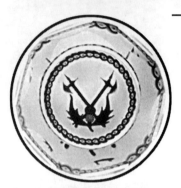

CT-382
CROSSED HALBERDS

Designer:	William Manson
Type:	Weight — Spherical
Edition:	1984 in a limited edition of 250
Status:	Fully subscribed
Series:	Traditional Collection
Original Issue Price:	£75.00, U.S. $265.00

Name	U.S. $	Can. $	U.K. £
Crossed Halberds	265.00	375.00	100.00

CT-383
KINGFISHER

Designer:	William Manson
Type:	Weight — Spherical
Edition:	1984 in a limited edition of 250
Status:	Fully subscribed
Series:	Traditional Collection
Original Issue Price:	£75.00, U.S. $265.00

Name	U.S. $	Can. $	U.K. £
Kingfisher	265.00	375.00	75.00

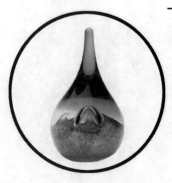

CT-384
MOONDROP

Designer:	Colin Terris
Type:	Weight — Drawn teardrop
Colour:	Many colour variations
Edition:	1984
Status:	Closed
Series:	Unlimited — Modern Design
Original Issue Price:	£12.95, U.S. $39.50

Name	U.S. $	Can. $	U.K. £
Moondrop (Many colourways)	40.00	55.00	15.00

CT-385
PEBBLE

Designer:	Colin Terris
Type:	Weight — Sculptural
Colour:	Many colour variations
Edition:	1984
Status:	Closed
Series:	Unlimited — Modern Design
Original Issue Price:	£17.95, U.S. $39.50

Name	U.S. $	Can. $	U.K. £
Pebble	50.00	70.00	20.00

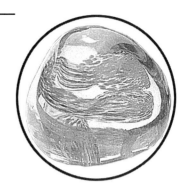

CT-386
DOUBLE MAGNUM AMETHYST

Designer:	Colin Terris
Type:	Weight — Spherical, double magnum
Edition:	1984
Status:	Closed
Original Issue Price:	£130.00, U.S. $425.00

Name	U.S. $	Can. $	U.K. £
Double Magnum Amethyst	425.00	600.00	175.00

CT-387
FLOWER CRYSTAL PINK CARNATIONS

Designer:	Colin Terris
Type:	Weight — Rectangular freeform
Edition:	1984
Status:	Closed
Original Issue Price:	£19.95, U.S. $85.00

Name	U.S. $	Can. $	U.K. £
Flower Crystal Pink Carnations	85.00	120.00	25.00

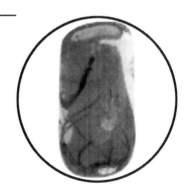

CT-388
FLOWER CRYSTAL BLACK ORCHIDS

Designer:	Colin Terris
Type:	Weight — Rectangular freeform
Edition:	1984
Status:	Closed
Original Issue Price:	£19.95, U.S. $85.00

Name	U.S. $	Can. $	U.K. £
Flower Crystal Black Orchids	85.00	120.00	25.00

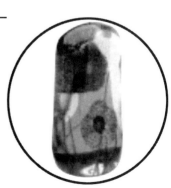

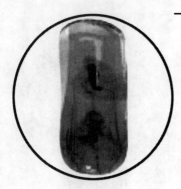

CT-389
FLOWER CRYSTAL BLUE PANSIES

Designer: Colin Terris
Type: Weight — Rectangular freeform
Edition: 1984
Status: Closed
Original Issue Price: £19.95, U.S. $85.00

Name	U.S. $	Can. $	U.K. £
Flower Crystal Blue Pansies	85.00	120.00	25.00

CT-390
FLOWER CRYSTAL RED POPPIES

Designer: Colin Terris
Type: Weight — Rectangular freeform
Edition: 1984
Status: Closed
Original Issue Price: £19.95, U.S. $85.00

Name	U.S. $	Can. $	U.K. £
Flower Crystal Red Poppies	85.00	120.00	25.00

CT-391
CHIFFON

Designer: Colin Terris
Type: Weight — Spherical
Edition: 1985 in a limited edition of 750
Status: Fully subscribed
Series: Limited — Modern Design
Original Issue Price: £39.95, U.S. $125.00

Name	U.S. $	Can. $	U.K. £
Chiffon	125.00	180.00	60.00

CT-392
DERVISH

Designer: Colin Terris
Type: Weight — Spherical
Edition: 1985 in a limited edition of 750
Status: Fully subscribed
Series: Limited — Modern Design
Original Issue Price: £41.95, U.S. $125.00

Name	U.S. $	Can. $	U.K. £
Dervish	125.00	180.00	60.00

CT-393
EVENSONG

Designer:	Colin Terris	
Type:	Weight — Domed	
Edition:	1985 in a limited edition of 250	
Status:	Fully subscribed	
Series:	Limited — Modern Design	
Original Issue Price:	£41.95, U.S. $135.00	

Name	U.S. $	Can. $	U.K. £
Evensong	135.00	190.00	75.00

CT-394
GALACTICA

Designer:	Colin Terris	
Type:	Weight — Spherical	
Edition:	1985 in a limited edition of 750	
Status:	Fully subscribed	
Series:	Limited — Modern Design	
Original Issue Price:	£39.95, U.S. $125.00	

Name	U.S. $	Can. $	U.K. £
Galactica	125.00	180.00	60.00

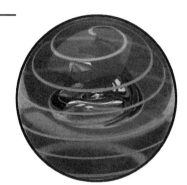

CT-395
ICE PRINCESS

Designer:	Colin Terris	
Type:	Weight — Domed	
Edition:	1985 in a limited edition of 500	
Status:	Fully subscribed	
Series:	Limited — Modern Design	
Original Issue Price:	£60.00, U.S. $185.00	

Name	U.S. $	Can. $	U.K. £
Ice Princess	185.00	250.00	100.00

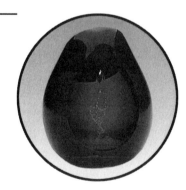

CT-396
LABYRINTH

Designer:	Colin Terris	
Type:	Weight — Domed	
Edition:	1985 in a limited edition of 500	
Status:	Fully subscribed	
Series:	Limited — Modern Design	
Original Issue Price:	£60.00, U.S. $185.00	

Name	U.S. $	Can. $	U.K. £
Labyrinth	185.00	250.00	75.00

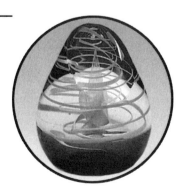

CT-397
MISTRAL

Designer:	Colin Terris
Type:	Weight — Spherical
Edition:	1985 in a limited edition of 750
Status:	Fully subscribed
Series:	Limited — Modern Design
Original Issue Price:	£41.95, U.S. $125.00

Name	U.S. $	Can. $	U.K. £
Mistral	125.00	185.00	80.00

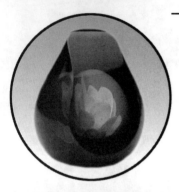

CT-398
SERENITY

Designer:	Colin Terris
Type:	Weight — Domed
Edition:	1985 in a limited edition of 500
Status:	Fully subscribed
Series:	Limited — Modern Design
Original Issue Price:	£60.00, U.S. $185.00

Name	U.S. $	Can. $	U.K. £
Serenity	185.00	250.00	100.00

CT-399
SUMMER POOL

Designer:	Colin Terris
Type:	Weight — Spherical
Edition:	1985 in a limited edition of 250
Status:	Fully subscribed
Series:	Limited — Modern Design
Original Issue Price:	£50.00, U.S. $150.00

Name	U.S. $	Can. $	U.K. £
Summer Pool	150.00	200.00	60.00

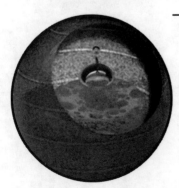

CT-400
TELSTAR

Designer:	Colin Terris
Type:	Weight — Spherical
Edition:	1985 in a limited edition of 750
Status:	Fully subscribed
Series:	Limited — Modern Design
Original Issue Price:	£39.95, U.S. $125.00

Name	U.S. $	Can. $	U.K. £
Telstar	125.00	180.00	45.00

CT-401
TRITON

Designer:	Colin Terris
Type:	Weight — Spherical
Edition:	1985 in a limited edition of 750
Status:	Fully subscribed
Series:	Limited — Modern Design

Original Issue Price: £41.95, U.S. $125.00

Name	*U.S. $*	*Can. $*	*U.K. £*
Triton	125.00	180.00	50.00

CT-402
VIRTUE

Designer:	Colin Terris
Type:	Weight — Domed
Edition:	1985 in a limited edition of 250
Status:	Fully subscribed
Series:	Limited — Modern Design

Original Issue Price: £63.00, U.S. $195.00

Name	*U.S. $*	*Can. $*	*U.K. £*
Virtue	200.00	275.00	100.00

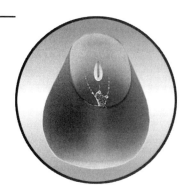

CT-403
WATER LILIES

Designer:	Colin Terris
Type:	Weight — Teardrop
Edition:	1985 in a limited edition of 250
Status:	Fully subscribed
Series:	Limited — Modern Design

Original Issue Price: £65.00, U.S. $195.00

Name	*U.S. $*	*Can. $*	*U.K. £*
Water Lilies	200.00	275.00	125.00

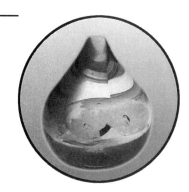

CT-404
20,000 LEAGUES

Designer:	Colin Terris
Type:	Weight — Spherical
Edition:	1985 in a limited edition of 500
Status:	Fully subscribed
Series:	Limited — Modern Design

Original Issue Price: £45.95, U.S. $150.00

Name	*U.S. $*	*Can. $*	*U.K. £*
20,000 Leagues	150.00	200.00	60.00

CT-405
CHANTILLY PERFUME BOTTLE

Designer: Jeneo Lewis
Type: Perfume bottle
Edition: 1985 in a limited edition of 250
Status: Fully subscribed
Series: Limited — Modern Design
Original Issue Price: £75.00, U.S. $250.00

Name	U.S. $	Can. $	U.K. £
Chantilly Perfume Bottle	250.00	325.00	130.00

CT-406A
LILAC TIME PERFUME BOTTLE

Designer: Jeneo Lewis
Type: Perfume bottle
Edition: 1985 in a limited edition of 150
Status: Fully subscribed
Series: Limited — Modern Design
Original Issue Price: £150.00/set, U.S. $495.00/set

Name	U.S. $	Can. $	U.K. £
Lilac Time Perfume Bottle	325.00	450.00	200.00
Set	500.00	700.00	300.00

Note: CT-406A and B were issuedand sold as a set.

CT-406B
LILAC TIME

Designer: Jeneo Lewis
Type: Weight — Spherical
Edition: 1985 in a limited edition of 150
Status: Fully subscribed
Series: Limited — Modern Design
Original Issue Price: £150.00/set, U.S. $495.00/set

Name	U.S. $	Can. $	U.K. £
Lilac Time	175.00	250.00	100.00

CT-407
HONEY BEE

Designer: William Manson
Type: Weight — Spherical
Edition: 1985 in a limited edition of 100
Status: Fully subscribed
Series: Traditional Collection
Original Issue Price: £175.00, U.S. $550.00

Name	U.S. $	Can. $	U.K. £
Honey Bee	575.00	750.00	200.00

CT-408
TROPICAL FISH

Designer: William Manson
Type: Weight — Spherical
Edition: 1985 in a limited edition of 100
Status: Closed at No. 80
Series: Traditional Collection
Original Issue Price: £150.00, U.S. $500.00

Name	U.S. $	Can. $	U.K. £
Tropical Fish	500.00	700.00	175.00

CT-409
APPLE BLOSSOM

Designer: Allan Scott
Type: Weight — Spherical
Edition: 1985 in a limited edition of 250
Status: Fully subscribed
Series: Whitefriars Collection
Original Issue Price: £69.50, U.S. $225.00

Name	U.S. $	Can. $	U.K. £
Apple Blossom	225.00	325.00	75.00

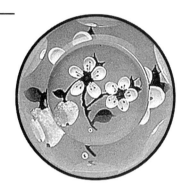

CT-410
PANSY

Designer: Allan Scott
Type: Weight — Spherical
Edition: 1985 in a limited edition of 250
Status: Fully subscribed
Series: Whitefriars Collection
Original Issue Price: £59.50, U.S. $210.00

Name	U.S. $	Can. $	U.K. £
Pansy	210.00	300.00	75.00

CT-411
PRIMROSES

Designer: Allan Scott
Type: Weight — Spherical
Edition: 1985 in a limited edition of 250
Status: Fully subscribed
Series: Whitefriars Collection
Original Issue Price: £69.50, U.S. $225.00

Name	U.S. $	Can. $	U.K. £
Primroses	225.00	325.00	75.00

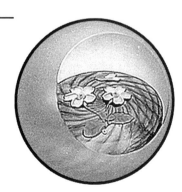

CT-412
SUMMER MEADOW BUTTERFLY

Designer:	Allan Scott and Harry McKay
Type:	Weight — Spherical
Edition:	1985 in a limited edition of 150
Status:	Fully subscribed
Series:	Whitefriars Collection
Original Issue Price:	£125.00, U.S. $395.00

Name	U.S. $	Can. $	U.K. £
Summer Meadow Butterfly	395.00	550.00	200.00

CT-413
SUMMER MEADOW DRAGONFLY

Designer:	Allan Scott and Harry McKay
Type:	Weight — Spherical
Edition:	1985 in a limited edition of 150
Status:	Fully subscribed
Series:	Whitefriars Collection
Original Issue Price:	£125.00, U.S. $395.00

Name	U.S. $	Can. $	U.K. £
Summer Meadow Dragonfly	395.00	550.00	200.00

CT-414
BOUQUET PERFUME BOTTLE

Designer:	Allan Scott
Type:	Perfume bottle
Edition:	1985 in a limited edition of 100
Status:	Fully subscribed
Series:	Traditional Collection
Original Issue Price:	£150.00, U.S. $495.00

Name	U.S. $	Can. $	U.K. £
Bouquet Perfume Bottle	500.00	700.00	175.00

CT-415
CARNIVAL

Designer:	Colin Terris
Type:	Weight — Spherical
Colour:	See below
Edition:	1985
Status:	Closed
Series:	Unlimited — Modern Design
Original Issue Price:	£19.95, U.S. $65.00

Colourways	U.S. $	Can. $	U.K. £
1. Emerald	65.00	90.00	25.00
2. Ruby	65.00	90.00	25.00
3. Yellow	65.00	90.00	25.00

CT-416
DOUBLE MAGNUM EMERALD

Designer:	Colin Terris
Type:	Weight — Spherical, double magnum
Edition:	1985
Status:	Closed
Series:	Unlimited — Modern Design
Original Issue Price:	£131.00, U.S. $425.00

Name	U.S. $	Can. $	U.K. £
Double Magnum Emerald	425.00	600.00	150.00

CT-417
QUICKSILVER

Designer:	Colin Terris
Type:	Weight — Spherical
Edition:	1985
Status:	Active
Series:	Unlimited — Modern Design
Original Issue Price:	£24.95, U.S. $75.00

Name	U.S. $	Can. $	U.K. £
Quicksilver	125.00	160.00	38.00

CT-418
STARWATCH

Designer:	Colin Terris
Type:	Weight — Spherical
Colour:	Many colour variations
Edition:	1985
Status:	Closed
Series:	Unlimited — Modern Design
Original Issue Price:	£29.95, U.S. $90.00

Name	U.S. $	Can. $	U.K. £
Starwatch	90.00	130.00	35.00

CT-419
MOONCRYSTAL

Designer:	Colin Terris
Type:	Weight — Spherical, miniature
Colour:	Many colour variations
Edition:	1985
Status:	Active
Series:	Medium and Miniature Size
Original Issue Price:	£9.95, U.S. $30.00

Name	U.S. $	Can. $	U.K. £
Mooncrystal	49.50	85.00	15.00

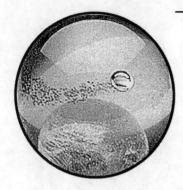

CT-420
HALLEY'S COMET

Designer:	Colin Terris
Type:	Weight — Spherical
Edition:	1985 in a limited edition of 750
Status:	Fully subscribed
Series:	Limited — Modern Design
Original Issue Price:	£37.95, U.S. $135.00

Name	U.S. $	Can. $	U.K. £
Halley's Comet	165.00	225.00	125.00

CT-421
BLUE VELVET

Designer:	Colin Terris
Type:	Weight — Spherical
Edition:	1985 in a limited edition of 500
Status:	Fully subscribed
Series:	Limited — Modern Design
Original Issue Price:	£41.95, U.S. $150.00

Name	U.S. $	Can. $	U.K. £
Blue Velvet	150.00	200.00	60.00

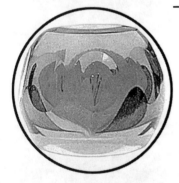

CT-422
DAMASK

Designer:	Colin Terris
Type:	Weight — Spherical
Edition:	1985 in a limited edition of 250
Status:	Fully subscribed
Series:	Limited — Modern Design
Original Issue Price:	£85.00, U.S. $265.00

Name	U.S. $	Can. $	U.K. £
Damask	265.00	375.00	95.00

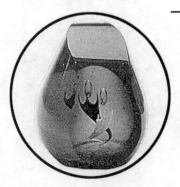

CT-423
ICE DANCE

Designer:	Colin Terris
Type:	Weight — Domed, single overlay
Edition:	1985 in a limited edition of 500
Status:	Fully subscribed
Series:	Limited — Modern Design
Original Issue Price:	£65.00, U.S. $225.00

Name	U.S. $	Can. $	U.K. £
Ice Dance	225.00	325.00	100.00

CT-424
AQUARELLE

Designer:	Colin Terris
Type:	Weight — Spherical
Edition:	1985 in a limited edition of 500
Status:	Fully subscribed
Series:	Limited — Modern Design
Original Issue Price:	£50.00, U.S. $175.00

Name	U.S. $	Can. $	U.K. £
Aquarelle	175.00	250.00	60.00

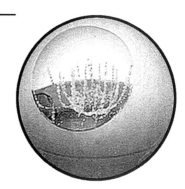

CT-425A
QUINTESSENCE PERFUME BOTTLE

Designer:	Stuart Cumming
Type:	Perfume bottle
Edition:	1985 in a limited edition of 250
Status:	Closed at No. 188
Series:	Limited Edition — Modern Design
Original Issue Price:	£150.00/set, U.S. $550.00/set

Name	U.S. $	Can. $	U.K. £
Quintessence Perfume Bottle	375.00	525.00	150.00
Set	550.00	775.00	250.00

Note: CT-425A and B were issued and sold as a set.

CT-425B
QUINTESSENCE

Designer:	Stuart Cumming
Type:	Weight — Spherical
Edition:	1985 in a limited edition of 250
Status:	Closed at No. 188
Series:	Limited Edition — Modern Design
Original Issue Price:	£150.00/set, U.S. $550.00/set

Name	U.S. $	Can. $	U.K. £
Quintessence	175.00	250.00	100.00

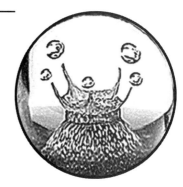

CT-426
WINDFLOWER RUBY

Designer:	Colin Terris
Type:	Weight — Spherical
Edition:	1985 in a limited edition of 750
Status:	Closed at No. 506
Series:	
Original Issue Price:	£41.95, U.S. $135.00

Name	U.S. $	Can. $	U.K. £
Windflower Ruby	135.00	190.00	45.00

CT-427
BLUE MARLIN

Designer:	William Manson	
Type:	Weight — Spherical	
Edition:	1985 in a limited edition of 100	
Status:	Fully subscribed	
Original Issue Price:	£150.00, U.S. $500.00	

Name	U.S. $	Can. $	U.K. £
Blue Marlin	600.00	900.00	200.00

CT-428
POND LIFE

Designer:	William Manson	
Type:	Weight — Spherical	
Edition:	1985 in a limited edition of 100	
Status:	Fully subscribed	
Series:	Traditional Collection	
Original Issue Price:	£250.00, U.S. $750.00	

Name	U.S. $	Can. $	U.K. £
Pond Life	750.00	1,050.00	275.00

CT-429
MAYFLY and FLOWERS

Designer:	William Manson	
Type:	Weight — Spherical	
Edition:	1985 in a limited edition of 250	
Status:	Closed at No. 155	
Original Issue Price:	£125.00, U.S. $425.00	

Name	U.S. $	Can. $	U.K. £
Mayfly and Flowers	425.00	600.00	150.00

CT-430
PHEASANT

Designer:	William Manson	
Type:	Weight — Domed	
Edition:	1985 in a limited edition of 150	
Status:	Closed at No. 72	
Original Issue Price:	£175.00, U.S. $550.00	

Name	U.S. $	Can. $	U.K. £
Pheasant	600.00	900.00	250.00

CT-431
ANEMONE

Designer:	Jeneo Lewis	
Type:	Weight — Spherical	
Edition:	1985 in a limited edition of 500	
Status:	Fully subscribed	
Series:	Limited Edition — Modern Design	
Original Issue Price:	£48.00, U.S. $165.00	

Name	U.S. $	Can. $	U.K. £
Anemone	165.00	225.00	60.00

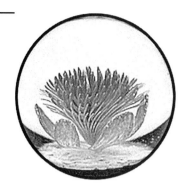

CT-432
PASTORALE

Designer:	Colin Terris
Type:	Weight — Domed
Edition:	1985 in a limited edition of 500
Status:	Fully subscribed
Series:	Limited — Modern Design
Original Issue Price:	£65.00, U.S. $200.00

Name	U.S. $	Can. $	U.K. £
Pastorale	200.00	275.00	75.00

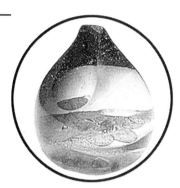

CT-433
FLORETTE

Designer:	Colin Terris
Type:	Weight — Disk, ribbed
Colour:	Many colour variations
Edition:	1985
Status:	Closed
Original Issue Price:	£9.50, U.S. $30.00

Name	U.S. $	Can. $	U.K. £
Florette	30.00	40.00	10.00

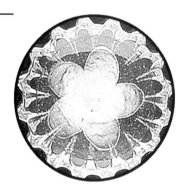

CT-434
THE FIREFLY

Designer:	Colin Terris
Type:	Weight — Spherical
Edition:	1985 in a limited edition of 500
Status:	Closed at No. 154
Original Issue Price:	£54.95, U.S. $195.00

Name	U.S. $	Can. $	U.K. £
The Firefly	195.00	275.00	60.00

Note: This paperweight was issued to commemorate the invention of the famous railway engine.

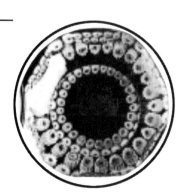

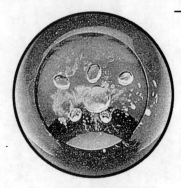

CT-435
MOON ORCHID

Designer: Colin Terris
Type: Weight — Spherical
Edition: 1985 in a limited edition of 1,000
Status: Closed at No. 604
Original Issue Price: £29.95, U.S. $100.00

Name	U.S. $	Can. $	U.K. £
Moon Orchid	100.00	140.00	60.00

Note: This is the 1985 Collectors' Weight.

CT-436
JUBILEE

Designer: Colin Terris
Type: Weight — Spherical
Edition: 1986 in a limited edition of 500
Status: Fully subscribed
Series: Limited Edition — Modern Design
Original Issue Price: £50.00, U.S. $175.00

Name	U.S. $	Can. $	U.K. £
Jubilee	175.00	250.00	95.00

Note: This paperweight was issued to celebrate Caithness's 25th anniversary.

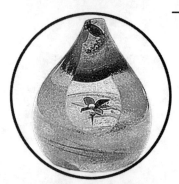

CT-437
CABARET

Designer: Colin Terris
Type: Weight — Teardrop
Edition: 1986 in a limited edition of 650
Status: Closed at No. 556
Original Issue Price: £53.00, U.S. $185.00

Name	U.S. $	Can. $	U.K. £
Cabaret	185.00	250.00	60.00

CT-438
AQUAMARINE

Designer: Colin Terris
Type: Weight — Spherical, single overlay
Edition: 1986 in a limited edition of 350
Status: Fully subscribed
Original Issue Price: £85.00, U.S. $295.00

Name	U.S. $	Can. $	U.K. £
Aquamarine	295.00	425.00	100.00

CT-439
CELESTE

Designer: Colin Terris
Type: Weight — Domed
Edition: 1986 in a limited edition of 500
Status: Fully subscribed
Series: Limited Edition — Modern Design
Original Issue Price: £60.00, U.S. $200.00

Name	U.S. $	Can. $	U.K. £
Celeste	200.00	275.00	75.00

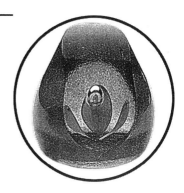

CT-440
FLYING FISH

Designer: Colin Terris
Type: Weight — Spherical
Edition: 1986 in a limited edition of 500
Status: Closed at No. 455
Series: Limited — Modern Design
Original Issue Price: £50.00, U.S. $175.00

Name	U.S. $	Can. $	U.K. £
Flying Fish	175.00	250.00	60.00

CT-441
THE WANDERER

Designer: Colin Terris
Type: Weight — Spherical
Edition: 1986 in a limited edition of 750
Status: Closed at No. 232
Series: Limited Edition — Modern Design
Original Issue Price: £37.95, U.S. $135.00

Name	U.S. $	Can. $	U.K. £
The Wanderer	135.00	190.00	40.00

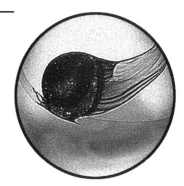

CT-442
AUTUMN LEAVES

Designer: Colin Terris
Type: Weight — Spherical
Edition: 1986 in a limited edition of 750
Status: Closed at No. 250
Series: Limited Edition — Modern Design
Original Issue Price: £42.00, U.S. $150.00

Name	U.S. $	Can. $	U.K. £
Autumn Leaves	150.00	200.00	45.00

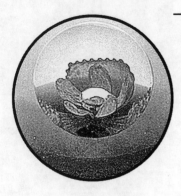

CT-443
RENAISSANCE

Designer: Colin Terris
Type: Weight — Spherical
Edition: 1986 in a limited edition of 500
Status: Fully subscribed
Series: Limited Edition — Modern Design
Original Issue Price: £50.00, U.S. $175.00

Name	U.S. $	Can. $	U.K. £
Renaissance	175.00	250.00	75.00

CT-444
NEPTUNE'S KINGDOM

Designer: Colin Terris
Type: Weight — Spherical
Edition: 1986 in a limited edition of 500
Status: Closed at No. 215
Series: Limited Edition — Modern Design
Original Issue Price: £68.00, U.S. $260.00

Name	U.S. $	Can. $	U.K. £
Neptune's Kingdom	260.00	375.00	85.00

CT-445
STAR SHIP

Designer: Colin Terris
Type: Weight — Spherical
Edition: 1986 in a limited edition of 750
Status: Fully subscribed
Series: Limited Edition — Modern Design
Original Issue Price: £44.95, U.S. $150.00

Name	U.S. $	Can. $	U.K. £
Star Ship	150.00	200.00	60.00

CT-446
SEA SPRAY

Designer: Colin Terris
Type: Weight — Spherical
Edition: 1986 in a limited edition of 750
Status: Fully subscribed
Series: Limited Edition — Modern Design
Original Issue Price: £47.95, U.S. $165.00

Name	U.S. $	Can. $	U.K. £
Sea Spray	165.00	225.00	50.00

CT-447
HELIX

Designer:	Colin Terris
Type:	Weight — Spherical
Edition:	1986 in a limited edition of 750
Status:	Fully subscribed
Series:	Limited Edition — Modern Design
Original Issue Price:	£50.00, U.S. $175.00

Name	U.S. $	Can. $	U.K. £
Helix	175.00	250.00	60.00

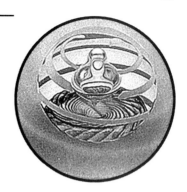

CT-448
ZEST

Designer:	Colin Terris
Type:	Weight — Spherical
Edition:	1986 in a limited edition of 750
Status:	Fully subscribed
Series:	Limited — Modern Design
Original Issue Price:	£42.00, U.S. $150.00

Name	U.S. $	Can. $	U.K. £
Zest	150.00	200.00	70.00

CT-449
GEMINI

Designer:	Colin Terris
Type:	Weight — Spherical
Edition:	1986 in a limited edition of 650
Status:	Fully subscribed
Series:	Limited — Modern Design
Original Issue Price:	£55.00, U.S. $195.00

Name	U.S. $	Can. $	U.K. £
Gemini	195.00	275.00	65.00

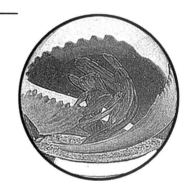

CT-450
HONEYSUCKLE PERFUME BOTTLE

Designer:	Jeneo Lewis
Type:	Perfume bottle
Edition:	1986 in a limited edition of 250
Status:	Fully subscribed
Series:	Limited — Modern Design
Original Issue Price:	£85.00, U.S. $295.00

Name	U.S. $	Can. $	U.K. £
Honeysuckle Perfume Bottle	295.00	425.00	100.00

CT-451
BLUE SPRAY

Designer: Allan Scott
Type: Weight — Spherical
Edition: 1986 in a limited edition of 250
Status: Closed at No. 104
Series: Whitefriars Collection
Original Issue Price: £85.00, U.S. $295.00

Name	U.S. $	Can. $	U.K. £
Blue Spray	295.00	425.00	95.00

CT-452
SPRING BOUQUET

Designer: Allan Scott
Type: Weight — Spherical
Edition: 1986 in a limited edition of 250
Status: Closed at No. 230
Series: Four Seasons
Original Issue Price: £125.00, U.S. $450.00

Name	U.S. $	Can. $	U.K. £
Spring Bouquet	450.00	650.00	150.00

CT-453
SUMMER BOUQUET

Designer: Allan Scott
Type: Weight — Spherical
Edition: 1986 in a limited edition of 250
Status: Closed at No. 215
Series: Four Seasons
Original Issue Price: £125.00, U.S. $450.00

Name	U.S. $	Can. $	U.K. £
Summer Bouquet	450.00	650.00	150.00

CT-454
AUTUMN BOUQUET

Designer: Allan Scott
Type: Weight — Spherical
Edition: 1986 in a limited edition of 250
Status: Closed at No. 211
Series: Four Seasons
Original Issue Price: £125.00, U.S. $450.00

Name	U.S. $	Can. $	U.K. £
Autumn Bouquet	450.00	650.00	150.00

CT-455
WINTER BOUQUET

Designer:	Allan Scott
Type:	Weight — Spherical
Edition:	1986 in a limited edition of 250
Status:	Closed at No. 211
Series:	Four Seasons
Original Issue Price:	£125.00, U.S. $450.00

Name	U.S. $	Can. $	U.K. £
Winter Bouquet	450.00	650.00	150.00

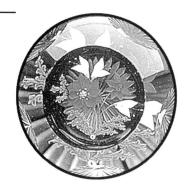

CT-456
PASTEL

Designer:	Colin Terris
Type:	Weight — Spherical, miniature
Colour:	Many colour variations
Edition:	1986
Status:	Closed
Series:	Medium and Miniature Size
Original Issue Price:	£14.95, U.S. $50.00

Name	U.S. $	Can. $	U.K. £
Pastel	50.00	70.00	15.00

CT-457
PEBBLE

Designer:	Colin Terris
Type:	Weight — Sculptural, medium-sized
Edition:	1986
Status:	Active
Series:	Medium and Miniature Size
Original Issue Price:	£8.95, U.S. $30.00

Name	U.S. $	Can. $	U.K. £
Pebble	35.00	65.00	11.00

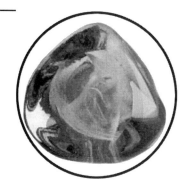

CT-458
VALENTINE PERFUME BOTTLE

Designer:	Colin Terris
Type:	Perfume bottle
Edition:	1986 in a limited edition of 350
Status:	Closed at No. 320
Series:	Watercolours
Original Issue Price:	£65.00, U.S. $275.00

Name	U.S. $	Can. $	U.K. £
Valentine Perfume Bottle	275.00	375.00	85.00

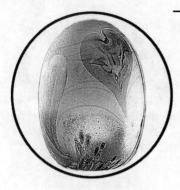

CT-459
JULIET

Designer:	Colin Terris
Type:	Weight — Domed
Edition:	1986 in a limited edition of 500
Status:	Closed at No. 341
Series:	Watercolours
Original Issue Price:	£37.95, U.S. $135.00

Name	U.S. $	Can. $	U.K. £
Juliet	135.00	190.00	40.00

CT-460
ORCHIDS

Designer:	Colin Terris
Type:	Weight — Spherical
Edition:	1986 in a limited edition of 750
Status:	Closed at No. 575
Series:	Watercolours
Original Issue Price:	£37.95, U.S. $135.00

Name	U.S. $	Can. $	U.K. £
Orchids	135.00	190.00	40.00

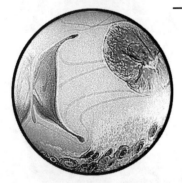

CT-461
BUTTERFLIES

Designer:	Colin Terris
Type:	Weight — Spherical
Edition:	1986 in a limited edition of 750
Status:	Closed at No. 671
Series:	Watercolours
Original Issue Price:	£37.95, U.S. $135.00

Name	U.S. $	Can. $	U.K. £
Butterflies	135.00	190.00	40.00

CT-462
HEARTS

Designer:	Colin Terris
Type:	Weight — Spherical
Edition:	1986 in a limited edition of 750
Status:	Closed at No. 540
Series:	Watercolours
Original Issue Price:	£37.95, U.S. $135.00

Name	U.S. $	Can. $	U.K. £
Hearts	135.00	190.00	40.00

CT-463
YULETIDE

Designer:	Colin Terris
Type:	Weight — Spherical
Edition:	1986 in a limited edition of 500
Status:	Closed at No. 118
Series:	Traditional Collection
Original Issue Price:	£75.00, U.S. 250.00

Name	U.S. $	Can. $	U.K. £
Yuletide	250.00	350.00	80.00

CT-464
SEAHORSE

Designer:	William Manson
Type:	Weight — Domed
Edition:	1986 in a limited edition of 150
Status:	Closed at No. 78
Original Issue Price:	£150.00, U.S. $550.00

Name	U.S. $	Can. $	U.K. £
Seahorse	550.00	775.00	300.00

CT-465
CAMELIA

Designer:	William Manson
Type:	Weight — Spherical
Edition:	1986 in a limited edition of 250
Status:	Closed at No. 208
Series:	Traditional Collection
Original Issue Price:	£100.00, U.S. $350.00

Name	U.S. $	Can. $	U.K. £
Camelia	350.00	500.00	125.00

CT-466
GOLDEN CORSAGE

Designer:	William Manson
Type:	Weight — Spherical
Edition:	1986 in a limited edition of 250
Status:	Fully subscribed
Series:	Traditional Collection
Original Issue Price:	£85.00, U.S. $295.00

Name	U.S. $	Can. $	U.K. £
Golden Corsage	295.00	425.00	85.00

CT-467
FIELD STUDY BUTTERFLY

Designer:	William Manson
Type:	Weight — Spherical
Edition:	1986 in a limited edition of 250
Status:	Closed at No. 228
Series:	Traditional Collection
Original Issue Price:	£125.00, U.S. $450.00

Name	U.S. $	Can. $	U.K. £
Field Study Butterfly	450.00	650.00	150.00

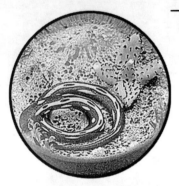

CT-468
RATTLESNAKE

Designer:	William Manson
Type:	Weight — Spherical
Edition:	1986 in a limited edition of 150
Status:	Closed at No. 105
Original Issue Price:	£200.00, U.S. $695.00

Name	U.S. $	Can. $	U.K. £
Rattlesnake	695.00	1,000.00	225.00

CT-469
RED ROSE

Designer:	William Manson
Type:	Weight — Spherical
Edition:	1986 in a limited edition of 500
Status:	Closed at No. 159
Series:	Traditional Collection
Original Issue Price:	£70.00, U.S. $250.00

Name	U.S. $	Can. $	U.K. £
Red Rose	250.00	350.00	75.00

CT-470
INFERNO

Designer:	Colin Terris
Type:	Weight — Spherical
Edition:	1986
Status:	Closed
Series:	Unlimited — Modern Design
Original Issue Price:	£18.95, U.S. $65.00

Name	U.S. $	Can. $	U.K. £
Inferno	65.00	90.00	25.00

CT-471
BLUSH

Designer:	Colin Terris
Type:	Weight — Spherical
Edition:	1986
Status:	Closed
Series:	Unlimited — Modern Design
Original Issue Price:	£19.95, U.S. $65.00

Name	U.S. $	Can. $	U.K. £
Blush	65.00	90.00	20.00

CT-472
DOUBLE MAGNUM VIOLET

Designer:	Colin Terris
Type:	Weight — Spherical, double magnum
Edition:	1986
Status:	Closed
Series:	Unlimited — Modern Design
Original Issue Price:	£136.00, U.S. $495.00

Name	U.S. $	Can. $	U.K. £
Double Magnum Violet	495.00	700.00	150.00

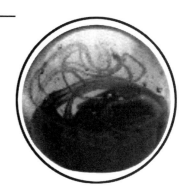

CT-473
ROYAL WEDDING ANCHOR

Designer:	Colin Terris
Type:	Weight — Spherical
Canes:	A & S (Andrew and Sarah)
Edition:	1986 in a limited edition of 500
Status:	Closed at No. 362
Original Issue Price:	£75.00, U.S. $265.00

Name	U.S. $	Can. $	U.K. £
Royal Wedding Anchor	265.00	375.00	75.00

Note: Weights CT-473 through 477 were issued to commemorate the wedding of Prince Andrew and Sarah Ferguson.

CT-474
ROYAL WEDDING HEART

Designer:	Colin Terris
Type:	Weight — Spherical
Cane:	A & S (Andrew and Sarah)
Edition:	1986 in a limited edition of 500
Status:	Closed at No. 329
Original Issue Price:	£65.00, U.S. $265.00

Name	U.S. $	Can. $	U.K. £
Royal Wedding Heart	265.00	375.00	65.00

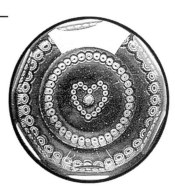

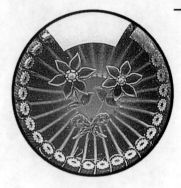

CT-475
ROYAL WEDDING TRIBUTE

Designer:	Colin Terris
Type:	Weight — Spherical
Canes:	A & S (Andrew and Sarah)
Edition:	1986 in a limited edition of 150
Status:	Fully subscribed
Original Issue Price:	£150.00, U.S. $225.00

Name	U.S. $	Can. $	U.K. £
Royal Wedding Tribute	300.00	400.00	200.00

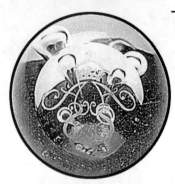

CT-476
ROYAL WEDDING MONOGRAM

Designer:	Colin Terris
Type:	Weight — Spherical
Edition:	1986 in a limited edition of 1,500
Status:	Closed at No. 751
Original Issue Price:	£39.95, U.S. $135.00

Name	U.S. $	Can. $	U.K. £
Royal Wedding Monogram	135.00	190.00	40.00

CT-477
ROYAL BOUQUET PERFUME BOTTLE

Designer:	Colin Terris
Type:	Perfume bottle
Canes:	A & S ((Andrew and Sarah — in bottle)
Edition:	1986 in a limited edition of 100
Status:	Fully subscribed
Original Issue Price:	£150.00, U.S. $225.00

Name	U.S. $	Can. $	U.K. £
Royal Bouquet Perfume Bottle	450.00	600.00	175.00

CT-478
VIVAT REGINA

Designer:	Colin Terris
Type:	Weight — Spherical
Cane:	60
Edition:	1986 in a limited edition of 250
Status:	Fully subscribed
Original Issue Price:	£85.00, U.S. $295.00

Name	U.S. $	Can. $	U.K. £
Vivat Regina	295.00	425.00	100.00

Note: This paperweight was issued to commemorate the 60th birthday of HM Queen Elizabeth II.

CT-479
ASTRAL

Designer: Colin Terris
Type: Weight — Spherical
Edition: 1986 in a limited edition of 750
Status: Fully subscribed
Series: Limited — Modern Design
Original Issue Price: £44.95, U.S. $150.00

Name	U.S. $	Can. $	U.K. £
Astral	150.00	200.00	50.00

CT-480
OCEAN TREASURE

Designer: Colin Terris
Type: Weight — Domed
Edition: 1986 in a limited edition of 650
Status: Closed at No. 597
Series: Limited — Modern Design
Original Issue Price: £60.00, U.S. $210.00

Name	U.S. $	Can. $	U.K. £
Ocean Treasure	210.00	300.00	65.00

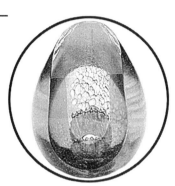

CT-481
QUADRILLE

Designer: Colin Terris
Type: Weight — Spherical
Edition: 1986 in a limited edition of 500
Status: Fully subscribed
Series: Limited — Modern Design
Original Issue Price: £55.00, U.S. $195.00

Name	U.S. $	Can. $	U.K. £
Quadrille	195.00	275.00	65.00

CT-482
IMPULSE

Designer: Colin Terris
Type: Weight — Spherical
Edition: 1986 in a limited edition of 750
Status: Fully subscribed
Series: Limited — Modern Design
Original Issue Price: £42.00, U.S. $150.00

Name	U.S. $	Can. $	U.K. £
Impulse	150.00	200.00	45.00

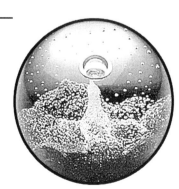

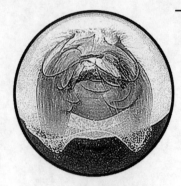

CT-483
KISMET

Designer:	Colin Terris
Type:	Weight — Spherical
Edition:	1986 in a limited edition of 750
Status:	Fully subscribed
Series:	Limited — Modern Design
Original Issue Price:	£47.95, U.S. $175.00

Name	U.S. $	Can. $	U.K. £
Kismet	175.00	250.00	50.00

CT-484
ENCOUNTER

Designer:	Colin Terris
Type:	Weight — Spherical
Edition:	1986 in a limited edition of 750
Status:	Fully subscribed
Series:	Limited — Modern Design
Original Issue Price:	£50.00, U.S. $175.00

Name	U.S. $	Can. $	U.K. £
Encounter	175.00	250.00	50.00

CT-485
MAGIC CARPET

Designer:	Colin Terris
Type:	Weight — Spherical
Edition:	1986 in a limited edition of 750
Status:	Fully subscribed
Series:	Limited — Modern Design
Original Issue Price:	£47.95, U.S. $175.00

Name	U.S. $	Can. $	U.K. £
Magic Carpet	175.00	250.00	50.00

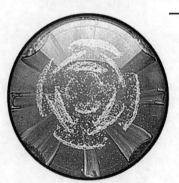

CT-486
JUBILEE ROSE

Designer:	Colin Terris
Type:	Weight — Spherical
Edition:	1986 in a limited edition of 750
Status:	Fully subscribed
Series:	Limited — Modern Design
Original Issue Price:	£50.00, U.S. $175.00

Name	U.S. $	Can. $	U.K. £
Jubilee Rose	175.00	250.00	50.00

Note: This paperweight was issued to celebrate the 25th anniversary of Caithness Glass.

CT-487
TRILOGY

Designer:	Colin Terris	
Type:	Weight — Spherical	
Edition:	1986 in a limited edition of 750	
Status:	Fully subscribed	
Series:	Limited — Modern Design	
Original Issue Price:	£39.95, U.S. $150.00	

Name	U.S. $	Can. $	U.K. £
Trilogy	150.00	200.00	45.00

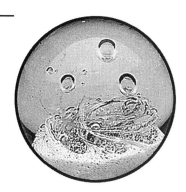

CT-488
IRIS

Designer:	Colin Terris
Type:	Weight — Spherical
Edition:	1986 in a limited edition of 750
Status:	Closed at No. 239
Series:	Watercolours
Original Issue Price:	£37.95, U.S. $135.00

Name	U.S. $	Can. $	U.K. £
Iris	135.00	190.00	45.00

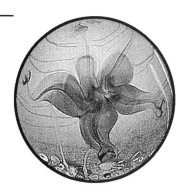

CT-489
CAMILLA PERFUME BOTTLE

Designer:	Colin Terris
Type:	Perfume bottle
Edition:	1986 in a limited edition of 350
Status:	Closed at No. 250
Series:	Watercolours
Original Issue Price:	£65.00, U.S. $275.00

Name	U.S. $	Can. $	U.K. £
Camilla Perfume Bottle	275.00	375.00	85.00

CT-490
MICHAELMAS DAISY

Designer:	William Manson
Type:	Weight — Spherical
Edition:	1986 in a limited edition of 250
Status:	Closed at No. 127
Series:	Traditional Collection
Original Issue Price:	£100.00, U.S. $350.00

Name	U.S. $	Can. $	U.K. £
Michaelmas Daisy	350.00	500.00	100.00

CT-491
FLUTTER BY

Designer:	William Manson
Type:	Weight — Spherical
Edition:	1986 in a limited edition of 250
Status:	Closed at No. 157
Series:	Traditional Collection
Original Issue Price:	£175.00, U.S. $595.00

Name	U.S. $	Can. $	U.K. £
Flutter By	595.00	850.00	175.00

CT-492
SHARK

Designer:	William Manson
Type:	Weight — Spherical
Edition:	1986 in a limited edition of 150
Status:	Closed at No. 123
Original Issue Price:	£200.00, U.S. $695.00

Name	U.S. $	Can. $	U.K. £
Shark	695.00	1,000.00	200.00

CT-493
THISTLE

Designer:	William Manson
Type:	Weight — Spherical
Edition:	1986 in a limited edition of 750
Status:	Closed at No. 429
Series:	Traditional Collection
Original Issue Price:	£55.00, U.S. $195.00

Name	U.S. $	Can. $	U.K. £
Thistle	195.00	275.00	55.00

CT-494
FLOURISH

Designer:	William Manson
Type:	Weight — Spherical
Edition:	1986 in a limited edition of 750
Status:	Closed at No. 244
Series:	Traditional Collection
Original Issue Price:	£50.00, U.S. $175.00

Name	U.S. $	Can. $	U.K. £
Flourish	175.00	250.00	50.00

CT-495
NOSEGAY

Designer: Allan Scott
Type: Weight — Spherical
Edition: 1986 in a limited edition of 250
Status: Closed at No. 151
Series: Whitefriars Collection
Original Issue Price: £85.00, U.S. $295.00

Name	U.S. $	Can. $	U.K. £
Nosegay	295.00	425.00	85.00

CT-496
CANDIDA

Designer: Allan Scott
Type: Weight — Spherical
Edition: 1986 in a limited edition of 250
Status: Closed at No. 152
Series: Whitefriars Collection
Original Issue Price: £85.00, U.S. $295.00

Name	U.S. $	Can. $	U.K. £
Candida	295.00	425.00	85.00

CT-497
ROSETTE

Designer: Allan Scott
Type: Weight — Spherical
Edition: 1986 in a limited edition of 500
Status: Closed at No. 164
Series: Whitefriars Collection
Original Issue Price: £55.00, U.S. $195.00

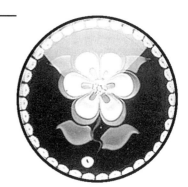

Name	U.S. $	Can. $	U.K. £
Rosette	195.00	275.00	55.00

CT-498
DOMINO

Designer: Colin Terris
Type: Weight — Domed
Edition: 1986 in a limited edition of 1,000
Status: Closed at No. 792
Original Issue Price: £35.00, U.S. $115.00

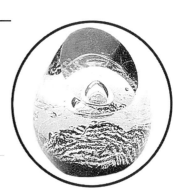

Name	U.S. $	Can. $	U.K. £
Domino	115.00	160.00	60.00

Note: This is the 1986 Collectors' Weight.

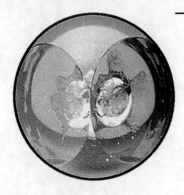

CT-499
NIGHT OWL

Designer: Colin Terris
Type: Weight — Spherical
Edition: 1987 in a limited edition of 500
Status: Fully subscribed
Series: Limited — Modern Design
Original Issue Price: £50.00, U.S. $175.00

Name	U.S. $	Can. $	U.K. £
Night Owl	175.00	250.00	70.00

CT-500
VIGIL

Designer: Colin Terris
Type: Weight — Spherical
Edition: 1987 in a limited edition of 750
Status: Fully subscribed
Series: Limited — Modern Design
Original Issue Price: £39.95, U.S. $135.00

Name	U.S. $	Can. $	U.K. £
Vigil	135.00	190.00	45.00

CT-501
SHANGRI-LA

Designer: Colin Terris
Type: Weight — Spherical
Edition: 1987 in a limited edition of 150
Status: Fully subscribed
Series: Limited — Modern Design
Original Issue Price: £99.00, U.S. $350.00

Name	U.S. $	Can. $	U.K. £
Shangri-La	350.00	500.00	200.00

CT-502
ADAGIO

Designer: Val Coghlin
Type: Weight — Spherical
Edition: 1987 in a limited edition of 750
Status: Fully subscribed
Series: Limited — Modern Design
Original Issue Price: £54.00, U.S. $195.00

Name	U.S. $	Can. $	U.K. £
Adagio	195.00	275.00	65.00

CT-503
VAGABOND

Designer:	Colin Terris
Type:	Weight — Spherical
Edition:	1987 in a limited edition of 750
Status:	Closed at No. 312
Series:	Limited — Modern Design
Original Issue Price:	£42.00, U.S. $150.00

Name	U.S. $	Can. $	U.K. £
Vagabond	150.00	200.00	50.00

CT-504
LOOP THE LOOP

Designer:	Colin Terris
Type:	Weight — Spherical
Edition:	1987 in a limited edition of 750
Status:	Closed at No. 596
Series:	Limited — Modern Design
Original Issue Price:	£54.00, U.S. $195.00

Name	U.S. $	Can. $	U.K. £
Loop the Loop	195.00	275.00	60.00

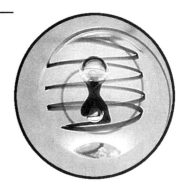

CT-505
MAGENTA

Designer:	Colin Terris
Type:	Weight — Spherical
Edition:	1987 in a limited edition of 750
Status:	Fully subscribed
Series:	Limited — Modern Design
Original Issue Price:	£50.00, U.S. $175.00

Name	U.S. $	Can. $	U.K. £
Magenta	175.00	250.00	55.00

CT-506
MINUET

Designer:	Colin Terris
Type:	Weight — Spherical
Edition:	1987 in a limited edition of 750
Status:	Fully subscribed
Series:	Limited — Modern Design
Original Issue Price:	£45.00, U.S. $165.00

Name	U.S. $	Can. $	U.K. £
Minuet	165.00	225.00	55.00

CT-507
EMERALD

Designer:	Colin Terris
Type:	Weight — Spherical
Edition:	1987 in a limited edition of 250
Status:	Fully subscribed
Series:	Limited — Modern Design
Original Issue Price:	£60.00, U.S. $210.00

Name	U.S. $	Can. $	U.K. £
Emerald	210.00	300.00	85.00

CT-508
ORACLE

Designer:	Colin Terris
Type:	Weight — Spherical
Edition:	1987 in a limited edition of 500
Status:	Closed at No. 468
Series:	Limited — Modern Design
Original Issue Price:	£55.00, U.S. $195.00

Name	U.S. $	Can. $	U.K. £
Oracle	195.00	275.00	60.00

CT-509
MINARET

Designer:	Colin Terris
Type:	Weight — Domed
Edition:	1987 in a limited edition of 650
Status:	Fully subscribed
Series:	Limited — Modern Design
Original Issue Price:	£53.00, U.S. $195.00

Name	U.S. $	Can. $	U.K. £
Minaret	195.00	275.00	75.00

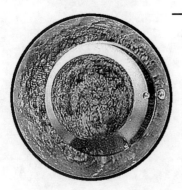

CT-510
JUPITER

Designer:	Colin Terris
Type:	Weight — Spherical
Edition:	1987 in a limited edition of 750
Status:	Fully subscribed
Series:	Limited — Modern Design
Original Issue Price:	£37.95, U.S. $135.00

Name	U.S. $	Can. $	U.K. £
Jupiter	135.00	190.00	50.00

CT-511
FLIGHT

Designer:	Colin Terris
Type:	Weight — Spherical
Edition:	1987 in a limited edition of 750
Status:	Fully subscribed
Series:	Limited — Modern Design
Original Issue Price:	£50.00, U.S. $185.00

Name	U.S. $	Can. $	U.K. £
Flight	185.00	250.00	95.00

CT-512
RENDEZVOUS

Designer:	Colin Terris
Type:	Weight — Spherical
Edition:	1987 in a limited edition of 750
Status:	Fully subscribed
Series:	Limited — Modern Design
Original Issue Price:	£45.00, U.S. $165.00

Name	U.S. $	Can. $	U.K. £
Rendezvous	165.00	225.00	150.00

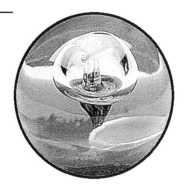

CT-513
EIGHTY EIGHT

Designer:	Colin Terris
Type:	Weight — Spherical
Edition:	1987 in a limited edition of 150
Status:	Fully subscribed
Series:	Limited — Modern Design
Original Issue Price:	£99.00, U.S. $350.00

Name	U.S. $	Can. $	U.K. £
Eighty Eight	350.00	500.00	125.00

Note: There are 88 facets cut and polished on the surface of this paperweight.

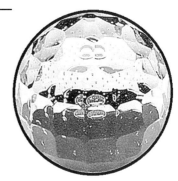

CT-514
BALLOON SELLER

Designer:	Colin Terris
Type:	Weight — Domed
Edition:	1987 in a limited edition of 650
Status:	Fully subscribed
Series:	Limited — Modern Design
Original Issue Price:	£55.00, U.S. $195.00

Name	U.S. $	Can. $	U.K. £
Balloon Seller	195.00	275.00	65.00

CT-515
SHAMAL

Designer:	Colin Terris
Type:	Weight — Spherical
Edition:	1987 in a limited edition of 750
Status:	Fully subscribed
Series:	Limited — Modern Design
Original Issue Price:	£37.95, U.S. $135.00

Name	U.S. $	Can. $	U.K. £
Shamal	135.00	190.00	45.00

CT-516
REVERIE

Designer:	Colin Terris
Type:	Weight — Spherical
Edition:	1987 in a limited edition of 750
Status:	Fully subscribed
Series:	Limited — Modern Design
Original Issue Price:	£47.95, U.S. $165.00

Name	U.S. $	Can. $	U.K. £
Reverie	165.00	225.00	55.00

CT-517
SOLACE

Designer:	Colin Terris
Type:	Weight — Spherical
Edition:	1987 in a limited edition of 750
Status:	Fully subscribed
Series:	Limited — Modern Design
Original Issue Price:	£42.00, U.S. $150.00

Name	U.S. $	Can. $	U.K. £
Solace	150.00	200.00	45.00

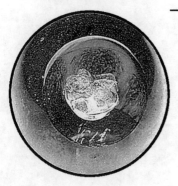

CT-518
ALPHA

Designer:	Colin Terris
Type:	Weight — Spherical
Edition:	1987 in a limited edition of 750
Status:	Closed at No. 692
Series:	Limited — Modern Design
Original Issue Price:	£45.00, U.S. $165.00

Name	U.S. $	Can. $	U.K. £
Alpha	165.00	225.00	50.00

CT-519
FLEUR

Designer:	Colin Terris
Type:	Weight — Spherical
Colour:	See below
Edition:	1987
Status:	Closed
Original Issue Price:	£12.95, U.S. $45.00

Colourways	U.S. $	Can. $	U.K. £
1. Blue	45.00	65.00	15.00
2. Pink	45.00	65.00	15.00
3. Violet	45.00	65.00	15.00

CT-520
TANGO

Designer:	Colin Terris
Type:	Weight — Spherical
Colour:	See below
Edition:	1987
Status:	Closed
Series:	Unlimited — Modern Design
Original Issue Price:	£16.95, U.S. $49.50

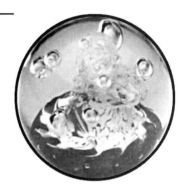

Colourways	U.S. $	Can. $	U.K. £
1. Crimson	50.00	70.00	20.00
2. Lapis blue	50.00	70.00	20.00
3. Sable	50.00	70.00	20.00
4. Topaz	50.00	70.00	20.00

CT-521
SWEETHEART

Designer:	Colin Terris
Type:	Weight — Spherical
Edition:	1987
Status:	Closed
Series:	Romance
Original Issue Price:	£15.95, U.S. $49.50

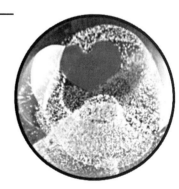

Name	U.S. $	Can. $	U.K. £
Sweetheart	50.00	70.00	20.00

CT-522
DOUBLE MAGNUM CRIMSON

Designer:	Colin Terris
Type:	Weight — Spherical, double magnum
Edition:	1987
Status:	Closed
Series:	Unlimited — Modern Design
Original Issue Price:	£136.00, U.S. $450.00

Name	U.S. $	Can. $	U.K. £
Double Magnum Crimson	450.00	650.00	150.00

CT-523
DOUBLE DRAGONFLY

Designer:	William Manson
Type:	Weight — Spherical
Edition:	1987 in a limited edition of 150
Status:	Fully subscribed
Series:	Traditional Collection
Original Issue Price:	£130.00, U.S. $450.00

Name	U.S. $	Can. $	U.K. £
Double Dragonfly	450.00	650.00	150.00

CT-524
AMETHYST SPRAY

Designer:	Allan Scott
Type:	Weight — Spherical
Edition:	1987 in a limited edition of 350
Status:	Closed at No. 160
Series:	Traditional Collection
Original Issue Price:	£85.00, U.S. $295.00

Name	U.S. $	Can. $	U.K. £
Amethyst Spray	295.00	425.00	85.00

CT-525
WHITE HEATHER

Designer:	William Manson
Type:	Weight — Spherical
Edition:	1987 in a limited edition of 500
Status:	Closed at No. 93
Series:	Traditional Collection
Original Issue Price:	£50.00, U.S. $175.00

Name	U.S. $	Can. $	U.K. £
White Heather	175.00	250.00	50.00

CT-526
SNOWDROPS

Designer: William Manson
Type: Weight — Spherical
Edition: 1987 in a limited edition of 500
Status: Closed at No. 409
Series: Traditional Collection
Original Issue Price: £55.00, U.S. $195.00

Name	U.S. $	Can. $	U.K. £
Snowdrops	195.00	275.00	60.00

CT-527
ZINNIA

Designer: William Manson
Type: Weight — Spherical
Edition: 1987 in a limited edition of 350
Status: Closed at No. 170
Series: Traditional Collection
Original Issue Price: £85.00, U.S. $295.00

Name	U.S. $	Can. $	U.K. £
Zinnia	295.00	425.00	85.00

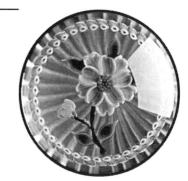

CT-528
NATIONAL FLOWERS

Designer: William Manson
Type: Weight — Spherical
Edition: 1987 in a limited edition of 250
Status: Closed at No. 184
Series: Traditional Collection
Original Issue Price: £150.00, U.S. $495.00

Name	U.S. $	Can. $	U.K. £
National Flowers	495.00	700.00	150.00

CT-529
DUCK POND

Designer: William Manson
Type: Weight — Spherical
Edition: 1987 in a limited edition of 150
Status: Fully subscribed
Series: Traditional Collection
Original Issue Price: £150.00, U.S. $495.00

Name	U.S. $	Can. $	U.K. £
Duck Pond	495.00	700.00	200.00

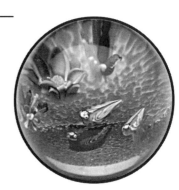

CT-530
HEDGEHOG

Designer:	William Manson
Type:	Weight — Spherical
Edition:	1987 in a limited edition of 100
Status:	Fully subscribed
Series:	Traditional Collection
Original Issue Price:	£200.00, U.S. $695.00

Name	*U.S. $*	*Can. $*	*U.K. £*
Hedgehog	695.00	1,000.00	225.00

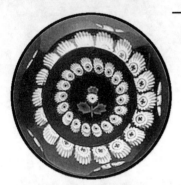

CT-531
MINI SCOTS THISTLE

Designer:	Allan Scott
Type:	Weight — Spherical
Edition:	1987
Status:	Closed
Series:	Millefiori Miniatures
Original Issue Price:	£19.95, U.S. $65.00

Name	*U.S. $*	*Can. $*	*U.K. £*
Mini Scots Thistle	65.00	90.00	30.00

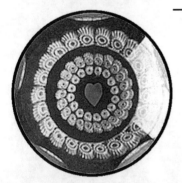

CT-532
MINI HEART

Designer:	Allan Scott
Type:	Weight — Spherical
Edition:	1987
Status:	Closed
Series:	Millefiori Miniatures
Original Issue Price:	£19.95, U.S. $65.00

Name	*U.S. $*	*Can. $*	*U.K. £*
Mini Heart	65.00	90.00	30.00

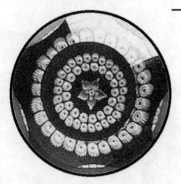

CT-533
MINI FORGET-ME-NOT

Designer:	Allan Scott
Type:	Weight — Spherical
Edition:	1987
Status:	Closed
Series:	Millefiori Miniatures
Original Issue Price:	£19.95, U.S. $65.00

Name	*U.S. $*	*Can. $*	*U.K. £*
Mini Forget-Me-Not	65.00	90.00	30.00

CT-534
MINI DRAGONFLY

Designer: Allan Scott
Type: Weight — Spherical
Edition: 1987
Status: Closed
Series: Millefiori Miniatures
Original Issue Price: £19.95, U.S. $65.00

Name	U.S. $	Can. $	U.K. £
Mini Dragonfly	65.00	90.00	30.00

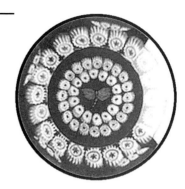

CT-535
MINI NARCISSUS

Designer: Allan Scott
Type: Weight — Spherical
Edition: 1987
Status: Closed
Series: Millefiori Miniatures
Original Issue Price: £19.95, U.S. $65.00

Name	U.S. $	Can. $	U.K. £
Mini Narcissus	65.00	90.00	30.00

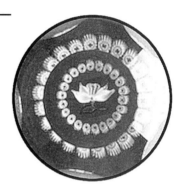

CT-536
BUTTERFLY DUET

Designer: Allan Scott
Type: Weight — Spherical
Edition: 1987 in a limited edition of 250
Status: Closed at No. 165
Series: Whitefriars Collection
Original Issue Price: £100.00, U.S. $350.00

Name	U.S. $	Can. $	U.K. £
Butterfly Duet	350.00	500.00	100.00

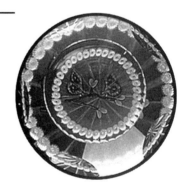

CT-537
OPIUM POPPY

Designer: Allan Scott
Type: Weight — Spherical
Edition: 1987 in a limited edition of 250
Status: Closed at No. 218
Series: Whitefriars Collection
Original Issue Price: £75.00, U.S. $275.00

Name	U.S. $	Can. $	U.K. £
Opium Poppy	275.00	375.00	75.00

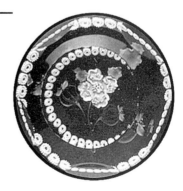

CT-538
BLUE and WHITE GARLAND

Designer:	Allan Scott
Type:	Weight — Spherical
Edition:	1987 in a limited edition of 250
Status:	Fully subscribed
Series:	Whitefriars Collection

Original Issue Price: £100.00, U.S. $350.00

Name	U.S. $	Can. $	U.K. £
Blue and White Garland	350.00	500.00	125.00

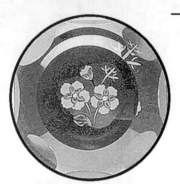

CT-539
SCARLET PIMPERNEL

Designer:	Allan Scott
Type:	Weight — Spherical
Edition:	1987 in a limited edition of 250
Status:	Closed at No. 227
Series:	Whitefriars Collection

Original Issue Price: £75.00, U.S. $275.00

Name	U.S. $	Can. $	U.K. £
Scarlet Pimpernel	275.00	375.00	125.00

CT-540
REGATTA

Designer:	Margot Thomson
Type:	Weight — Domed
Edition:	1987 in a limited edition of 350
Status:	Closed at No. 333
Series:	Limited — Modern Design

Original Issue Price: £64.00, U.S. $225.00

Name	U.S. $	Can. $	U.K. £
Regatta	225.00	325.00	70.00

CT-541
WILL O' THE WISP

Designer:	Colin Terris
Type:	Weight — Spherical
Edition:	1987 in a limited edition of 150
Status:	Fully subscribed
Series:	Limited — Modern Design

Original Issue Price: £99.00, U.S. $350.00

Name	U.S. $	Can. $	U.K. £
Will o' the Wisp	350.00	500.00	200.00

CT-542
VALHALLA

Designer: Colin Terris
Type: Weight — Domed
Edition: 1987 in a limited edition of 650
Status: Fully subscribed
Series: Limited — Modern Design
Original Issue Price: £55.00, U.S. $195.00

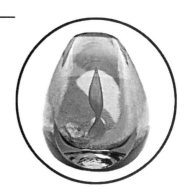

Name	U.S. $	Can. $	U.K. £
Valhalla	195.00	275.00	65.00

CT-543
ODYSSEY

Designer: Margot Thomson
Type: Weight — Spherical
Edition: 1987 in a limited edition of 750
Status: Closed at No. 718
Series: Limited — Modern Design
Original Issue Price: £47.95, U.S. $165.00

Name	U.S. $	Can. $	U.K. £
Odyssey	165.00	225.00	50.00

CT-544
SPRING BREEZE

Designer: Colin Terris
Type: Weight — Spherical
Edition: 1987 in a limited edition of 750
Status: Fully subscribed
Series: Limited — Modern Design
Original Issue Price: £39.95, U.S. $135.00

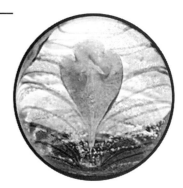

Name	U.S. $	Can. $	U.K. £
Spring Breeze	135.00	190.00	45.00

CT-545
MARRAKESH

Designer: Colin Terris
Type: Weight — Spherical
Edition: 1987 in a limited edition of 500
Status: Fully subscribed
Series: Limited — Modern Design
Original Issue Price: £50.00, U.S. $175.00

Name	U.S. $	Can. $	U.K. £
Marrakesh	175.00	250.00	65.00

CT-546
NEBULA

Designer:	Colin Terris
Type:	Weight — Spherical
Edition:	1987 in a limited edition of 750
Status:	Fully subscribed
Series:	Limited — Modern Design
Original Issue Price:	£45.00, U.S. $165.00

Name	U.S. $	Can. $	U.K. £
Nebula	165.00	225.00	50.00

CT-547
HOBGOBLIN

Designer:	Margot Thomson
Type:	Weight — Spherical
Edition:	1987 in a limited edition of 750
Status:	Closed at No. 711
Series:	Limited — Modern Design
Original Issue Price:	£42.00, U.S. $150.00

Name	U.S. $	Can. $	U.K. £
Hobgoblin	150.00	200.00	45.00

CT-548
SPACE FRONTIER

Designer:	Colin Terris
Type:	Weight — Spherical
Edition:	1987 in a limited edition of 750
Status:	Fully subscribed
Series:	Limited — Modern Design
Original Issue Price:	£47.95, U.S. $165.00

Name	U.S. $	Can. $	U.K. £
Space Frontier	165.00	225.00	50.00

CT-549
ACROBAT

Designer:	Margot Thomson
Type:	Weight — Spherical
Colour:	See below
Edition:	1987
Status:	Closed
Series:	Unlimited — Modern Design
Original Issue Price:	£19.95, U.S. $69.50

Colourways	U.S. $	Can. $	U.K. £
1. Emerald	70.00	100.00	20.00
2. Jet	70.00	100.00	20.00
3. Sapphire	70.00	100.00	20.00

CT-550
PINK CHAMPAGNE

Designer:	Colin Terris
Type:	Weight — Spherical
Edition:	1987
Status:	Active
Series:	Unlimited — Modern Design
Original Issue Price:	£19.95, U.S. $69.50

Name	U.S. $	Can. $	U.K. £
Pink Champagne	95.00	125.00	30.00

CT-551
STRAWBERRY FAYRE

Designer:	Margot Thomson
Type:	Weight — Spherical
Edition:	1987
Status:	Closed
Series:	Unlimited — Modern Design
Original Issue Price:	£19.95, U.S. $69.50

Name	U.S. $	Can. $	U.K. £
Strawberry Fayre	69.50	100.00	25.00

CT-552
TEMPEST

Designer:	Margot Thomson
Type:	Weight — Spherical
Colour:	See below
Edition:	1987
Status:	Closed
Series:	Unlimited — Modern Design
Original Issue Price:	£21.95, U.S. $75.00

Colourways	U.S. $	Can. $	U.K. £
1. Cobalt	75.00	100.00	25.00
2. Magenta	75.00	100.00	25.00

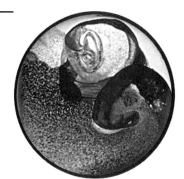

CT-553
MINI ANGEL

Designer:	Allan Scott
Type:	Weight — Spherical
Edition:	1987
Status:	Closed
Series:	Millefiori Miniatures
Original Issue Price:	£22.50, U.S. $75.00

Name	U.S. $	Can. $	U.K. £
Mini Angel	75.00	100.00	30.00

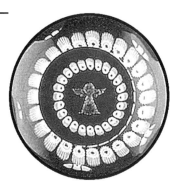

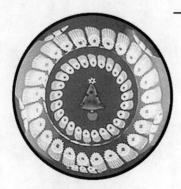

CT-554
MINI CHRISTMAS TREE

Designer: Allan Scott
Type: Weight — Spherical
Edition: 1987
Status: Closed
Series: Millefiori Miniatures
Original Issue Price: £22.50, U.S. $75.00

Name	U.S. $	Can. $	U.K. £
Mini Christmas Tree	75.00	100.00	30.00

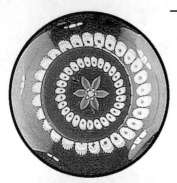

CT-555
MINI POINSETTIA

Designer: Allan Scott
Type: Weight — Spherical
Edition: 1987
Status: Closed
Series: Millefiori Miniatures
Original Issue Price: £22.50, U.S. $75.00

Name	U.S. $	Can. $	U.K. £
Mini Poinsettia	75.00	100.00	30.00

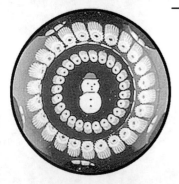

CT-556
MINI SNOWMAN

Designer: Allan Scott
Type: Weight — Spherical
Edition: 1987
Status: Closed
Series: Millefiori Miniatures
Original Issue Price: £22.50, U.S. $75.00

Name	U.S. $	Can. $	U.K. £
Mini Snowman	75.00	100.00	30.00

CT-557
CHRISTMAS DECORATION

Designer: William Manson
Type: Weight — Spherical
Edition: 1987 in a limited edition of 250
Status: Closed at No. 79
Series: Christmas Traditional Collection
Original Issue Price: £70.00, U.S. $250.00

Name	U.S. $	Can. $	U.K. £
Christmas Decoration	250.00	350.00	100.00

CT-558
CHRISTMAS STAR

Designer:	William Manson		
Type:	Weight — Spherical		
Edition:	1987 in a limited edition of 250		
Status:	Closed at No. 157		
Series:	Christmas Traditional Collection		
Original Issue Price:	£80.00, U.S. $295.00		

Name	U.S. $	Can. $	U.K. £
Christmas Star	295.00	425.00	80.00

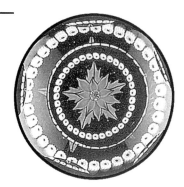

CT-559
NOEL

Designer:	William Manson		
Type:	Weight — Spherical		
Edition:	1987 in a limited edition of 250		
Status:	Closed at No. 97		
Series:	Christmas Traditional Collection		
Original Issue Price:	£70.00, U.S. $250.00		

Name	U.S. $	Can. $	U.K. £
Noel	250.00	350.00	75.00

CT-560
CHORALE

Designer:	Colin Terris		
Type:	Weight — Pyramid facets		
Edition:	1987 in a limited edition of 1,000		
Status:	Closed at No. 816		
Original Issue Price:	£50.00, U.S. $175.00		

Name	U.S. $	Can. $	U.K. £
Chorale	175.00	250.00	85.00

Note: This is the 1987 Collectors' Paperweight.

CT-561
NECTAR

Designer:	Alastair MacIntosh		
Type:	Weight — Spherical		
Edition:	1988 in a limited edition of 750		
Status:	Closed at No. 375		
Series:	Limited — Modern Design		
Original Issue Price:	£50.00, U.S. $190.00		

Name	U.S. $	Can. $	U.K. £
Nectar	190.00	275.00	60.00

CT-562
READY STEADY GO

Designer:	Colin Terris
Type:	Weight — Spherical
Edition:	1988 in a limited edition of 150
Status:	Fully subscribed
Series:	Limited — Modern Design
Original Issue Price:	£120.00, U.S. $450.00

Name	U.S. $	Can. $	U.K. £
Ready Steady Go	450.00	650.00	160.00

CT-563
ETHERIA

Designer:	Colin Terris
Type:	Weight — Spherical
Edition:	1988 in a limited edition of 750
Status:	Closed at No. 726
Series:	Limited — Modern Design
Original Issue Price:	£69.00, U.S. $275.00

Name	U.S. $	Can. $	U.K. £
Etheria	275.00	375.00	75.00

CT-564
MERRY GO ROUND

Designer:	Colin Terris
Type:	Weight — Spherical
Edition:	1988 in a limited edition of 750
Status:	Closed at No. 730
Series:	Limited — Modern Design
Original Issue Price:	£60.00, U.S. $225.00

Name	U.S. $	Can. $	U.K. £
Merry Go Round	225.00	325.00	65.00

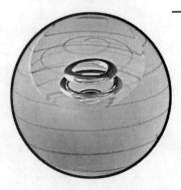

CT-565
WHEELSPIN

Designer:	Colin Terris
Type:	Weight — Spherical
Edition:	1988 in a limited edition of 750
Status:	Closed at No. 372
Series:	Limited — Modern Design
Original Issue Price:	£65.00, U.S. $250.00

Name	U.S. $	Can. $	U.K. £
Wheelspin	250.00	350.00	75.00

CT-566
MAGIC LANTERN

Designer: Colin Terris
Type: Weight — Spherical
Edition: 1988 in a limited edition of 750
Status: Fully subscribed
Series: Limited — Modern Design
Original Issue Price: £45.00, U.S. $175.00

Name	U.S. $	Can. $	U.K. £
Magic Lantern	175.00	250.00	55.00

CT-567
FIRECRACKER

Designer: Alastair MacIntosh
Type: Weight — Spherical
Edition: 1988 in a limited edition of 750
Status: Closed at No. 741
Series: Limited — Modern Design
Original Issue Price: £50.00, U.S. $190.00

Name	U.S. $	Can. $	U.K. £
Firecracker	190.00	275.00	55.00

CT-568
CHAMELEON

Designer: Colin Terris
Type: Weight — Spherical
Edition: 1988 in a limited edition of 750
Status: Closed at No. 184
Series: Limited — Modern Design
Original Issue Price: £65.00, U.S. $250.00

Name	U.S. $	Can. $	U.K. £
Chameleon	250.00	350.00	65.00

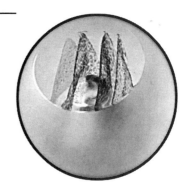

CT-569
AUTUMN BREEZE

Designer: Colin Terris
Type: Weight — Spherical
Edition: 1988 in a limited edition of 750
Status: Closed at No. 723
Series: Limited — Modern Design
Original Issue Price: £43.00, U.S. $165.00

Name	U.S. $	Can. $	U.K. £
Autumn Breeze	165.00	225.00	45.00

CT-570
JAMBOREE

Designer:	Alastair MacIntosh
Type:	Weight — Spherical
Edition:	1988 in a limited edition of 500
Status:	Fully subscribed
Series:	Limited — Modern Design
Original Issue Price:	£65.00, U.S. $250.00

Name	U.S. $	Can. $	U.K. £
Jamboree	250.00	350.00	70.00

CT-571
POINSETTIA PERFUME BOTTLE

Designer:	Colin Terris
Type:	Perfume bottle
Edition:	1988 in a limited edition of 250
Status:	Closed at No. 174
Original Issue Price:	£85.00, U.S. $350.00

Name	U.S. $	Can. $	U.K. £
Poinsettia Perfume Bottle	350.00	500.00	100.00

CT-572
EQUINOX

Designer:	Alastair MacIntosh
Type:	Weight — Spherical
Edition:	1988 in a limited edition of 750
Status:	Closed at No. 573
Series:	Limited — Modern Design
Original Issue Price:	£50.00, U.S. $190.00

Name	U.S. $	Can. $	U.K. £
Equinox	190.00	275.00	60.00

CT-573
REPOSE

Designer:	Colin Terris
Type:	Weight — Spherical
Edition:	1988 in a limited edition of 750
Status:	Closed at No. 725
Series:	Limited — Modern Design
Original Issue Price:	£50.00, U.S. $190.00

Name	U.S. $	Can. $	U.K. £
Repose	190.00	275.00	50.00

CT-574
MERRY MAKER

Designer:	Colin Terris
Type:	Weight — Spherical
Edition:	1988 in a limited edition of 750
Status:	Fully subscribed
Series:	Limited — Modern Design
Original Issue Price:	£45.00, U.S. $175.00

Name	U.S. $	Can. $	U.K. £
Merry Maker	175.00	250.00	50.00

CT-575A
MERCURY BOTTLE

Designer:	Colin Terris
Type:	Bottle
Edition:	1988 in a limited edition of 150
Status:	Closed at No. 142
Series:	Limited — Modern Design
Original Issue Price:	£175.00/set, U.S. $695.00/set

Name	U.S. $	Can. $	U.K. £
Mercury Bottle	475.00	675.00	150.00
Set	700.00	1,000.00	250.00

Note: CT-575A and B were issued and sold as a set.

CT-575B
MERCURY

Designer:	Colin Terris
Type:	Weight — Spherical
Edition:	1988 in a limited edition of 150
Status:	Closed at No. 142
Series:	Limited — Modern Design
Original Issue Price:	£175.00/set, U.S. $695.00/set

Name	U.S. $	Can. $	U.K. £
Mercury	225.00	325.00	100.00

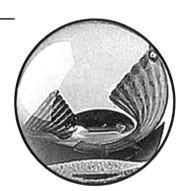

CT-576
AMMONITE

Designer:	Margot Thomson
Type:	Weight — Spherical
Edition:	1988 in a limited edition of 500
Status:	Closed at No. 444
Series:	Limited — Modern Design
Original Issue Price:	£50.00, U.S. $190.00

Name	U.S. $	Can. $	U.K. £
Ammonite	190.00	275.00	50.00

CT-577
AURORA

Designer:	Colin Terris
Type:	Weight — Spherical
Edition:	1988 in a limited edition of 250
Status:	Fully subscribed
Series:	Limited — Modern Design
Original Issue Price:	£85.00, U.S. $350.00

Name	U.S. $	Can. $	U.K. £
Aurora	350.00	500.00	100.00

CT-578
COUNTERPOINT

Designer:	Colin Terris
Type:	Weight — Spherical
Edition:	1988 in a limited edition of 750
Status:	Fully subscribed
Series:	Limited — Modern Design
Original Issue Price:	£50.00, U.S. $190.00

Name	U.S. $	Can. $	U.K. £
Counterpoint	190.00	275.00	60.00

CT-579
CYCLONE

Designer:	Colin Terris
Type:	Weight — Spherical
Edition:	1988 in a limited edition of 750
Status:	Fully subscribed
Series:	Limited — Modern Design
Original Issue Price:	£43.00, U.S. $165.00

Name	U.S. $	Can. $	U.K. £
Cyclone	165.00	225.00	45.00

CT-580
LISTENER

Designer:	Colin Terris
Type:	Weight — Spherical
Edition:	1988 in a limited edition of 750
Status:	Fully subscribed
Series:	Limited — Modern Design
Original Issue Price:	£45.00, U.S. $175.00

Name	U.S. $	Can. $	U.K. £
Listener	175.00	250.00	50.00

CT-581
CRUSADER

Designer:	Margot Thomson
Type:	Weight — Spherical
Edition:	1988 in a limited edition of 750
Status:	Fully subscribed
Series:	Limited — Modern Design
Original Issue Price:	£60.00, U.S. $225.00

Name	U.S. $	Can. $	U.K. £
Crusader	225.00	325.00	75.00

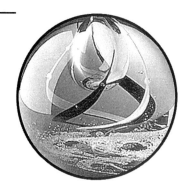

CT-582
WOOD NYMPH

Designer:	Margot Thomson
Type:	Weight — Domed
Edition:	1988 in a limited edition of 650
Status:	Closed at No. 452
Series:	Limited — Modern Design
Original Issue Price:	£55.00, U.S. $210.00

Name	U.S. $	Can. $	U.K. £
Wood Nymph	210.00	300.00	60.00

CT-583
ADVENTURE

Designer:	Colin Terris
Type:	Weight — Spherical
Edition:	1988 in a limited edition of 500
Status:	Fully subscribed
Series:	Limited — Modern Design
Original Issue Price:	£69.00, U.S. $275.00

Name	U.S. $	Can. $	U.K. £
Adventure	275.00	375.00	75.00

Note: This paperweight has basket facets and an opaque spatter overlay.

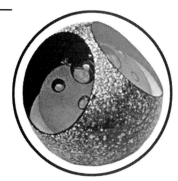

CT-584
SEA SPRITE

Designer:	Colin Terris
Type:	Weight — Spherical
Edition:	1988 in a limited edition of 250
Status:	Fully subscribed
Series:	Limited — Modern Design
Original Issue Price:	£85.00, U.S. $350.00

Name	U.S. $	Can. $	U.K. £
Sea Sprite	350.00	500.00	85.00

CT-585
SPINNING TOP

Designer: Colin Terris
Type: Weight — Spherical
Edition: 1988 in a limited edition of 750
Status: Fully subscribed
Series: Limited — Modern Design
Original Issue Price: £55.00, U.S. $210.00

Name	U.S. $	Can. $	U.K. £
Spinning Top	210.00	300.00	60.00

CT-586
MADRIGAL

Designer: Colin Terris
Type: Weight — Spherical
Edition: 1988 in a limited edition of 350
Status: Fully subscribed
Series: Limited — Modern Design
Original Issue Price: £69.00, U.S. $275.00

Name	U.S. $	Can. $	U.K. £
Madrigal	275.00	375.00	75.00

CT-587
MAELSTROM

Designer: Margot Thomson
Type: Weight — Conical
Edition: 1988 in a limited edition of 650
Status: Closed at No. 501
Series: Limited — Modern Design
Original Issue Price: £55.00, U.S. $210.00

Name	U.S. $	Can. $	U.K. £
Maelstrom	210.00	300.00	60.00

CT-588
PINNACLE

Designer: Colin Terris
Type: Weight — Spherical
Edition: 1988 in a limited edition of 150
Status: Fully subscribed
Series: Limited — Modern Design
Original Issue Price: £120.00, U.S. $450.00

Name	U.S. $	Can. $	U.K. £
Pinnacle	450.00	650.00	150.00

CT-589
BLITHE SPIRIT

Designer:	Colin Terris
Type:	Weight — Spherical
Edition:	1988 in a limited edition of 150
Status:	Fully subscribed
Series:	Limited — Modern Design
Original Issue Price:	£99.00, U.S. $395.00

Name	U.S. $	Can. $	U.K. £
Blithe Spirit	395.00	550.00	150.00

CT-590
FLIGHT OF FANCY

Designer:	Colin Terris
Type:	Weight — Domed
Edition:	1988 in a limited edition of 650
Status:	Fully subscribed
Original Issue Price:	£69.00, U.S. $275.00

Name	U.S. $	Can. $	U.K. £
Flight of Fancy	275.00	375.00	100.00

CT-591
SPRING BREEZE PERFUME BOTTLE

Designer:	Colin Terris
Type:	Perfume bottle
Edition:	1988 in a limited edition of 250
Status:	Closed at No. 235
Series:	Limited — Modern Design
Original Issue Price:	£85.00, U.S. $350.00

Name	U.S. $	Can. $	U.K. £
Spring Breeze Perfume Bottle	350.00	500.00	85.00

CT-592
VICTORIAN BOUQUET

Designer:	Allan Scott
Type:	Weight — Spherical
Edition:	1988 in a limited edition of 500
Status:	Closed at No. 272
Series:	Whitefriars Collection
Original Issue Price:	£70.00, U.S. $275.00

Name	U.S. $	Can. $	U.K. £
Victorian Bouquet	275.00	375.00	70.00

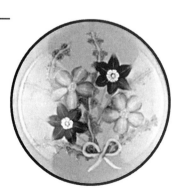

CT-593
STILL LIFE

Designer:	Allan Scott
Type:	Weight — Spherical
Edition:	1988 in a limited edition of 100
Status:	Fully subscribed
Series:	Whitefriars Collection
Original Issue Price:	£125.00, U.S. $475.00

Name	U.S. $	Can. $	U.K. £
Still Life	475.00	675.00	175.00

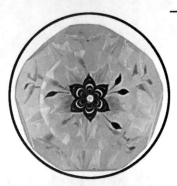

CT-594
SAPPHIRE STAR

Designer:	Allan Scott
Type:	Weight — Spherical
Edition:	1988 in a limited edition of 100
Status:	Fully subscribed
Series:	Whitefriars Collection
Original Issue Price:	£125.00, U.S. $475.00

Name	U.S. $	Can. $	U.K. £
Sapphire Star	475.00	675.00	150.00

CT-595
MIDNIGHT BOUQUET

Designer:	Allan Scott
Type:	Weight — Spherical
Edition:	1988 in a limited edition of 250
Status:	Closed at No. 222
Series:	Whitefriars Collection
Original Issue Price:	£90.00, U.S. $350.00

Name	U.S. $	Can. $	U.K. £
Midnight Bouquet	350.00	500.00	90.00

CT-596
BROCADE BUTTERFLY

Designer:	Allan Scott
Type:	Weight — Spherical
Edition:	1988 in a limited edition of 250
Status:	Closed at No. 206
Series:	Whitefriars Collection
Original Issue Price:	£90.00, U.S. $350.00

Name	U.S. $	Can. $	U.K. £
Brocade Butterfly	350.00	500.00	90.00

CT-597
LACE

Designer: Allan Scott
Type: Weight — Spherical
Edition: 1988 in a limited edition of 250
Status: Closed at No. 209
Series: Whitefriars Collection
Original Issue Price: £90.00, U.S. $350.00

Name	U.S. $	Can. $	U.K. £
Lace	350.00	500.00	90.00

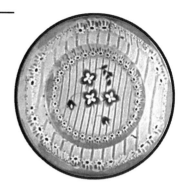

CT-598
FLORAL WHIMSY

Designer: Allan Scott
Type: Weight — Spherical
Edition: 1988 in a limited edition of 500
Status: Closed at No. 121
Series: Whitefriars Collection
Original Issue Price: £70.00, U.S. $275.00

Name	U.S. $	Can. $	U.K. £
Floral Whimsy	275.00	375.00	70.00

CT-599
SUMMER BLUE

Designer: Allan Scott
Type: Weight — Spherical
Edition: 1988 in a limited edition of 100
Status: Closed at No. 91
Series: Whitefriars Collection
Original Issue Price: £125.00, U.S. $475.00

Name	U.S. $	Can. $	U.K. £
Summer Blue	475.00	675.00	125.00

CT-600
CARNIVAL SILVER

Designer: Colin Terris
Type: Weight — Spherical
Edition: 1988
Status: Closed
Series: Unlimited — Modern Design
Original Issue Price: £13.30, U.S. $69.50

Name	U.S. $	Can. $	U.K. £
Carnival Silver	70.00	100.00	30.00

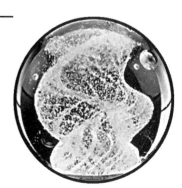

CT-601
FROG and LADYBIRD

Designer: William Manson
Type: Weight — Spherical
Edition: 1988 in a limited edition of 150
Status: Fully subscribed
Series: Traditional Collection
Original Issue Price: £200.00, U.S. $775.00

Name	U.S. $	Can. $	U.K. £
Frog and Ladybird	775.00	1,100.00	225.00

CT-602
NESTING BLUEBIRD

Designer: William Manson
Type: Weight — Spherical
Edition: 1988 in a limited edition of 250
Status: Closed at No. 230
Series: Traditional Collection
Original Issue Price: £150.00, U.S. $575.00

Name	U.S. $	Can. $	U.K. £
Nesting Bluebird	575.00	825.00	150.00

CT-603
HARVEST MOUSE

Designer: William Manson
Type: Weight — Spherical
Edition: 1988 in a limited edition of 200
Status: Closed at No. 126
Series: Traditional Collection
Original Issue Price: £175.00, U.S. $695.00

Name	U.S. $	Can. $	U.K. £
Harvest Mouse	695.00	1,000.00	175.00

CT-604
NATURE STUDY

Designer: William Manson
Type: Weight — Spherical
Edition: 1988 in a limited edition of 200
Status: Closed at No. 137
Original Issue Price: £175.00, U.S. $695.00

Name	U.S. $	Can. $	U.K. £
Nature Study	695.00	1,000.00	200.00

CT-605
BADGER

Designer: William Manson
Type: Weight — Spherical
Edition: 1988 in a limited edition of 100
Status: Closed at No. 41
Series: Traditional Collection
Original Issue Price: £225.00, U.S. $850.00

Name	U.S. $	Can. $	U.K. £
Badger	950.00	1,350.00	250.00

CT-606
OCEAN HUNTER

Designer: William Manson
Type: Weight — Spherical
Edition: 1988 in a limited edition of 250
Status: Closed at No. 80
Series: Traditional Collection
Original Issue Price: £130.00, U.S. $495.00

Name	U.S. $	Can. $	U.K. £
Ocean Hunter	525.00	725.00	150.00

CT-607
SWAN LAKE

Designer: William Manson
Type: Weight — Spherical
Edition: 1988 in a limited edition of 250
Status: Closed at No. 241
Series: Traditional Collection
Original Issue Price: £150.00, U.S. $575.00

Name	U.S. $	Can. $	U.K. £
Swan Lake	575.00	825.00	175.00

CT-608
CROCODILE

Designer: William Manson
Type: Weight — Spherical
Edition: 1988 in a limited edition of 150
Status: Closed at No. 104
Series: Traditional Collection
Original Issue Price: £200.00, U.S. $775.00

Name	U.S. $	Can. $	U.K. £
Crocodile	775.00	1,100.00	200.00

CT-609
STARWATCH SILVER

Designer: Colin Terris
Type: Weight — Spherical
Edition: 1988
Status: Active
Series: Unlimited — Modern Design
Original Issue Price: £25.95, U.S. $99.50

Name	U.S. $	Can. $	U.K. £
Starwatch Silver	125.00	160.00	38.00

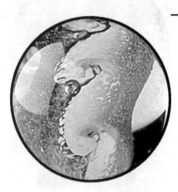

CT-610
TIDAL WAVE

Designer: Margot Thomson
Type: Weight — Spherical
Edition: 1988
Status: Active
Series: Unlimited — Modern Design
Original Issue Price: £19.95, U.S. $79.50

Name	U.S. $	Can. $	U.K. £
Tidal Wave	95.00	130.00	29.50

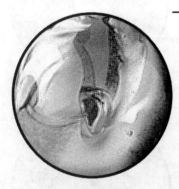

CT-611
NEON

Designer: Alastair MacIntosh
Type: Weight — Spherical
Colour: See below
Edition: 1988
Status: Closed
Series: Unlimited — Modern Design
Original Issue Price: £23.95, U.S. $95.00

Colourways	U.S. $	Can. $	U.K. £
1. Green, white and blue	95.00	130.00	25.00
2. Pink, white and blue	95.00	130.00	25.00
3. Purple, white and yellow	95.00	130.00	25.00

CT-612
PETALS

Designer:	Colin Terris
Type:	Weight — Spherical
Colour:	See below
Edition:	1988
Status:	Closed
Series:	Unlimited — Modern Design
Original Issue Price:	£25.95, U.S. $99.50

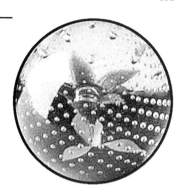

Colourways	U.S. $	Can. $	U.K. £
1. Blue	100.00	140.00	30.00
2. Gold	100.00	140.00	30.00
3. Red	100.00	140.00	30.00
4. Yellow	100.00	140.00	30.00

CT-613
SNOW TRAIL

Designer:	Margot Thomson
Type:	Weight — Spherical
Colour:	See below
Edition:	1988
Status:	Closed
Series:	Unlimited — Modern Design
Original Issue Price:	£25.95, U.S. $99.50

Colourways	U.S. $	Can. $	U.K. £
1. Amethyst	100.00	140.00	30.00
2. Clear	100.00	140.00	30.00

CT-614
CALYPSO

Designer:	Margot Thomson
Type:	Weight — Spherical
Colour:	See below
Edition:	1988
Status:	Closed
Series:	Unlimited — Modern Design
Original Issue Price:	£21.95, U.S. $79.50

Colourways	U.S. $	Can. $	U.K. £
1. Pink	80.00	110.00	25.00
2. Topaz	80.00	110.00	25.00

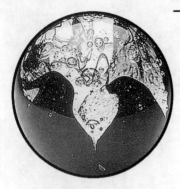

CT-615
DOUBLE MAGNUM SABLE

Designer: Colin Terris
Type: Weight — Spherical, double magnum
Edition: 1988
Status: Closed
Series: Unlimited — Modern Design
Original Issue Price: £145.00, U.S. $495.00

Name	U.S. $	Can. $	U.K. £
Double Magnum Sable	495.00	700.00	175.00

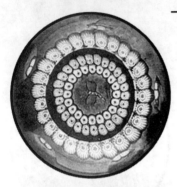

CT-616
MINIATURE DRAGONFLY

Designer: Allan Scott
Type: Weight — Spherical
Edition: 1988
Status: Closed
Series: Millefiori Miniatures
Original Issue Price: £23.95, U.S. $79.50

Name	U.S. $	Can. $	U.K. £
Miniature Dragonfly	80.00	110.00	30.00

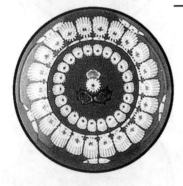

CT-617
MINIATURE THISTLE

Designer: Allan Scott
Type: Weight — Spherical
Edition: 1988
Status: Closed
Series: Millefiori Miniatures
Original Issue Price: £23.95, U.S. $79.50

Name	U.S. $	Can. $	U.K. £
Miniature Thistle	80.00	110.00	30.00

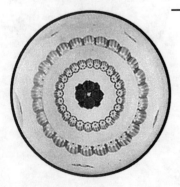

CT-618
MINIATURE ROSE

Designer: Allan Scott
Type: Weight — Spherical
Edition: 1988
Status: Closed
Series: Millefiori Miniatures
Original Issue Price: £23.95, U.S. $79.50

Name	U.S. $	Can. $	U.K. £
Miniature Rose	80.00	110.00	30.00

CT-619
MINIATURE DAFFODIL

Designer: Allan Scott
Type: Weight — Spherical
Edition: 1988
Status: Closed
Series: Millefiori Minatures
Original Issue Price: £23.95, U.S. $79.50

Name	*U.S. $*	*Can. $*	*U.K. £*
Miniature Daffodil	80.00	110.00	30.00

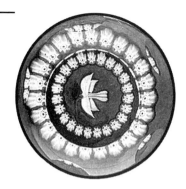

CT-620
MINIATURE SHAMROCK

Designer: Allan Scott
Type: Weight — Spherical
Edition: 1988
Status: Closed
Series: Millefiori Miniatures
Original Issue Price: £23.95, U.S. $79.50

Name	*U.S. $*	*Can. $*	*U.K. £*
Miniature Shamrock	80.00	110.00	30.00

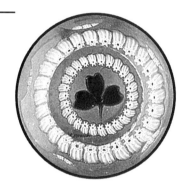

CT-621
MINIATURE HEART

Designer: Allan Scott
Type: Weight — Spherical
Edition: 1988
Status: Closed
Series: Millefiori Miniatures
Original Issue Price: £23.95, U.S. $79.50

Name	*U.S. $*	*Can. $*	*U.K. £*
Miniature Heart	80.00	110.00	30.00

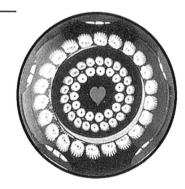

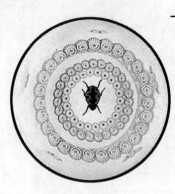

CT-622
MINIATURE LADYBIRD

Designer: Allan Scott
Type: Weight — Spherical
Edition: 1988
Status: Closed
Series: Millefiori Miniatures
Original Issue Price: £23.95, U.S. $79.50

Name	U.S. $	Can. $	U.K. £
Miniature Ladybird	80.00	110.00	30.00

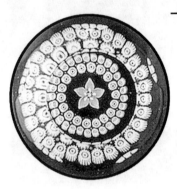

CT-623
MINIATURE FORGET-ME-NOT

Designer: Allan Scott
Type: Weight — Spherical
Edition: 1988
Status: Closed
Series: Millefiori Miniatures
Original Issue Price: £23.95, U.S. $79.50

Name	U.S. $	Can. $	U.K. £
Miniature Forget-me-not	80.00	110.00	30.00

CT-624
SERPENTINE

Designer: Stuart Cumming
Type: Weight — Spherical
Edition: 1988 in a limited edition of 750
Status: Closed at No. 733
Series: Limited — Modern Design
Original Issue Price: £43.00, U.S. $165.00

Name	U.S. $	Can. $	U.K. £
Serpentine	165.00	225.00	45.00

CT-625
CALIPH

Designer:	Margot Thomson
Type:	Weight — Spherical
Edition:	1988 in a limited edition of 750
Status:	Fully subscribed
Series:	Limited — Modern Design
Original Issue Price:	£45.00, U.S. $175.00

Name	U.S. $	Can. $	U.K. £
Caliph	175.00	250.00	50.00

CT-626
MERIDIAN

Designer:	Alastair MacIntosh
Type:	Weight — Domed
Edition:	1988 in a limited edition of 500
Status:	Fully subscribed
Series:	Limited — Modern Design
Original Issue Price:	£65.00, U.S. $250.00

Name	U.S. $	Can. $	U.K. £
Meridian	250.00	350.00	65.00

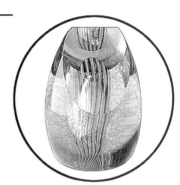

CT-627
VESUVIUS

Designer:	Colin Terris
Type:	Weight — Pyramid facets
Edition:	1988 in a limited edition of 650
Status:	Closed at No. 462
Series:	Limited — Modern Design
Original Issue Price:	£59.00, U.S. $225.00

Name	U.S. $	Can. $	U.K. £
Vesuvius	225.00	325.00	60.00

CT-628
TIME WARP

Designer:	Colin Terris
Type:	Weight — Spherical
Edition:	1988 in a limited edition of 750
Status:	Closed at No. 557
Series:	Limited — Modern Design
Original Issue Price:	£55.00, U.S. $210.00

Name	U.S. $	Can. $	U.K. £
Time Warp	210.00	300.00	55.00

CT-629
ARGOSY

Designer:	Colin Terris
Type:	Weight — Spherical
Edition:	1988 in a limited edition of 250
Status:	Fully subscribed
Series:	Limited — Modern Design
Original Issue Price:	£90.00, U.S. $350.00

Name	U.S. $	Can. $	U.K. £
Argosy	350.00	500.00	100.00

CT-630
SNOWFLAME

Designer:	Margot Thomson
Type:	Weight — Spherical
Edition:	1988 in a limited edition of 750
Status:	Fully subscribed
Series:	Limited — Modern Design
Original Issue Price:	£45.00, U.S. $175.00

Name	U.S. $	Can. $	U.K. £
Snowflame	175.00	250.00	50.00

CT-631
MISTS OF TIME

Designer:	Margot Thomson
Type:	Weight — Pyramid facets
Edition:	1988 in a limited edition of 500
Status:	Closed at No. 368
Series:	Limited — Modern Design
Original Issue Price:	£75.00, U.S. $295.00

Name	U.S. $	Can. $	U.K. £
Mists of Time	295.00	425.00	80.00

CT-632
GALLEON

Designer:	Colin Terris
Type:	Weight — Spherical
Edition:	1988 in a limited edition of 750
Status:	Closed at No. 696
Series:	Limited — Modern Design
Original Issue Price:	£50.00, U.S. $190.00

Name	U.S. $	Can. $	U.K. £
Galleon	190.00	275.00	50.00

CT-633
BRITANNIA

Designer:	Alastair MacIntosh
Type:	Weight — Spherical
Edition:	1988 in a limited edition of 250
Status:	Fully subscribed
Series:	Limited — Modern Design
Original Issue Price:	£85.00, U.S. $350.00

Name	U.S. $	Can. $	U.K. £
Britannia	350.00	500.00	100.00

CT-634
PARROT

Designer:	William Manson
Type:	Weight — Spherical
Edition:	1988 in a limited edition of 150
Status:	Closed at No. 142
Series:	Whitefriars Collection
Original Issue Price:	£200.00, U.S. $775.00

Name	U.S. $	Can. $	U.K. £
Parrot	775.00	1,100.00	225.00

CT-635
DRAGONFLY

Designer:	William Manson
Type:	Weight — Spherical
Edition:	1988 in a limited edition of 200
Status:	Fully subscribed
Series:	Traditional Collection
Original Issue Price:	£185.00, U.S. $695.00

Name	U.S. $	Can. $	U.K. £
Dragonfly	695.00	1,000.00	200.00

CT-636
ROSE and LADYBIRD

Designer:	William Manson
Type:	Weight — Spherical
Edition:	1988 in a limited edition of 250
Status:	Fully subscribed
Series:	Traditional Collection
Original Issue Price:	£150.00, U.S. $575.00

Name	U.S. $	Can. $	U.K. £
Rose and Ladybird	575.00	825.00	175.00

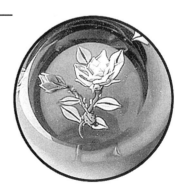

CT-637
SUMMER GARDEN

Designer: Allan Scott
Type: Weight — Spherical
Edition: 1988 in a limited edition of 250
Status: Fully subscribed
Series: Whitefriars Collection
Original Issue Price: £100.00, U.S. $375.00

Name	U.S. $	Can. $	U.K. £
Summer Garden	375.00	525.00	125.00

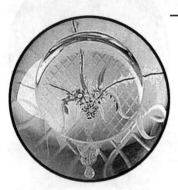

CT-638
HANGING BASKET

Designer: Allan Scott
Type: Weight — Spherical
Edition: 1988 in a limited edition of 250
Status: Closed at No. 244
Series: Whitefriars Collection
Original Issue Price: £100.00, U.S. $395.00

Name	U.S. $	Can. $	U.K. £
Hanging Basket	395.00	550.00	125.00

CT-639
MAGNUM OPUS '88

Designer: Colin Terris
Type: Weight — Spherical, treble magnum
Colour: Pink flower with aqua and green leaves
Edition: 1988 in a limited edition of 100
Status: Fully subscribed
Series: Limited — Modern Design
Original Issue Price: £450.00, U.S. $1,500

Name	U.S. $	Can. $	U.K. £
Magnum Opus '88	1,500.00	2,150.00	800.00

CT-640
FIESTA

Designer:	Alastair MacIntosh
Type:	Weight — Spherical
Colour:	See below
Edition:	1988
Status:	Closed
Series:	Unlimited — Modern Design
Original Issue Price:	£23.95, U.S. $90.00

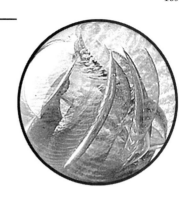

Colourways	U.S. $	Can. $	U.K. £
1. Aqua	90.00	130.00	25.00
2. Lime	90.00	130.00	25.00
3. Orange	90.00	130.00	25.00
4. Ruby	90.00	130.00	25.00

CT-641
SPINNAKER

Designer:	Alastair MacIntosh
Type:	Weight — Spherical
Colour:	See below
Edition:	1988
Status:	Closed
Series:	Unlimited — Modern Design
Original Issue Price:	£14.95, U.S. $55.00

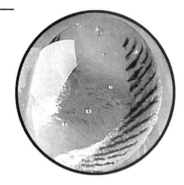

Colourways	U.S. $	Can. $	U.K. £
1. Cobalt	55.00	75.00	15.00
2. Lime	55.00	75.00	15.00
3. Orange	55.00	75.00	15.00
4. Ruby	55.00	75.00	15.00

CT-642
MINIATURE MISTLETOE

Designer:	Allan Scott
Type:	Weight — Spherical
Edition:	1988
Status:	Closed
Series:	Millefiori Miniatures
Original Issue Price:	£24.95, U.S. $79.50

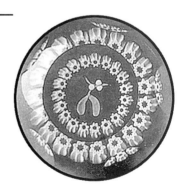

Name	U.S. $	Can. $	U.K. £
Miniature Mistletoe	80.00	110.00	30.00

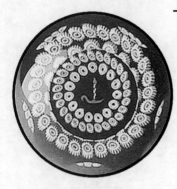

CT-643
MINIATURE CANDLE

Designer:	Allan Scott		
Type:	Weight — Spherical		
Edition:	1988		
Status:	Closed		
Series:	Millefiori Miniatures		
Original Issue Price:	£24.95, U.S. $79.50		

Name	U.S. $	Can. $	U.K. £
Miniature Candle	80.00	110.00	30.00

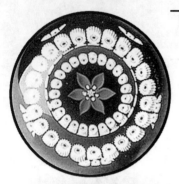

CT-644
MINIATURE POINSETTIA

Designer:	Allan Scott		
Type:	Weight — Spherical		
Edition:	1988		
Status:	Closed		
Series:	Millefiori Miniatures		
Original Issue Price:	£24.95, U.S. $79.50		

Name	U.S. $	Can. $	U.K. £
Miniature Poinsettia	80.00	110.00	30.00

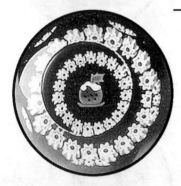

CT-645
MINIATURE FESTIVE FARE

Designer:	Allan Scott		
Type:	Weight — Spherical		
Edition:	1988		
Status:	Closed		
Series:	Millefiori Miniatures		
Original Issue Price:	£24.95, U.S. $79.50		

Name	U.S. $	Can. $	U.K. £
Miniature Festive Fare	80.00	110.00	30.00

CT-646
OPUS 88

Designer:	Colin Terris		
Type:	Weight — Spherical		
Colour:	Pink and white flower with blue leaves		
Edition:	1988 in a limited edition of 1,000		
Status:	Fully subscribed		
Original Issue Price:	£55.00, U.S. $195.00		

Name	U.S. $	Can. $	U.K. £
Opus 88	250.00	350.00	175.00

Note: This is the 1988 Collectors' Weight.

CT-647
AFFINITY

Designer: Margot Thomson
Type: Weight — Spherical
Edition: 1989 in a limited edition of 750
Status: Closed at No. 636
Series: Limited — Modern Design
Original Issue Price: £55.00, U.S. $275.00

Name	U.S. $	Can. $	U.K. £
Affinity	275.00	375.00	55.00

CT-648
ALPINE WINTER

Designer: Alastair MacIntosh
Type: Weight — Domed
Edition: 1989 in a limited edition of 650
Status: Fully subscribed
Series: Limited — Modern Design
Original Issue Price: £60.00, U.S. $250.00

Name	U.S. $	Can. $	U.K. £
Alpine Winter	250.00	350.00	60.00

CT-649
BONSAI

Designer: Alastair MacIntosh
Type: Weight — Domed
Edition: 1989 in a limited edition of 500
Status: Fully subscribed
Series: Limited — Modern Design
Original Issue Price: £69.00, U.S. $275.00

Name	U.S. $	Can. $	U.K. £
Bonsai	275.00	375.00	70.00

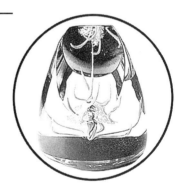

CT-650
BUTTERFLY ORCHID

Designer: Colin Terris
Type: Weight — Spherical
Edition: 1989 in a limited edition of 750
Status: Closed at No. 602
Series: Limited — Modern Design
Original Issue Price: £60.00, U.S. $225.00

Name	U.S. $	Can. $	U.K. £
Butterfly Orchid	225.00	325.00	60.00

CT-651
CLEOPATRA

Designer: Colin Terris
Type: Weight — Pyramid facets
Edition: 1989 in a limited edition of 500
Status: Closed at No. 465
Series: Limited — Modern Design
Original Issue Price: £80.00, U.S. $325.00

Name	U.S. $	Can. $	U.K. £
Cleopatra	325.00	450.00	80.00

CT-652
CONFUSION

Designer: Colin Terris
Type: Weight — Spherical
Edition: 1989 in a limited edition of 750
Status: Closed at No. 716
Series: Limited — Modern Design
Original Issue Price: £55.00, U.S. $210.00

Name	U.S. $	Can. $	U.K. £
Confusion	210.00	300.00	55.00

CT-653A
EARTH

Designer: Colin Terris
Type: Weight — Spherical
Edition: 1989 in a limited edition of 250
Status: Fully subscribed
Series: Elements, Set Two
Original Issue Price: £295.00/set, U.S. $1,000.00/set

Name	U.S. $	Can. $	U.K. £
Earth	250.00	350.00	90.00
Set	1,000.00	1,400.00	360.00

Note: CT-653A, B, C and D were issued and sold as a set.

CT-653B
AIR

Designer: Colin Terris
Type: Weight — Spherical
Edition: 1989 in a limited edition of 250
Status: Fully subscribed
Series: Elements, Set Two
Original Issue Price: £295.00/set, U.S. $1,000.00/set

Name	U.S. $	Can. $	U.K. £
Air	250.00	350.00	90.00

CT-653C
FIRE

Designer:	Colin Terris
Type:	Weight — Spherical
Edition:	1989 in a limited edition of 250
Status:	Fully subscribed
Series:	Elements, Set Two
Original Issue Price:	£295.00/set, U.S. $1,000/set

Name	U.S. $	Can. $	U.K. £
Fire	250.00	350.00	90.00

CT-653D
WATER

Designer:	Colin Terris
Type:	Weight — Spherical
Edition:	1989 in a limited edition of 250
Status:	Fully subscribed
Series:	Elements, Set Two
Original Issue Price:	£295.00/set, U.S. $1,000/set

Name	U.S. $	Can. $	U.K. £
Water	250.00	350.00	90.00

CT-654
EVOLUTION

Designer:	Alastair MacIntosh
Type:	Weight — Spherical
Edition:	1989 in a limited edition of 750
Status:	Closed at No. 651
Series:	Limited — Modern Design
Original Issue Price:	£55.00, U.S. $225.00

Name	U.S. $	Can. $	U.K. £
Evolution	225.00	325.00	55.00

CT-655
GLOBE TROTTER

Designer:	Margot Thomson
Type:	Weight — Spherical
Edition:	1989 in a limited edition of 650
Status:	Closed at No. 546
Series:	Limited — Modern Design
Original Issue Price:	£65.00, U.S. $250.00

Name	U.S. $	Can. $	U.K. £
Globe Trotter	250.00	350.00	65.00

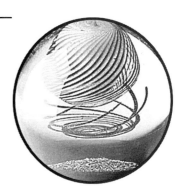

CT-656
HALLOWEEN

Designer:	Margot Thomson
Type:	Weight — Spherical
Edition:	1989 in a limited edition of 650
Status:	Closed at No. 602
Series:	Limited — Modern Design
Original Issue Price:	£69.00, U.S. $275.00

Name	U.S. $	Can. $	U.K. £
Halloween	275.00	375.00	70.00

CT-657
ICE FAIRY

Designer:	Margot Thomson
Type:	Weight — Teardrop
Edition:	1989 in a limited edition of 650
Status:	Fully subscribed
Series:	Limited — Modern Design
Original Issue Price:	£80.00, U.S. $325.00

Name	U.S. $	Can. $	U.K. £
Ice Fairy	325.00	450.00	80.00

CT-658
INCANTATION

Designer:	Colin Terris
Type:	Weight — Domed
Edition:	1989 in a limited edition of 500
Status:	Fully subscribed
Series:	Limited — Modern Design
Original Issue Price:	£69.00, U.S. $275.00

Name	U.S. $	Can. $	U.K. £
Incantation	275.00	375.00	70.00

CT-659
INTRIGUE

Designer:	Colin Terris
Type:	Weight — Spherical
Edition:	1989 in a limited edition of 750
Status:	Closed at No. 529
Series:	Limited — Modern Design
Original Issue Price:	£55.00, U.S. $225.00

Name	U.S. $	Can. $	U.K. £
Intrigue	225.00	325.00	55.00

CT-660
MARDI-GRAS

Designer: Margot Thomson
Type: Weight — Teardrop
Edition: 1989 in a limited edition of 650
Status: Fully subscribed
Series: Limited — Modern Design
Original Issue Price: £65.00, U.S. $250.00

Name	U.S. $	Can. $	U.K. £
Mardi-Gras	250.00	350.00	70.00

CT-661
MAZOURKA

Designer: Colin Terris
Type: Weight — Spherical
Edition: 1989 in a limited edition of 250
Status: Closed at No. 231
Series: Limited — Modern Design
Original Issue Price: £99.00, U.S. $395.00

Name	U.S. $	Can. $	U.K. £
Mazourka	395.00	550.00	100.00

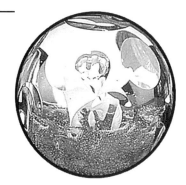

CT-662
MERCATOR

Designer: Alastair MacIntosh
Type: Weight — Spherical
Edition: 1989 in a limited edition of 650
Status: Closed at No. 610
Series: Limited — Modern Design
Original Issue Price: £69.00, U.S. $275.00

Name	U.S. $	Can. $	U.K. £
Mercator	275.00	375.00	70.00

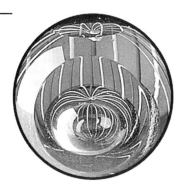

CT-663
MIDNIGHT

Designer: Colin Terris
Type: Weight — Spherical
Edition: 1989 in a limited edition of 750
Status: Closed at No. 440
Series: Limited — Modern Design
Original Issue Price: £60.00, U.S. $250.00

Name	U.S. $	Can. $	U.K. £
Midnight	250.00	350.00	60.00

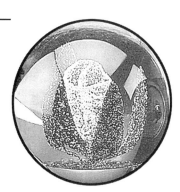

CT-664
MOONFLOWER CELEBRATION

Designer:	Colin Terris	
Type:	Weight — Spherical	
Colour:	Blue and silver	
Edition:	1989 in a limited edition of 500	
Series:	Limited — Modern Design	
Status:	Closed at No. 421	
Original Issue Price:	£120.00, U.S. $475.00	

Name	U.S. $	Can. $	U.K. £
Moonflower Celebration	475.00	675.00	125.00

Note: This paperweight was issued to celebrate the 20th anniversary of the *Moonflower* design (1969-1989).

CT-665
MOONLIGHT DANCER

Designer:	Colin Terris	
Type:	Weight — Spherical	
Edition:	1989 in a limited edition of 750	
Status:	Fully subscribed	
Series:	Limited — Modern Design	
Original Issue Price:	£45.00, U.S. $175.00	

Name	U.S. $	Can. $	U.K. £
Moonlight Dancer	175.00	250.00	55.00

CT-666
MYSTERIA

Designer:	Colin Terris	
Type:	Weight — Spherical	
Edition:	1989 in a limited edition of 750	
Status:	Closed at No. 496	
Series:	Limited — Modern Design	
Original Issue Price:	£55.00, U.S. $225.00	

Name	U.S. $	Can. $	U.K. £
Mysteria	225.00	325.00	55.00

CT-667
OASIS

Designer:	Stuart Cumming	
Type:	Weight — Spherical, magnum size	
Edition:	1989 in a limited edition of 350	
Series:	Limited — Modern Design	
Status:	Fully subscribed	
Original Issue Price:	£85.00, U.S. $350.00	

Name	U.S. $	Can. $	U.K. £
Oasis	350.00	500.00	95.00

CT-668
PETRONELLA

Designer:	Alastair MacIntosh
Type:	Weight — Spherical
Edition:	1989 in a limited edition of 250
Status:	Closed at No. 244
Series:	Limited — Modern Design
Original Issue Price:	£120.00, U.S. $475.00

Name	U.S. $	Can. $	U.K. £
Petronella	475.00	675.00	125.00

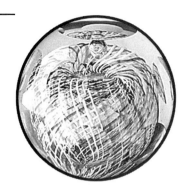

CT-669
PLANETARIUM

Designer:	Colin Terris
Type:	Weight — Spherical
Edition:	1989 in a limited edition of 750
Status:	Fully subscribed
Series:	Limited — Modern Design
Original Issue Price:	£50.00, U.S. $210.00

Name	U.S. $	Can. $	U.K. £
Planetarium	210.00	300.00	50.00

CT-670
PRINCESS

Designer:	Colin Terris
Type:	Weight — Spherical
Edition:	1989 in a limited edition of 250
Status:	Fully subscribed
Series:	Limited — Modern Design
Original Issue Price:	£150.00, U.S. $625.00

Name	U.S. $	Can. $	U.K. £
Princess	625.00	900.00	175.00

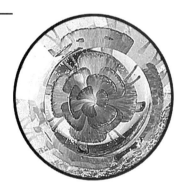

CT-671
RED ARROWS

Designer:	Alastair MacIntosh
Type:	Weight — Teardrop
Edition:	1989 in a limited edition of 750
Status:	Fully subscribed
Series:	Limited — Modern Design
Original Issue Price:	£45.00, U.S. $175.00

Name	U.S. $	Can. $	U.K. £
Red Arrows	175.00	250.00	45.00

CT-672
SCHEHERAZADE

Designer:	Margot Thomson
Type:	Weight — Teardrop
Edition:	1989 in a limited edition of 250
Status:	Fully subscribed
Series:	Limited — Modern Design
Original Issue Price:	£120.00, U.S. $475.00

Name	U.S. $	Can. $	U.K. £
Scheherazade	475.00	675.00	135.00

CT-673
SPACE JOURNEY

Designer:	Alastair MacIntosh
Type:	Weight — Spherical
Edition:	1989 in a limited edition of 650
Status:	Fully subscribed
Series:	Limited — Modern Design
Original Issue Price:	£65.00, U.S. $275.00

Name	U.S. $	Can. $	U.K. £
Space Journey	275.00	375.00	65.00

CT-674
SUMMIT

Designer:	Colin Terris
Type:	Weight — Spherical
Edition:	1989 in a limited edition of 750
Status:	Closed at No. 737
Series:	Limited — Modern Design
Original Issue Price:	£50.00, U.S. $210.00

Name	U.S. $	Can. $	U.K. £
Summit	210.00	300.00	50.00

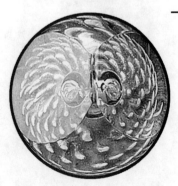

CT-675
TAWNY OWL

Designer:	Alastair MacIntosh
Type:	Weight — Spherical
Edition:	1989 in a limited edition of 500
Status:	Fully subscribed
Original Issue Price:	£80.00, U.S. $325.00

Name	U.S. $	Can. $	U.K. £
Tawny Owl	325.00	450.00	95.00

CT-676
TRINITY

Designer:	Colin Terris
Type:	Weight — Spherical
Edition:	1989 in a limited edition of 750
Status:	Closed at No. 425
Series:	Limited — Modern Design
Original Issue Price:	£60.00, U.S. $250.00

Name	U.S. $	Can. $	U.K. £
Trinity	250.00	350.00	60.00

CT-677
UNISON

Designer:	Colin Terris
Type:	Weight — Spherical
Edition:	1989 in a limited edition of 750
Status:	Closed at No. 445
Series:	Limited — Modern Design
Original Issue Price:	£50.00, U.S. $210.00

Name	U.S. $	Can. $	U.K. £
Unison	210.00	300.00	50.00

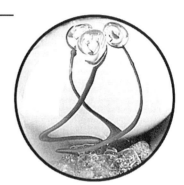

CT-678
VOLCANO

Designer:	Alastair MacIntosh
Type:	Weight — Domed
Edition:	1989 in a limited edition of 650
Status:	Closed at No. 627
Series:	Limited — Modern Design
Original Issue Price:	£65.00, U.S. $250.00

Name	U.S. $	Can. $	U.K. £
Volcano	250.00	350.00	65.00

CT-679
DOLPHIN

Designer:	William Manson
Type:	Weight — Spherical
Edition:	1989 in a limited edition of 250
Status:	Closed at No. 190
Series:	Traditional Collection
Original Issue Price:	£160.00, U.S. $650.00

Name	U.S. $	Can. $	U.K. £
Dolphin	650.00	925.00	175.00

CT-680
FESTIVE BOUQUET

Designer:	William Manson
Type:	Weight — Spherical
Edition:	1989 in a limited edition of 250
Status:	Closed at No. 90
Series:	Traditional Collection
Original Issue Price:	£175.00, U.S. $695.00

Name	U.S. $	Can. $	U.K. £
Festive Bouquet	695.00	1,000.00	175.00

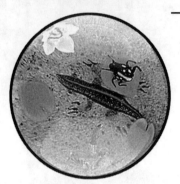

CT-681
NEWT

Designer:	William Manson
Type:	Weight — Spherical
Edition:	1989 in a limited edition of 150
Status:	Closed at No. 115
Series:	Traditional Collection
Original Issue Price:	£200.00, U.S. $775.00

Name	U.S. $	Can. $	U.K. £
Newt	775.00	1,100.00	200.00

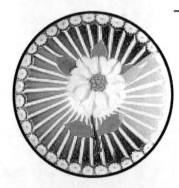

CT-682
ROYAL FLOURISH

Designer:	William Manson
Type:	Weight — Spherical
Edition:	1989 in a limited edition of 250
Status:	Closed at No. 99
Series:	Traditional Collection
Original Issue Price:	£130.00, U.S. $750.00

Name	U.S. $	Can. $	U.K. £
Royal Flourish	750.00	1,050.00	130.00

CT-683
TIGER FISH

Designer:	William Manson
Type:	Weight — Spherical
Edition:	1989 in a limited edition of 250
Status:	Closed at No. 52
Series:	Traditional Collection
Original Issue Price:	£185.00, U.S. $750.00

Name	U.S. $	Can. $	U.K. £
Tiger Fish	750.00	1,050.00	185.00

Modern - Limited

CT-8
Coral

CT-38
Vortex

CT-90
Sunflare

CT-159
Space Orchid

CT-206
Fantasia

CT-303
Antennae

CT-506
Minuet

CT-579
Cyclone

CT-654
Evolution

Modern - Limited

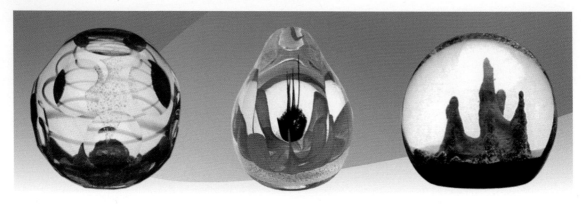

CT-716
Aladdin

CT-748
Radiance

CT-880
Painted Desert

CT-1031
Double Magnum 94

CT-1173
Fairyland

CT-1283
Oceanic

CT-1396
Innocence

CT-1485
Hallucination

CT-1531
Cinnabar

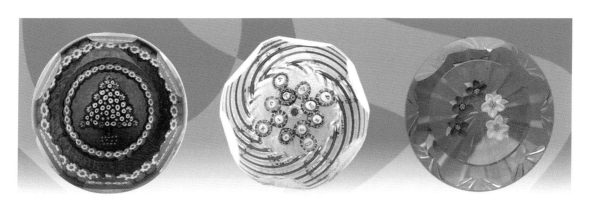

CT-302
Christmas Tree

CT-323
The Zodiac

CT-362
Amethyst Bouquet

CT-409
Apple Blossom

CT-451
Blue Spray

CT-537
Opium Poppy

CT-595
Midnight Bouquet

CT-637
Summer Garden

CT-685
Peacock

Whitefriars

CT-773	CT-833	CT-897
Scots Thistle	*Alpine Pink*	*Primula*

CT-1023A	CT-1023B	CT-1187
Summer Celebration (Pair)	*Summer Celebration (Pair)*	*Iris Bouquet*

CT-1575	CT-1661	CT-1740
Spring Florette - Cobalt	*Valentino*	*Diamond Reflections*

CT-46A
Spring

CT-103
Manta Ray

CT-105
Ladybird

CT-186
Seal

CT-232
Regency Stripe

CT-301
Christmas Rose

CT-327
Highland Fling

CT-348
Fire Lizard

CT-601
Frog and Ladybird

Traditional

CT-683
Tiger Fish

CT-842
Scorpion

CT-895
Butterfly

CT- 1013
Double Salamander

CT-1015
Humming Bird

CT-1248
Tropical Parakeet

CT-1308
Teddy Bear

CT-1584
Bunnies

CT-1586
Sunflowers

Modern - Unlimited

CT-92
Morning Dew

CT-177
Flamenco

CT-295
Seaform

CT-305
Fireball

CT-338
Spinaway

CT-417
Quicksilver

CT-552
Tempest Magenta

CT-693
Vibrance

CT-694
Windfall Emerald

Modern - Unlimited

CT-712
Sea Dance Sable

CT-852
Liberty

CT-853
Sirocco Aqua

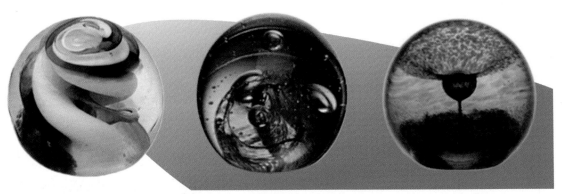

CT-859
Dizzy Green

CT-1132
Escapade

CT-1133
Flower of Scotland

CT-1213
Brushstrokes

CT-1334
Titania

CT-1371
Whizz

CT-684
FLORIANA

Designer:	Harry McKay
Type:	Weight — Spherical
Edition:	1989 in a limited edition of 250
Status:	Closed at No. 130
Series:	Whitefriars Collection
Original Issue Price:	£100.00, U.S. $395.00

Name	U.S. $	Can. $	U.K. £
Floriana	395.00	550.00	100.00

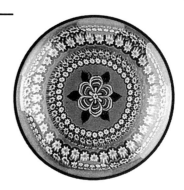

CT-685
PEACOCK

Designer:	Fiona Steele
Type:	Weight — Spherical
Edition:	1989 in a limited edition of 250
Status:	Closed at No. 205
Series:	Whitefriars Collection
Original Issue Price:	£125.00, U.S. $495.00

Name	U.S. $	Can. $	U.K. £
Peacock	495.00	700.00	125.00

CT-686
ROYAL BLUE

Designer:	Allan Scott
Type:	Weight — Spherical
Edition:	1989 in a limited edition of 250
Status:	Closed at No. 68
Series:	Whitefriars Collection
Original Issue Price:	£100.00, U.S. $395.00

Name	U.S. $	Can. $	U.K. £
Royal Blue	400.00	550.00	100.00

CT-687
SCARLET BOUQUET

Designer:	Allan Scott
Type:	Weight — Spherical
Edition:	1989 in a limited edition of 250
Status:	Closed at No. 153
Series:	Whitefriars Collection
Original Issue Price:	£110.00, U.S. $425.00

Name	U.S. $	Can. $	U.K. £
Scarlet Bouquet	425.00	600.00	110.00

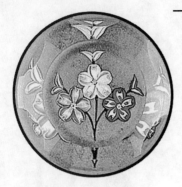

CT-688
TRIPLE FANCY

Designer: Allan Scott
Type: Weight — Spherical
Edition: 1989 in a limited edition of 250
Status: Closed at No. 81
Series: Whitefriars Collection
Original Issue Price: £100.00, U.S. $375.00

Name	U.S. $	Can. $	U.K. £
Triple Fancy	375.00	525.00	200.00

CT-689
CINDERELLA

Designer: Alastair MacIntosh
Type: Weight — Domed
Edition: 1989
Status: Closed
Series: Unlimited — Modern Design
Original Issue Price: £22.95, U.S. $87.50

Name	U.S. $	Can. $	U.K. £
Cinderella	90.00	150.00	28.50

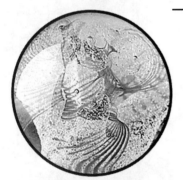

CT-690
DAYDREAMS

Designer: Margot Thomson
Type: Weight — Spherical
Edition: 1989
Status: Active
Series: Unlimited — Modern Design
Original Issue Price: £22.95, U.S. $87.50

Name	U.S. $	Can. $	U.K. £
Daydreams	95.00	130.00	29.50

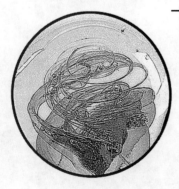

CT-691
DOUBLE MAGNUM AZURE

Designer: Margot Thomson
Type: Weight — Spherical, double magnum
Edition: 1989
Status: Closed
Series: Unlimited — Modern Design
Original Issue Price: £150.00, U.S. $495.00

Name	U.S. $	Can. $	U.K. £
Double Magnum Azure	495.00	700.00	150.00

CT-692
RIBBONS

Designer: Alastair MacIntosh
Type: Weight — Spherical
Colour: See below
Edition: 1989
Status: Closed
Series: Unlimited — Modern Design
Original Issue Price: £19.95, U.S. $72.50

Colourways	U.S. $	Can. $	U.K. £
1. Blue	100.00	145.00	27.50
2. Ruby	100.00	145.00	27.50
3. Topaz	100.00	145.00	27.50

CT-693
VIBRANCE

Designer: Alastair MacIntosh
Type: Weight — Spherical
Edition: 1989
Status: Closed
Series: Unlimited — Modern Design
Original Issue Price: £26.95, U.S. $99.50

Name	U.S. $	Can. $	U.K. £
Vibrance	100.00	140.00	30.00

CT-694
WINDFALL

Designer: Colin Terris
Type: Weight — Spherical
Colour: See below
Edition: 1989
Status: See below
Series: Unlimited — Modern Design
Original Issue Price: £27.95, U.S. $99.50

Colourways/Status	U.S. $	Can. $	U.K. £
1. Emerald (Closed)	110.00	145.00	35.00
2. Ruby (Active)	110.00	145.00	35.00

CT-695
MINIATURE CORNFLOWER

Designer: Allan Scott
Type: Weight — Spherical
Edition: 1989
Status: Closed
Series: Millefiori Miniatures
Original Issue Price: £27.95, U.S. $79.50

Name	U.S. $	Can. $	U.K. £
Miniature Cornflower	80.00	110.00	30.00

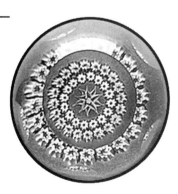

CT-696
MINIATURE POSY

Designer:	Allan Scott
Type:	Weight — Spherical
Edition:	1989
Status:	Closed
Series:	Millefiori Miniatures
Original Issue Price:	£27.95, U.S. $79.50

Name	U.S. $	Can. $	U.K. £
Miniature Posy	80.00	110.00	30.00

CT-697
BAGATELLE

Designer:	Alastair MacIntosh
Type:	Weight — Spherical
Edition:	1989 in a limited edition of 750
Status:	Closed at No. 481
Series:	Limited — Modern Design
Original Issue Price:	£45.00, U.S. $150.00

Name	U.S. $	Can. $	U.K. £
Bagatelle	150.00	200.00	45.00

CT-698
BEWITCHED

Designer:	Alastair MacIntosh
Type:	Weight — Spherical
Edition:	1989 in a limited edition of 750
Status:	Fully subscribed
Original Issue Price:	£55.00, U.S. $175.00

Name	U.S. $	Can. $	U.K. £
Bewitched	175.00	250.00	55.00

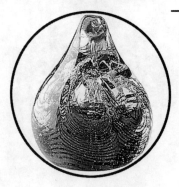

CT-699
ELIXIR

Designer:	Margot Thomson
Type:	Weight — Teardrop
Edition:	1989 in a limited edition of 500
Status:	Fully subscribed
Series:	Limited — Modern Design
Original Issue Price:	£69.00, U.S. $225.00

Name	U.S. $	Can. $	U.K. £
Elixir	225.00	325.00	70.00

CT-700
FANFARE

Designer: Alastair MacIntosh
Type: Weight — Spherical
Edition: 1989 in a limited edition of 750
Status: Closed at No. 693
Original Issue Price: £43.00, U.S. $135.00

Name	U.S. $	Can. $	U.K. £
Fanfare	135.00	190.00	45.00

CT-701
GOLDEN HAVEN

Designer: Colin Terris
Type: Weight — Spherical
Edition: 1989 in a limited edition of 500
Status: Closed at No. 414
Series: Limited — Modern Design
Original Issue Price: £90.00, U.S. $285.00

Name	U.S. $	Can. $	U.K. £
Golden Haven	285.00	400.00	90.00

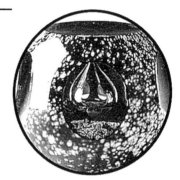

CT-702
LULLABY

Designer: Colin Terris
Type: Weight — Spherical
Edition: 1989 in a limited edition of 250
Status: Fully subscribed
Original Issue Price: £150.00, U.S. $475.00

Name	U.S. $	Can. $	U.K. £
Lullaby	475.00	675.00	200.00

CT-703
PHOENIX

Designer: Margot Thomson
Type: Weight — Domed
Edition: 1989 in a limited edition of 1,000
Status: Fully subscribed
Original Issue Price: £60.00, U.S. $175.00

Name	U.S. $	Can. $	U.K. £
Phoenix	175.00	250.00	75.00

Note: This is the 1989 Collectors' Weight.

CT-704
SECRET GARDEN

Designer: Colin Terris
Type: Weight — Domed
Edition: 1989 in a limited edition of 200
Status: Fully subscribed
Original Issue Price: £130.00, U.S. $425.00

Name	U.S. $	Can. $	U.K. £
Secret Garden	425.00	600.00	225.00

CT-705
SPELLBOUND

Designer: Colin Terris
Type: Weight — Spherical
Edition: 1989 in a limited edition of 750
Status: Fully subscribed
Series: Limited — Modern Design
Original Issue Price: £55.00, U.S. $175.00

Name	U.S. $	Can. $	U.K. £
Spellbound	175.00	250.00	55.00

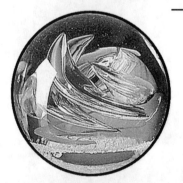

CT-706
TOPSY-TURVY

Designer: Margot Thomson
Type: Weight — Spherical
Edition: 1989 in a limited edition of 750
Status: Closed at No. 717
Original Issue Price: £48.00, U.S. $150.00

Name	U.S. $	Can. $	U.K. £
Topsy-Turvy	150.00	200.00	50.00

CT-707
OCEAN DUET

Designer: William Manson
Type: Weight — Spherical
Edition: 1989 in a limited edition of 250
Status: Closed at No. 124
Series: Traditional Collection
Original Issue Price: £185.00, U.S. $595.00

Name	U.S. $	Can. $	U.K. £
Ocean Duet	600.00	850.00	200.00

CT-708
PENGUINS

Designer: William Manson
Type: Weight — Spherical
Edition: 1989 in a limited edition of 250
Status: Closed at No. 140
Series: Traditional Collection
Original Issue Price: £185.00, U.S. $595.00

Name	U.S. $	Can. $	U.K. £
Penguins	595.00	850.00	250.00

CT-709
ARIES

Designer: Alastair MacIntosh
Type: Weight — Spherical
Colour: See below
Edition: 1989
Status: Closed
Series: Limited — Modern Design
Original Issue Price: £25.95, U.S. $90.00

Colourways	U.S. $	Can. $	U.K. £
1. Green	90.00	130.00	30.00
2. Purple	90.00	130.00	30.00
3. Rose	90.00	130.00	30.00

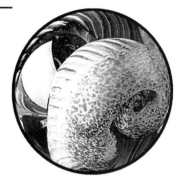

CT-710
HIGH SEAS

Designer: Alastair MacIntosh
Type: Weight — Spherical
Edition: 1989
Status: Closed
Series: Unlimited — Modern Design
Original Issue Price: £22.95, U.S. $79.50

Name	U.S. $	Can. $	U.K. £
High Seas	90.00	135.00	25.00

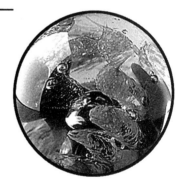

CT-711
MOMENTUM

Designer: Margot Thomson
Type: Weight — Spherical
Edition: 1989
Status: Closed
Series: Unlimited — Modern Design
Original Issue Price: £22.95, U.S. $79.50

Name	U.S. $	Can. $	U.K. £
Momentum	80.00	110.00	25.00

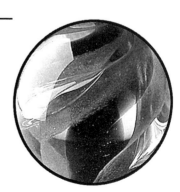

CT-712
SEA DANCE SABLE

Designer: Colin Terris
Type: Weight — Spherical
Edition: 1989
Status: Closed
Original Issue Price: £29.95, U.S. $99.50

Name	U.S. $	Can. $	U.K. £
Sea Dance Sable	100.00	140.00	35.00

CT-713
LUCKENBOOTH

Designer: Colin Terris
Type: Weight — Spherical
Edition: 1989
Status: Active
Series: Romance
Original Issue Price: £35.00, U.S. $135.00

Name	U.S. $	Can. $	U.K. £
Luckenbooth	150.00	200.00	48.50

Note: The Luckenbooth design is a traditional Scottish betrothal symbol.

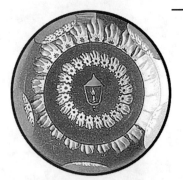

CT-714
CHRISTMAS LANTERN

Designer: Allan Scott
Type: Weight — Spherical
Edition: 1989
Status: Closed
Series: Millefiori Miniatures
Original Issue Price: £27.95, U.S. $79.50

Name	U.S. $	Can. $	U.K. £
Christmas Lantern	79.50	110.00	30.00

CT-715
ABSEIL

Designer: Alastair MacIntosh
Type: Weight — Domed
Edition: 1990 in a limited edition of 1,438
Status: Closed
Original Issue Price: £65.00, U.S. $195.00

Name	U.S. $	Can. $	U.K. £
Abseil	195.00	275.00	75.00

Note: This is the 1990 Collectors' Weight.

CT-716
ALADDIN

Designer:	Colin Terris
Type:	Weight — Spherical
Edition:	1990 in a limited edition of 250
Status:	Closed at No. 181
Series:	Limited — Modern Design
Original Issue Price:	£140.00, U.S. $495.00

Name	U.S. $	Can. $	U.K. £
Aladdin	495.00	700.00	150.00

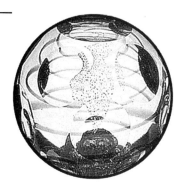

CT-717
ALCHEMY

Designer:	Colin Terris
Type:	Weight — Teardrop
Edition:	1990 in a limited edition of 650
Status:	Closed at No. 457
Series:	Limited — Modern Design
Original Issue Price:	£75.00, U.S. $295.00

Name	U.S. $	Can. $	U.K. £
Alchemy	295.00	425.00	80.00

CT-718
AQUARIUS

Designer:	Margot Thomson
Type:	Weight — Teardrop
Edition:	1990 in a limited edition of 500
Status:	Closed at No. 455
Series:	Limited — Modern Design
Original Issue Price:	£80.00, U.S. $325.00

Name	U.S. $	Can. $	U.K. £
Aquarius	325.00	450.00	80.00

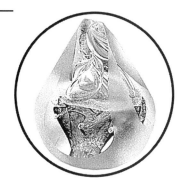

CT-719
BLACK NARCISSUS

Designer:	Colin Terris
Type:	Weight — Domed
Edition:	1990 in a limited edition of 500
Status:	Fully subscribed
Series:	Limited — Modern Design
Original Issue Price:	£85.00, U.S. $325.00

Name	U.S. $	Can. $	U.K. £
Black Narcissus	325.00	450.00	90.00

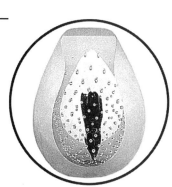

CT-720
BYZANTIUM

Designer:	Margot Thomson
Type:	Weight — Spherical
Edition:	1990 in a limited edition of 750
Status:	Closed at No. 651
Series:	Limited — Modern Design
Original Issue Price:	£55.00, U.S. $210.00

Name	U.S. $	Can. $	U.K. £
Byzantium	210.00	300.00	60.00

CT-721
CASTAWAY

Designer:	Margot Thomson
Type:	Weight — Spherical
Edition:	1990 in a limited edition of 750
Status:	Closed at No. 716
Series:	Limited — Modern Design
Original Issue Price:	£65.00, U.S. $250.00

Name	U.S. $	Can. $	U.K. £
Castaway	250.00	350.00	65.00

CT-722
CAVALCADE

Designer:	Alastair MacIntosh
Type:	Weight — Spherical
Edition:	1990 in a limited edition of 250
Status:	Closed at No. 150
Series:	Limited — Modern Design
Original Issue Price:	£125.00, U.S. $450.00

Name	U.S. $	Can. $	U.K. £
Cavalcade	450.00	650.00	125.00

CT-723
CHARISMA

Designer:	Alastair MacIntosh
Type:	Weight — Spherical
Edition:	1990 in a limited edition of 750
Status:	Fully subscribed
Series:	Limited — Modern Design
Original Issue Price:	£50.00, U.S. $175.00

Name	U.S. $	Can. $	U.K. £
Charisma	175.00	250.00	50.00

CT-724
CLARION CALL

Designer:	Margot Thomson
Type:	Weight — Teardrop
Edition:	1990 in a limited edition of 650
Status:	Closed at No. 401
Series:	Limited — Modern Design
Original Issue Price:	£59.00, U.S. $210.00

Name	U.S. $	Can. $	U.K. £
Clarion Call	210.00	300.00	60.00

CT-725
CRESCENDO

Designer:	Colin Terris
Type:	Weight — Spherical, magnum size
Edition:	1990 in a limited edition of 350
Status:	Closed at No. 287
Series:	Limited — Modern Design
Original Issue Price:	£110.00, U.S. $395.00

Name	U.S. $	Can. $	U.K. £
Crescendo	395.00	550.00	110.00

CT-726
DESERT ORCHID

Designer:	Colin Terris
Type:	Weight — Spherical
Edition:	1990 in a limited edition of 750
Status:	Fully subscribed
Series:	Limited — Modern Design
Original Issue Price:	£65.00, U.S. $250.00

Name	U.S. $	Can. $	U.K. £
Desert Orchid	250.00	350.00	65.00

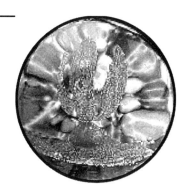

CT-727
DYNASTY

Designer:	Alastair MacIntosh
Type:	Weight — Pyramid facets
Edition:	1990 in a limited edition of 500
Status:	Closed at No. 317
Original Issue Price:	£65.00, U.S. $250.00

Name	U.S. $	Can. $	U.K. £
Dynasty	250.00	350.00	75.00

CT-728
ELFIN DANCE

Designer: Alastair MacIntosh
Type: Weight — Spherical
Edition: 1990 in a limited edition of 750
Status: Fully subscribed
Series: Limited — Modern Design
Original Issue Price: £60.00, U.S. $225.00

Name	U.S. $	Can. $	U.K. £
Elfin Dance	225.00	325.00	65.00

CT-729
FAR HORIZONS

Designer: Alastair MacIntosh
Type: Weight — Spherical
Edition: 1990 in a limited edition of 150
Status: Fully subscribed
Series: Limited — Modern Design
Original Issue Price: £150.00, U.S. $495.00

Name	U.S. $	Can. $	U.K. £
Far Horizons	495.00	700.00	200.00

CT-730
FREEDOM

Designer: Alastair MacIntosh
Type: Weight — Spherical
Edition: 1990 in a limited edition of 650
Status: Closed at No. 475
Series: Limited — Modern Design
Original Issue Price: £65.00, U.S. $225.00

Name	U.S. $	Can. $	U.K. £
Freedom	225.00	325.00	65.00

CT-731
GUARDIAN

Designer: Colin Terris and Alastair MacIntosh
Type: Weight — Domed
Edition: 1990 in a limited edition of 500
Status: Fully subscribed
Series: Limited — Modern Design
Original Issue Price: £85.00, U.S. $310.00

Name	U.S. $	Can. $	U.K. £
Guardian	310.00	425.00	90.00

CT-732
HELIUM

Designer:	Alastair MacIntosh
Type:	Weight — Spherical
Edition:	1990 in a limited edition of 750
Status:	Closed at No. 429
Series:	Limited — Modern Design
Original Issue Price:	£50.00, U.S. $190.00

Name	U.S. $	Can. $	U.K. £
Helium	190.00	275.00	50.00

CT-733
INTERLUDE

Designer:	Margot Thomson
Type:	Weight — Spherical
Edition:	1990 in a limited edition of 750
Status:	Closed at No. 266
Series:	Limited — Modern Design
Original Issue Price:	£65.00, U.S. $250.00

Name	U.S. $	Can. $	U.K. £
Interlude	250.00	350.00	70.00

CT-734
INTO FOCUS

Designer:	Margot Thomson
Type:	Weight — Spherical
Edition:	1990 in a limited edition of 750
Status:	Closed at No. 719
Series:	Limited — Modern Design
Original Issue Price:	£55.00, U.S. $210.00

Name	U.S. $	Can. $	U.K. £
Into Focus	210.00	300.00	60.00

CT-735
LAGOON

Designer:	Margot Thomson
Type:	Weight — Spherical
Edition:	1990 in a limited edition of 150
Status:	Fully subscribed
Series:	Limited — Modern Design
Original Issue Price:	£175.00, U.S. $650.00

Name	U.S. $	Can. $	U.K. £
Lagoon	650.00	925.00	225.00

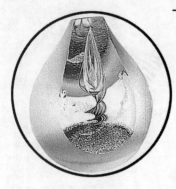

CT-736
MERLIN

Designer: Margot Thomson
Type: Weight — Teardrop
Edition: 1990 in a limited edition of 500
Status: Fully subscribed
Series: Limited — Modern Design
Original Issue Price: £80.00, U.S. $325.00

Name	U.S. $	Can. $	U.K. £
Merlin	325.00	450.00	95.00

CT-737
MESSENGER

Designer: Colin Terris
Type: Weight — Spherical
Edition: 1990 in a limited edition of 750
Status: Closed at No. 391
Original Issue Price: £43.00, U.S. $150.00

Name	U.S. $	Can. $	U.K. £
Messenger	150.00	200.00	45.00

CT-738
MIDSUMMER

Designer: Colin Terris and Helen MacDonald
Type: Weight — Domed
Edition: 1990 in a limited edition of 250
Status: Closed at No. 155
Series: Limited — Modern Design
Original Issue Price: £175.00, U.S. $575.00

Name	U.S. $	Can. $	U.K. £
Midsummer	575.00	825.00	250.00

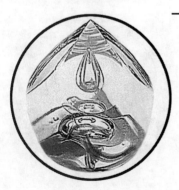

CT-739
MIRAGE

Designer: Colin Terris
Type: Weight — Teardrop
Edition: 1990 in a limited edition of 500
Status: Closed at No. 479
Series: Limited — Modern Design
Original Issue Price: £75.00, U.S. $275.00

Name	U.S. $	Can. $	U.K. £
Mirage	275.00	375.00	75.00

CT-740
NEW WORLD

Designer:	Stuart Cumming
Type:	Weight — Spherical
Edition:	1990 in a limited edition of 750
Status:	Fully subscribed
Series:	Limited — Modern Design
Original Issue Price:	£50.00, U.S. $190.00

Name	*U.S. $*	*Can. $*	*U.K. £*
New World	190.00	275.00	50.00

CT-741
NIRVANA

Designer:	Alastair MacIntosh
Type:	Weight — Domed
Edition:	1990 in a limited edition of 500
Status:	Fully subscribed
Series:	Limited — Modern Design
Original Issue Price:	£65.00, U.S. $250.00

Name	*U.S. $*	*Can. $*	*U.K. £*
Nirvana	250.00	350.00	65.00

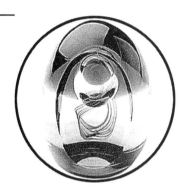

CT-742
PANACHE

Designer:	Alastair MacIntosh
Type:	Weight — Domed
Edition:	1990 in a limited edition of 750
Status:	Closed at No. 449
Series:	Limited — Modern Design
Original Issue Price:	£50.00, U.S. $190.00

Name	*U.S. $*	*Can. $*	*U.K. £*
Panache	190.00	275.00	55.00

CT-743
PATHFINDER

Designer:	Alastair MacIntosh
Type:	Weight — Spherical
Edition:	1990 in a limited edition of 750
Status:	Closed at No. 309
Series:	Limited — Modern Design
Original Issue Price:	£60.00, U.S. $250.00

Name	*U.S. $*	*Can. $*	*U.K. £*
Pathfinder	250.00	350.00	60.00

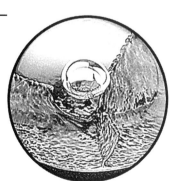

CT-744
POT POURRI

Designer:	Margot Thomson	
Type:	Weight — Spherical	
Edition:	1990 in a limited edition of 750	
Status:	Closed at No. 726	
Series:	Limited — Modern Design	
Original Issue Price:	£65.00, U.S. $250.00	

Name	U.S. $	Can. $	U.K. £
Pot Pourri	250.00	350.00	65.00

CT-745
PRELUDE

Designer:	Colin Terris	
Type:	Weight — Spherical	
Edition:	1990 in a limited edition of 750	
Status:	Closed at No. 410	
Series:	Limited — Modern Design	
Original Issue Price:	£65.00, U.S. $250.00	

Name	U.S. $	Can. $	U.K. £
Prelude	250.00	350.00	65.00

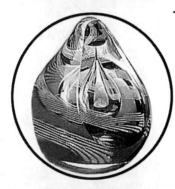

CT-746
QUEST

Designer:	Margot Thomson	
Type:	Weight — Teardrop	
Edition:	1990 in a limited edition of 650	
Status:	Closed at No. 628	
Original Issue Price:	£69.00, U.S. $250.00	

Name	U.S. $	Can. $	U.K. £
Quest	250.00	350.00	70.00

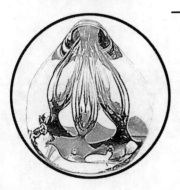

CT-747
QUORUM

Designer:	Margot Thomson	
Type:	Weight — Teardrop	
Edition:	1990 in a limited edition of 750	
Status:	Closed at No. 693	
Series:	Limited — Modern Design	
Original Issue Price:	£45.00, U.S. $175.00	

Name	U.S. $	Can. $	U.K. £
Quorum	175.00	250.00	45.00

CT-748
RADIANCE

Designer: Alastair MacIntosh
Type: Weight — Domed
Edition: 1990 in a limited edition of 650
Status: Closed at No. 526
Series: Limited — Modern Design
Original Issue Price: £75.00, U.S. $295.00

Name	U.S. $	Can. $	U.K. £
Radiance	295.00	425.00	80.00

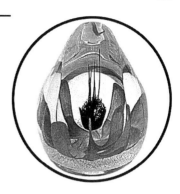

CT-749
SAND DEVIL

Designer: Margot Thomson
Type: Weight — Spherical
Edition: 1990 in a limited edition of 750
Status: Closed at No. 725
Series: Limited — Modern Design
Original Issue Price: £69.00, U.S. $250.00

Name	U.S. $	Can. $	U.K. £
Sand Devil	250.00	350.00	75.00

CT-750
SUMMER BREEZE

Designer: Colin Terris
Type: Weight — Spherical
Edition: 1990 in a limited edition of 750
Status: Closed at No. 522
Series: Limited — Modern Design
Original Issue Price: £43.00, U.S. $165.00

Name	U.S. $	Can. $	U.K. £
Summer Breeze	165.00	225.00	45.00

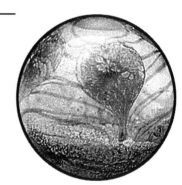

CT-751
TRAILBLAZER

Designer: Alastair MacIntosh
Type: Weight — Spherical
Edition: 1990 in a limited edition of 750
Status: Closed at No. 698
Series: Limited — Modern Design
Original Issue Price: £45.00, U.S. $175.00

Name	U.S. $	Can. $	U.K. £
Trailblazer	175.00	250.00	45.00

CT-752
VISION

Designer:	Colin Terris
Type:	Weight — Spherical
Edition:	1990 in a limited edition of 750
Status:	Closed at No. 478
Series:	Limited — Modern Design
Original Issue Price:	£65.00, U.S. $250.00

Name	U.S. $	Can. $	U.K. £
Vision	250.00	350.00	70.00

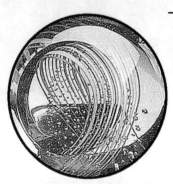

CT-753
ZOOM

Designer:	Alastair MacIntosh
Type:	Weight — Spherical
Edition:	1990 in a limited edition of 750
Status:	Closed at No. 740
Series:	Limited — Modern Design
Original Issue Price:	£60.00, U.S. $225.00

Name	U.S. $	Can. $	U.K. £
Zoom	225.00	325.00	60.00

CT-754A
BEZIQUE PERFUME BOTTLE

Designer:	Colin Terris
Type:	Perfume bottle
Edition:	1990 in a limited edition of 150
Status:	Closed at No. 61
Series:	Limited — Modern Design
Original Issue Price:	£350.00/set, U.S. $1,250.00/set

Name	U.S. $	Can. $	U.K. £
Bezique Perfume Bottle	950.00	1,350.00	600.00
Set	1,425.00	2,025.00	900.00

Note: CT-754A and B were issued and sold as a set.

CT-754B
BEZIQUE

Designer:	Colin Terris
Type:	Weight — Spherical
Edition:	1990 in a limited edition of 150
Status:	Closed at No. 61
Series:	Limited — Modern Design
Original Issue Price:	£350.00/set, U.S. $1,250.00/set

Name	U.S. $	Can. $	U.K. £
Bezique	475.00	675.00	300.00

CT-755
SUMMER BREEZE PERFUME BOTTLE

Designer:	Colin Terris		
Type:	Perfume bottle		
Edition:	1990 in a limited edition of 250		
Status:	Closed at No. 107		
Series:	Limited — Modern Design		
Original Issue Price:	£85.00, U.S. $350.00		

Name	U.S. $	Can. $	U.K. £
Summer Breeze Perfume Bottle	350.00	500.00	85.00

CT-756
BLACKBERRIES and LADYBIRD

Designer:	William Manson		
Type:	Weight — Spherical		
Edition:	1990 in a limited edition of 250		
Status:	Closed at No. 116		
Series:	Traditional Collection		
Original Issue Price:	£175.00, U.S. $595.00		

Name	U.S. $	Can. $	U.K. £
Blackberries and Ladybird	595.00	850.00	175.00

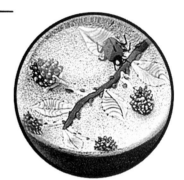

CT-757
CARNATION

Designer:	William Manson		
Type:	Weight — Spherical		
Edition:	1990 in a limited edition of 250		
Status:	Closed at No. 100		
Series:	Traditional Collection		
Original Issue Price:	£175.00, U.S. $595.00		

Name	U.S. $	Can. $	U.K. £
Carnation	595.00	850.00	175.00

CT-758
DAISY and LADYBIRD

Designer:	William Manson		
Type:	Weight — Spherical		
Edition:	1990 in a limited edition of 250		
Status:	Closed at No. 89		
Series:	Traditional Collection		
Original Issue Price:	£185.00, U.S. $595.00		

Name	U.S. $	Can. $	U.K. £
Daisy and Ladybird	725.00	1,000.00	185.00

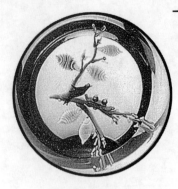

CT-759
DAWN CHORUS

Designer:	William Manson
Type:	Weight — Spherical
Edition:	1990 in a limited edition of 250
Status:	Closed at No. 128
Series:	Traditional Collection
Original Issue Price:	£175.00, U.S. $595.00

Name	U.S. $	Can. $	U.K. £
Dawn Chorus	595.00	850.00	175.00

CT-760
DRAGONFLY GARLAND

Designer:	William Manson
Type:	Weight — Spherical
Edition:	1990 in a limited edition of 250
Status:	Closed at No. 109
Series:	Traditional Collection
Original Issue Price:	£185.00, U.S. $595.00

Name	U.S. $	Can. $	U.K. £
Dragonfly Garland	595.00	850.00	185.00

CT-761
FLAMINGOES

Designer:	William Manson
Type:	Weight — Spherical
Edition:	1990 in a limited edition of 150
Status:	Closed at No. 141
Series:	Traditional Collection
Original Issue Price:	£200.00, U.S. $695.00

Name	U.S. $	Can. $	U.K. £
Flamingoes	695.00	1,000.00	200.00

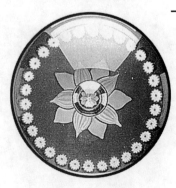

CT-762
FLORAL REFLECTIONS

Designer:	William Manson
Type:	Weight — Spherical
Edition:	1990 in a limited edition of 500
Status:	Closed at No. 213
Series:	Traditional Collection
Original Issue Price:	£70.00, U.S. $250.00

Name	U.S. $	Can. $	U.K. £
Floral Reflections	250.00	350.00	70.00

CT-763
SEALS

Designer:	William Manson
Type:	Weight — Spherical
Edition:	1990 in a limited edition of 150
Status:	Closed at No. 105
Series:	Traditional Collection
Original Issue Price:	£220.00, U.S. $775.00

Name	U.S. $	Can. $	U.K. £
Seals	775.00	1,100.00	225.00

CT-764
ANEMONE

Designer:	Margot Thomson
Type:	Weight — Spherical
Edition:	1990 in a limited edition of 250
Status:	Closed at No. 137
Series:	Whitefriars Collection
Original Issue Price:	£100.00, U.S. $375.00

Name	U.S. $	Can. $	U.K. £
Anemone	375.00	525.00	100.00

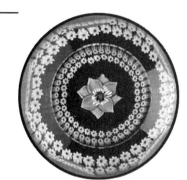

CT-765
AQUILEGIA

Designer:	Margot Thomson
Type:	Weight — Spherical
Edition:	1990 in a limited edition of 150
Status:	Closed at No. 133
Series:	Whitefriars Collection
Original Issue Price:	£165.00, U.S. $575.00

Name	U.S. $	Can. $	U.K. £
Aquilegia	575.00	825.00	175.00

CT-766
BUTTERFLIES

Designer:	Margot Thomson
Type:	Weight — Spherical
Edition:	1990 in a limited edition of 250
Status:	Closed at No. 115
Series:	Whitefriars Collection
Original Issue Price:	£100.00, U.S. $375.00

Name	U.S. $	Can. $	U.K. £
Butterflies	375.00	525.00	100.00

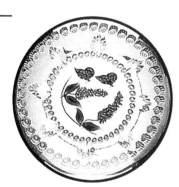

CT-767
DAISY CHAIN

Designer:	Margot Thomson
Type:	Weight — Spherical
Edition:	1990 in a limited edition of 250
Status:	Closed at No. 117
Series:	Whitefriars Collection
Original Issue Price:	£125.00, U.S. $425.00

Name	U.S. $	Can. $	U.K. £
Daisy Chain	425.00	600.00	125.00

CT-768
DELPHINIUM

Designer:	Margot Thomson
Type:	Weight — Spherical
Edition:	1990 in a limited edition of 250
Status:	Closed at No. 77
Series:	Whitefriars Collection
Original Issue Price:	£125.00, U.S. $425.00

Name	U.S. $	Can. $	U.K. £
Delphinium	475.00	675.00	125.00

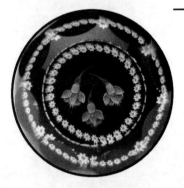

CT-769
FUCHSIAS

Designer:	Margot Thomson
Type:	Weight — Spherical
Edition:	1990 in a limited edition of 250
Status:	Fully subscribed
Series:	Whitefriars Collection
Original Issue Price:	£100.00, U.S. $375.00

Name	U.S. $	Can. $	U.K. £
Fuchsias	375.00	525.00	100.00

CT-770
ORCHIDS

Designer:	Allan Scott
Type:	Weight — Spherical
Edition:	1990 in a limited edition of 250
Status:	Closed at No. 224
Series:	Whitefriars Collection
Original Issue Price:	£90.00, U.S. $325.00

Name	U.S. $	Can. $	U.K. £
Orchids	325.00	450.00	90.00

CT-771
POPPIES

Designer:	Margot Thomson
Type:	Weight — Spherical
Edition:	1990 in a limited edition of 250
Status:	Closed at No. 93
Series:	Whitefriars Collection
Original Issue Price:	£90.00, U.S. $325.00

Name	U.S. $	Can. $	U.K. £
Poppies	325.00	450.00	90.00

CT-772
PRIMULA

Designer:	Margot Thomson
Type:	Weight — Spherical
Edition:	1990 in a limited edition of 250
Status:	Closed at No. 143
Series:	Whitefriars Collection
Original Issue Price:	£100.00, U.S. $325.00

Name	U.S. $	Can. $	U.K. £
Primula	325.00	450.00	100.00

CT-773
SCOTS THISTLE

Designer:	Allan Scott
Type:	Weight — Spherical
Edition:	1990 in a limited edition of 250
Status:	Closed at No. 136
Series:	Whitefriars Collection
Original Issue Price:	£90.00, U.S. $325.00

Name	U.S. $	Can. $	U.K. £
Scots Thistle	325.00	450.00	9 0.00

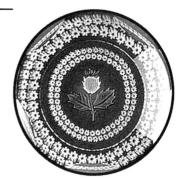

CT-774
SPRING FLOWERS

Designer:	Margot Thomson
Type:	Weight — Spherical
Edition:	1990 in a limited edition of 250
Status:	Closed at No. 127
Series:	Whitefriars Collection
Original Issue Price:	£125.00, U.S. $425.00

Name	U.S. $	Can. $	U.K. £
Spring Flowers	425.00	600.00	125.00

CT-775
SWEET PEA

Designer:	Margot Thomson
Type:	Weight — Spherical
Edition:	1990 in a limited edition of 250
Status:	Closed at No. 244
Series:	Whitefriars Collection
Original Issue Price:	£125.00, U.S. $425.00

Name	U.S. $	Can. $	U.K. £
Sweet Pea	425.00	600.00	135.00

CT-776
ROYAL BIRTHDAY BOUQUET

Designer:	Allan Scott
Type:	Weight — Spherical
Edition:	1990 in a limited edition of 90
Status:	Fully subscribed
Original Issue Price:	£250.00

Name	U.S. $	Can. $	U.K. £
Royal Birthday Bouquet	500.00	750.00	300.00

Note: CT-776, 777 and 778 were issued to commemorate HM The Queen Mother's 90th birthday. This paperweight was not issued in the U.S.

CT-777
ROYAL BIRTHDAY PERFUME BOTTLE

Designer:	Colin Terris
Type:	Perfume bottle
Edition:	1990 in a limited edition of 90
Status:	Fully subscribed
Original Issue Price:	£250.00

Name	U.S. $	Can. $	U.K. £
Royal Birthday Perfume Bottle	500.00	750.00	300.00

Note: This perfume bottle was not issued in the U.S.

CT-778
ROYAL BIRTHDAY GLAMIS ROSE

Designer:	Colin Terris
Type:	Weight — Spherical, engraved
Edition:	1990 in a limited edition of 500
Status:	Fully subscribed
Original Issue Price:	£65.00

Name	U.S. $	Can. $	U.K. £
Royal Birthday Glamis Rose	95.00	130.00	65.00

CT-779
COSMOS

Designer:	Margot Thomson
Type:	Weight — Spherical
Edition:	1990
Status:	Active
Series:	Unlimited — Modern Design
Original Issue Price:	£26.95, U.S. $99.50

Name	U.S. $	Can. $	U.K. £
Cosmos	110.00	150.00	35.00

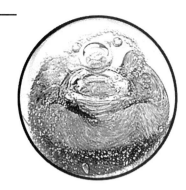

CT-780
DOUBLE MAGNUM JADE

Designer:	Margot Thomson
Type:	Weight — Spherical, double magnum
Edition:	1990
Status:	Closed
Series:	Unlimited — Modern Design
Original Issue Price:	£150.00, U.S. $495.00

Name	U.S. $	Can. $	U.K. £
Double Magnum Jade	495.00	700.00	150.00

CT-781
FREEFORM

Designer:	Alastair MacIntosh
Type:	Weight — Spherical
Colour:	See below
Edition:	1990
Status:	Closed
Series:	Unlimited — Modern Design
Original Issue Price:	£24.95, U.S. $87.50

Colourways	U.S. $	Can. $	U.K. £
1. Gold	90.00	120.00	25.00
2. Green	90.00	120.00	25.00

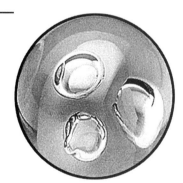

CT-782
LIMELIGHT

Designer:	Margot Thomson
Type:	Weight — Spherical
Edition:	1990
Status:	Closed
Series:	Unlimited — Modern Design
Original Issue Price:	£21.95, U.S. $87.50

Name	U.S. $	Can. $	U.K. £
Limelight	90.00	120.00	25.00

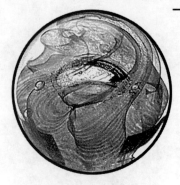

CT-783
MISCHIEF

Designer:	Margot Thomson
Type:	Weight — Spherical
Edition:	1990
Status:	Closed
Series:	Unlimited — Modern Design
Original Issue Price:	£24.95, U.S. $87.50

Name	U.S. $	Can. $	U.K. £
Mischief	90.00	120.00	30.00

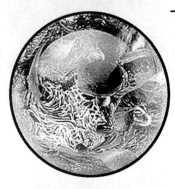

CT-784
BRIMSTONE

Designer:	Alastair MacIntosh
Type:	Weight — Spherical
Colour:	See below
Edition:	1990
Status:	Closed
Series:	Medium and Miniature Size
Original Issue Price:	£16.95, U.S. $62.50

Colourways	U.S. $	Can. $	U.K. £
1. Blue	65.00	90.00	17.00
2. Red	65.00	90.00	17.00

CT-785
FANDANGO

Designer:	Margot Thomson
Type:	Weight — Spherical
Edition:	1990
Status:	Closed
Series:	Unlimited — Modern Design
Original Issue Price:	£19.95, U.S. $62.50

Name	U.S. $	Can. $	U.K. £
Fandango	65.00	90.00	20.00

CT-786
STREAMERS

Designer:	Margot Thomson
Type:	Weight — Spherical
Colour:	See below
Edition:	1990
Status:	Closed
Series:	Medium and Miniature Size
Original Issue Price:	£16.95, U.S. $62.50

Colourways	U.S. $	Can. $	U.K. £
1. Aqua	65.00	90.00	17.00
2. Rose	65.00	90.00	17.00
3. Sable	65.00	90.00	17.00

CT-787
TRAPEZE

Designer: Margot Thomson
Type: Weight — Spherical
Colour: See below
Edition: 1990
Status: Closed
Series: Unlimited — Modern Design
Original Issue Price: £15.95, U.S. $62.50

Colourways	U.S. $	Can. $	U.K. £
1. Coral	65.00	90.00	16.00
2. Emerald	65.00	90.00	16.00
3. Jet	65.00	90.00	16.00
4. Sapphire	65.00	90.00	16.00

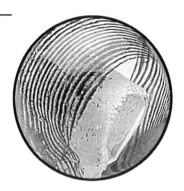

CT-788
MINI CORNFLOWER

Designer: Allan Scott
Type: Weight — Spherical
Edition: 1990
Status: Closed
Series: Millefiori Miniatures
Original Issue Price: £24.95, U.S. $89.50

Name	U.S. $	Can. $	U.K. £
Mini Cornflower	90.00	120.00	25.00

Note: This paperweight has a top facet only.

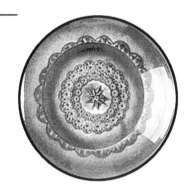

CT-789
MINI FORGET-ME-NOT

Designer: Allan Scott
Type: Weight — Spherical
Edition: 1990
Status: Closed
Series: Millefiori Miniatures
Original Issue Price: £24.95, U.S. $89.50

Name	U.S. $	Can. $	U.K. £
Mini Forget-me-not	90.00	120.00	25.00

Note: This paperweight has a top facet only.

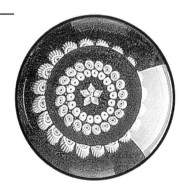

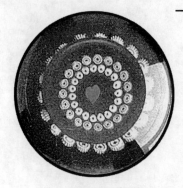

CT-790
MINI HEART

Designer:	Allan Scott
Type:	Weight — Spherical
Edition:	1990
Status:	Closed
Series:	Romance
Original Issue Price:	£24.95, U.S. $89.50

Name	U.S. $	Can. $	U.K. £
Mini Heart	90.00	120.00	25.00

Note: This paperweight has a top facet only.

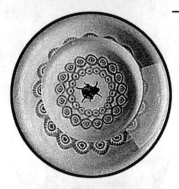

CT-791
MINI LADYBIRD

Designer:	Allan Scott
Type:	Weight — Spherical
Edition:	1990
Status:	Closed
Series:	Millefiori Miniatures
Original Issue Price:	£24.95, U.S. $89.50

Name	U.S. $	Can. $	U.K. £
Mini Ladybird	90.00	120.00	25.00

Note: This paperweight has a top facet only.

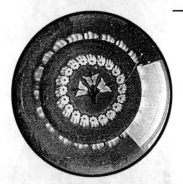

CT-792
MINI POSY

Designer:	Allan Scott
Type:	Weight — Spherical
Edition:	1990
Status:	Closed
Series:	Millefiori Miniatures
Original Issue Price:	£24.95, U.S. $89.50

Name	U.S. $	Can. $	U.K. £
Mini Posy	90.00	120.00	25.00

Note: This paperweight has a top facet only.

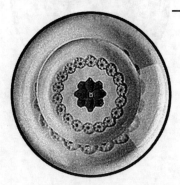

CT-793
MINI ROSE

Designer:	Allan Scott
Type:	Weight — Spherical
Edition:	1990
Status:	Closed
Series:	Millefiori Miniatures
Original Issue Price:	£24.95, U.S. $89.50

Name	U.S. $	Can. $	U.K. £
Mini Rose	90.00	120.00	25.00

Note: This paperweight has a top facet only.

CT-794
MINI THISTLE

Designer: Allan Scott
Type: Weight — Spherical
Edition: 1990
Status: Closed
Series: Millefiori Miniatures
Original Issue Price: £24.95, U.S. $89.50

Name	U.S. $	Can. $	U.K. £
Mini Thistle	89.50	120.00	25.00

Note: This paperweight has a top facet only.

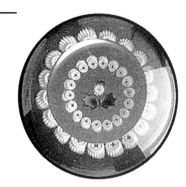

CT-795
ARABESQUE

Designer: Margot Thomson
Type: Weight — Teardrop
Edition: 1991 in a limited edition of 750
Status: Closed at No. 504
Series: Limited — Modern Design
Original Issue Price: £65.00, U.S. $230.00

Name	U.S. $	Can. $	U.K. £
Arabesque	230.00	325.00	65.00

CT-796
ARCTIC ORCHID

Designer: Colin Terris
Type: Weight — Spherical
Edition: 1991 in a limited edition of 750
Status: Closed at No. 736
Series: Limited — Modern Design
Original Issue Price: £75.00, U.S. $275.00

Name	U.S. $	Can. $	U.K. £
Arctic Orchid	275.00	375.00	75.00

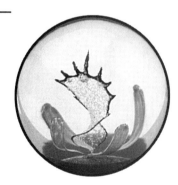

CT-797
ARGON

Designer: Colin Terris
Type: Weight — Spherical
Edition: 1991 in a limited edition of 750
Status: Closed at No. 472
Series: Limited — Modern Design
Original Issue Price: £70.00, U.S. $250.00

Name	U.S. $	Can. $	U.K. £
Argon	250.00	350.00	70.00

CT-798
ASPIRATION

Designer: Colin Terris
Type: Weight — Spherical
Edition: 1991 in a limited edition of 750
Status: Fully subscribed
Series: Limited — Modern Design
Original Issue Price: £55.00, U.S. $195.00

Name	U.S. $	Can. $	U.K. £
Aspiration	195.00	275.00	55.00

CT-799
BECALMED

Designer: Margot Thomson
Type: Weight — Spherical
Edition: 1991 in a limited edition of 750
Status: Closed at No. 263
Series: Limited — Modern Design
Original Issue Price: £55.00, U.S. $200.00

Name	U.S. $	Can. $	U.K. £
Becalmed	200.00	275.00	55.00

CT-800
CHRYSALIS

Designer: Margot Thomson
Type: Weight — Spherical
Edition: 1991 in a limited edition of 750
Status: Closed at No. 718
Series: Limited — Modern Design
Original Issue Price: £60.00, U.S. $225.00

Name	U.S. $	Can. $	U.K. £
Chrysalis	225.00	325.00	60.00

CT-801
CLAIRVOYANT

Designer: Alastair MacIntosh
Type: Weight — Spherical
Edition: 1991 in a limited edition of 750
Status: Closed at No. 371
Series: Limited — Modern Design
Original Issue Price: £60.00, U.S. $225.00

Name	U.S. $	Can. $	U.K. £
Clairvoyant	225.00	325.00	60.00

CT-802
CORAL VOYAGER

Designer: Margot Thomson
Type: Weight — Teardrop
Edition: 1991 in a limited edition of 500
Status: Closed at No. 268
Series: Limited — Modern Design
Original Issue Price: £95.00, U.S. $350.00

Name	U.S. $	Can. $	U.K. £
Coral Voyager	350.00	500.00	100.00

CT-803
DISCOVERY

Designer: Colin Terris
Type: Weight — Spherical
Edition: 1991 in a limited edition of 750
Status: Fully subscribed
Series: Limited — Modern Design
Original Issue Price: £69.00, U.S. $250.00

Name	U.S. $	Can. $	U.K. £
Discovery	250.00	350.00	75.00

CT-804
EXPLORER

Designer: Colin Terris
Type: Weight — Spherical
Edition: 1991 in a limited edition of 750
Status: Closed at No. 630
Series: Limited — Modern Design
Original Issue Price: £70.00, U.S. $250.00

Name	U.S. $	Can. $	U.K. £
Explorer	250.00	350.00	70.00

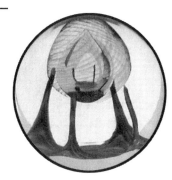

CT-805
FLORAL ILLUSION

Designer: Colin Terris
Type: Weight — Spherical
Edition: 1991 in a limited edition of 1,773
Status: Closed
Original Issue Price: £75.00, U.S. $215.00

Name	U.S. $	Can. $	U.K. £
Floral Illusion	215.00	300.00	80.00

Note: This is the 1991 Collectors' Paperweight.

CT-806
FREE FALL

Designer:	Colin Terris
Type:	Weight — Spherical
Edition:	1991 in a limited edition of 750
Status:	Fully subscribed
Series:	Limited — Modern Design
Original Issue Price:	£45.00, U.S. $150.00

Name	U.S. $	Can. $	U.K. £
Free Fall	150.00	200.00	45.00

CT-807
HIGH FLYER

Designer:	Margot Thomson
Type:	Weight — Domed
Edition:	1991 in a limited edition of 650
Status:	Closed at No. 641
Series:	Limited — Modern Design
Original Issue Price:	£85.00, U.S. $310.00

Name	U.S. $	Can. $	U.K. £
High Flyer	310.00	425.00	85.00

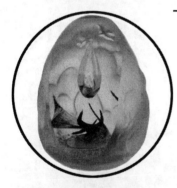

CT-808
INDIAN SUMMER

Designer:	Helen MacDonald and Alastair MacIntosh
Type:	Weight — Domed
Edition:	1991 in a limited edition of 250
Status:	Closed at No. 194
Series:	Limited — Modern Design
Original Issue Price:	£200.00, U.S. $735.00

Name	U.S. $	Can. $	U.K. £
Indian Summer	735.00	1,050.00	250.00

CT-809
MILKY WAY

Designer:	Colin Terris
Type:	Weight — Spherical
Edition:	1991 in a limited edition of 750
Status:	Fully subscribed
Series:	Limited — Modern Design
Original Issue Price:	£55.00, U.S. $200.00

Name	U.S. $	Can. $	U.K. £
Milky Way	200.00	275.00	55.00

CT-810
MISSION

Designer:	Colin Terris
Type:	Weight — Spherical
Edition:	1991 in a limited edition of 750
Status:	Closed at No. 233
Series:	Limited — Modern Design
Original Issue Price:	£72.00, U.S. $265.00

Name	U.S. $	Can. $	U.K. £
Mission	265.00	375.00	75.00

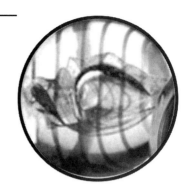

CT-811
OPTIMA

Designer:	Colin Terris
Type:	Weight — Teardrop
Edition:	1991 in a limited edition of 500
Status:	Fully subscribed
Series:	Limited — Modern Design
Original Issue Price:	£85.00, U.S. $310.00

Name	U.S. $	Can. $	U.K. £
Optima	310.00	425.00	85.00

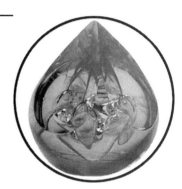

CT-812
PAINTBOX

Designer:	Alastair MacIntosh
Type:	Weight — Spherical
Edition:	1991 in a limited edition of 750
Status:	Closed at No. 714
Series:	Limited — Modern Design
Original Issue Price:	£45.00, U.S. $150.00

Name	U.S. $	Can. $	U.K. £
Paintbox	150.00	200.00	45.00

CT-813
PARADE

Designer:	Margot Thomson
Type:	Weight — Spherical
Edition:	1991 in a limited edition of 750
Status:	Fully subscribed
Series:	Limited — Modern Design
Original Issue Price:	£43.00, U.S. $150.00

Name	U.S. $	Can. $	U.K. £
Parade	150.00	200.00	45.00

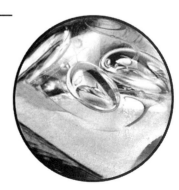

CT-814
PURSUIT

Designer:	Margot Thomson
Type:	Weight — Spherical
Edition:	1991 in a limited edition of 750
Status:	Closed at No. 385
Series:	Limited — Modern Design
Original Issue Price:	£55.00, U.S. $200.00

Name	U.S. $	Can. $	U.K. £
Pursuit	200.00	275.00	55.00

CT-815
PYROTECHNICS

Designer:	Alastair MacIntosh
Type:	Weight — Spherical
Edition:	1991 in a limited edition of 750
Status:	Fully subscribed
Series:	Limited — Modern Design
Original Issue Price:	£49.00, U.S. $175.00

Name	U.S. $	Can. $	U.K. £
Pyrotechnics	175.00	250.00	50.00

CT-816
REVELATION

Designer:	Colin Terris
Type:	Weight — Spherical
Edition:	1991 in a limited edition of 250
Status:	Closed at No. 235
Original Issue Price:	£110.00, U.S. $385.00

Name	U.S. $	Can. $	U.K. £
Revelation	385.00	550.00	125.00

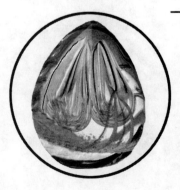

CT-817
SKYHIGH

Designer:	Margot Thomson
Type:	Weight — Domed
Edition:	1991 in a limited edition of 750
Status:	Fully subscribed
Series:	Limited — Modern Design
Original Issue Price:	£53.00, U.S. $175.00

Name	U.S. $	Can. $	U.K. £
Skyhigh	175.00	250.00	55.00

CT-818
SNOWFLAKE ORCHID

Designer: Colin Terris
Type: Weight — Spherical
Edition: 1991 in a limited edition of 150
Status: Fully subscribed
Series: Limited — Modern Design
Original Issue Price: £175.00, U.S. $635.00

Name	U.S. $	Can. $	U.K. £
Snowflake Orchid	635.00	900.00	225.00

CT-819
SPLASH

Designer: Margot Thomson
Type: Weight — Teardrop
Edition: 1991 in a limited edition of 750
Status: Closed at No. 306
Original Issue Price: £85.00, U.S. $310.00

Name	U.S. $	Can. $	U.K. £
Splash	310.00	425.00	85.00

CT-820
SPRING MELODY

Designer: Colin Terris
Type: Weight — Spherical
Edition: 1991 in a limited edition of 150
Status: Fully subscribed
Series: Limited — Modern Design
Original Issue Price: £175.00, U.S. $635.00

Name	U.S. $	Can. $	U.K. £
Spring Melody	635.00	900.00	275.00

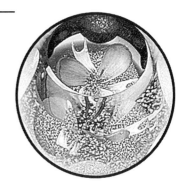

CT-821
STARGAZER

Designer: Alastair MacIntosh
Type: Weight — Spherical
Edition: 1991 in a limited edition of 750
Status: Closed at No. 733
Series: Limited — Modern Design
Original Issue Price: £49.00, U.S. $175.00

Name	U.S. $	Can. $	U.K. £
Stargazer	175.00	250.00	50.00

CT-822
SUN SEEKERS

Designer:	Colin Terris
Type:	Weight — Spherical, magnum size
Edition:	1991 in a limited edition of 350
Status:	Closed at No. 323
Series:	Limited — Modern Design
Original Issue Price:	£110.00, U.S. $385.00

Name	U.S. $	Can. $	U.K. £
Sun Seekers	385.00	550.00	125.00

CT-823
SUPER NOVA

Designer:	Colin Terris
Type:	Weight — Spherical
Edition:	1991 in a limited edition of 750
Status:	Closed at No. 622
Series:	Limited — Modern Design
Original Issue Price:	£65.00, U.S. $230.00

Name	U.S. $	Can. $	U.K. £
Super Nova	230.00	325.00	65.00

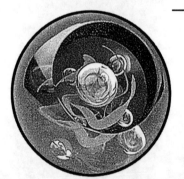

CT-824
SWORD DANCE

Designer:	Alastair MacIntosh
Type:	Weight — Spherical
Edition:	1991 in a limited edition of 750
Status:	Closed at No. 714
Series:	Limited — Modern Design
Original Issue Price:	£65.00, U.S. $230.00

Name	U.S. $	Can. $	U.K. £
Sword Dance	230.00	325.00	65.00

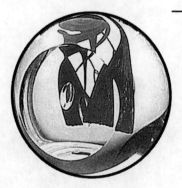

CT-825
TAILSPIN

Designer:	Alastair MacIntosh
Type:	Weight — Spherical
Edition:	1991 in a limited edition of 750
Status:	Closed at No. 409
Series:	Limited — Modern Design
Original Issue Price:	£65.00, U.S. $230.00

Name	U.S. $	Can. $	U.K. £
Tailspin	230.00	325.00	65.00

CT-826
TAPESTRY

Designer: Margot Thomson
Type: Weight — Domed
Edition: 1991 in a limited edition of 500
Status: Closed at No. 496
Series: Limited — Modern Design
Original Issue Price: £100.00, U.S. $365.00

Name	U.S. $	Can. $	U.K. £
Tapestry	365.00	525.00	100.00

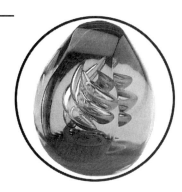

CT-827
TRAMPOLINE

Designer: Alastair MacIntosh
Type: Weight — Domed
Edition: 1991 in a limited edition of 650
Status: Closed at No. 635
Original Issue Price: £75.00, U.S. $275.00

Name	U.S. $	Can. $	U.K. £
Trampoline	275.00	375.00	75.00

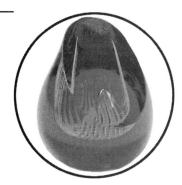

CT-828
TRIUMPH

Designer: Alastair MacIntosh
Type: Weight — Spherical
Edition: 1991 in a limited edition of 750
Status: Closed at No. 394
Series: Limited — Modern Design
Original Issue Price: £55.00, U.S. $200.00

Name	U.S. $	Can. $	U.K. £
Triumph	200.00	275.00	55.00

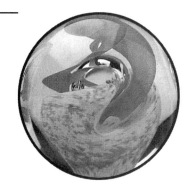

CT-829
UTOPIA

Designer: Margot Thomson
Type: Weight — Spherical
Edition: 1991 in a limited edition of 650
Status: Closed at No. 438
Series: Limited — Modern Design
Original Issue Price: £85.00, U.S. $310.00

Name	U.S. $	Can. $	U.K. £
Utopia	310.00	425.00	85.00

CT-830
VIRTUOSO

Designer:	Alastair MacIntosh
Type:	Weight — Spherical
Edition:	1991 in a limited edition of 750
Status:	Closed at No. 631
Series:	Limited — Modern Design
Original Issue Price:	£60.00, U.S. $225.00

Name	U.S. $	Can. $	U.K. £
Virtuoso	225.00	325.00	60.00

CT-831
WANDERLUST

Designer:	Margot Thomson
Type:	Weight — Spherical
Edition:	1991 in a limited edition of 350
Status:	Closed at No. 298
Series:	Limited — Modern Design
Original Issue Price:	£95.00, U.S. $350.00

Name	U.S. $	Can. $	U.K. £
Wanderlust	350.00	500.00	95.00

CT-832
WINDCHIMES

Designer:	Colin Terris
Type:	Weight — Spherical
Edition:	1991 in a limited edition of 750
Status:	Closed at No. 302
Series:	Limited — Modern Design
Original Issue Price:	£65.00, U.S. $230.00

Name	U.S. $	Can. $	U.K. £
Windchimes	230.00	325.00	65.00

CT-833
ALPINE PINK

Designer:	Margot Thomson
Type:	Weight — Spherical
Edition:	1991 in a limited edition of 250
Status:	Closed at No. 145
Series:	Whitefriars Collection
Original Issue Price:	£150.00, U.S. $540.00

Name	U.S. $	Can. $	U.K. £
Alpine Pink	540.00	775.00	150.00

CT-834
CLEMATIS

Designer:	Margot Thomson
Type:	Weight — Spherical
Edition:	1991 in a limited edition of 150
Status:	Closed at No. 112
Series:	Whitefriars Collection

Original Issue Price: £185.00, U.S. $675.00

Name	U.S. $	Can. $	U.K. £
Clematis	675.00	975.00	185.00

CT-835
EDELWEISS

Designer:	Margot Thomson
Type:	Weight — Spherical
Edition:	1991 in a limited edition of 250
Status:	Closed at No. 209
Series:	Whitefriars Collection

Original Issue Price: £135.00, U.S. $495.00

Name	U.S. $	Can. $	U.K. £
Edelweiss	495.00	700.00	135.00

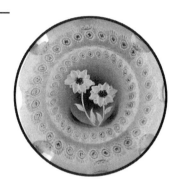

CT-836
FLAG IRIS

Designer:	Margot Thomson
Type:	Weight — Spherical
Edition:	1991 in a limited edition of 250
Status:	Closed at No. 165
Series:	Whitefriars Collection

Original Issue Price: £135.00, U.S. $495.00

Name	U.S. $	Can. $	U.K. £
Flag Iris	495.00	700.00	135.00

CT-837
PERUVIAN LILIES

Designer:	Margot Thomson
Type:	Weight — Spherical
Edition:	1991 in a limited edition of 250
Status:	Closed at No. 145
Series:	Whitefriars Collection

Original Issue Price: £125.00, U.S. $450.00

Name	U.S. $	Can. $	U.K. £
Peruvian Lilies	450.00	650.00	125.00

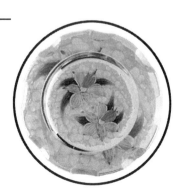

CT-838
BARRIER REEF

Designer: William Manson
Type: Weight — Spherical
Edition: 1991 in a limited edition of 250
Status: Closed at No. 183
Series: Traditional Collection
Original Issue Price: £175.00, U.S. $635.00

Name	U.S. $	Can. $	U.K. £
Barrier Reef	635.00	900.00	175.00

CT-839
CAVERN

Designer: William Manson
Type: Weight — Spherical
Edition: 1991 in a limited edition of 250
Status: Closed at No. 145
Series: Traditional Collection
Original Issue Price: £160.00, U.S. $575.00

Name	U.S. $	Can. $	U.K. £
Cavern	575.00	825.00	160.00

CT-840
DRAGONFLY and WATERLILIES

Designer: William Manson
Type: Weight — Spherical
Edition: 1991 in a limited edition of 250
Status: Closed at No. 192
Series: Traditional Collection
Original Issue Price: £175.00, U.S. $635.00

Name	U.S. $	Can. $	U.K. £
Dragonfly and Waterlilies	635.00	900.00	175.00

CT-841
LILIES and LADYBIRD

Designer: William Manson
Type: Weight — Spherical
Edition: 1991 in a limited edition of 250
Status: Closed at No. 86
Series: Traditional Collection
Original Issue Price: £175.00, U.S. $635.00

Name	U.S. $	Can. $	U.K. £
Lilies and Ladybird	635.00	900.00	175.00

CT-842
SCORPION

Designer:	William Manson
Type:	Weight — Spherical
Edition:	1991 in a limited edition of 250
Status:	Closed at No. 76
Series:	Traditional Collection
Original Issue Price:	£185.00, U.S. $675.00

Name	U.S. $	Can. $	U.K. £
Scorpion	700.00	1,000.00	185.00

CT-843
SEA BED

Designer:	William Manson
Type:	Weight — Spherical
Edition:	1991 in a limited edition of 250
Status:	Closed at No. 154
Series:	Traditional Collection
Original Issue Price:	£175.00, U.S. $635.00

Name	U.S. $	Can. $	U.K. £
Sea Bed	635.00	900.00	175.00

CT-844
WILD ROSE BOUQUET

Designer:	William Manson
Type:	Weight — Spherical
Edition:	1991 in a limited edition of 250
Status:	Closed at No. 113
Original Issue Price:	£200.00, U.S. $735.00

Name	U.S. $	Can. $	U.K. £
Wild Rose Bouquet	735.00	1,050.00	200.00

CT-845
CRUCIBLE

Designer:	Alastair MacIntosh
Type:	Weight — Spherical
Edition:	1991
Status:	Closed
Series:	Unlimited —Modern Design
Original Issue Price:	£29.95, U.S. $99.50

Name	U.S. $	Can. $	U.K. £
Crucible	100.00	140.00	30.00

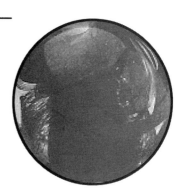

CT-846
DOUBLE MAGNUM MAGENTA

Designer: Margot Thomson
Type: Weight — Spherical, double magnum
Edition: 1991
Status: Closed
Series: Unlimited — Modern Design
Original Issue Price: £165.00, U.S. $575.00

Name	U.S. $	Can. $	U.K. £
Double Magnum Magenta	575.00	825.00	175.00

CT-847
ECHO

Designer: Alastair MacIntosh
Type: Weight — Spherical
Edition: 1991
Status: Closed
Series: Unlimited — Modern Design
Original Issue Price: £29.95, U.S. $99.50

Name	U.S. $	Can. $	U.K. £
Echo	100.00	140.00	30.00

CT-848
ESCAPE

Designer: Alastair MacIntosh
Type: Weight — Spherical
Edition: 1991
Status: Closed
Series: Unlimited — Modern Design
Original Issue Price: £32.50, U.S. $115.00

Name	U.S. $	Can. $	U.K. £
Escape	115.00	160.00	33.00

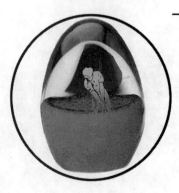

CT-849
GOLF DOME

Designer: Caithness Studios
Type: Weight — Domed
Edition: 1991
Status: Closed
Series: Unlimited — Modern Design
Original Issue Price: £29.95, U.S. $115.00

Name	U.S. $	Can. $	U.K. £
Golf Dome	115.00	160.00	30.00

CT-850
GOLFER

Designer:	Caithness Studios
Type:	Weight — Spherical
Edition:	1991
Status:	Closed
Series:	Unlimited — Modern Design
Original Issue Price:	£37.50, U.S. $135.00

Name	U.S. $	Can. $	U.K. £
Golfer	135.00	190.00	40.00

CT-851
JACOB'S LADDER

Designer:	Alastair MacIntosh
Type:	Weight — Spherical
Edition:	1991
Status:	Closed
Series:	Unlimited — Modern Design
Original Issue Price:	£29.95, U.S. $110.00

Name	U.S. $	Can. $	U.K. £
Jacob's Ladder	110.00	150.00	30.00

CT-852
LIBERTY

Designer:	Alastair MacIntosh
Type:	Weight — Spherical
Edition:	1991
Status:	Closed
Series:	Unlimited — Modern Design
Original Issue Price:	£29.95, U.S. $110.00

Name	U.S. $	Can. $	U.K. £
Liberty	110.00	150.00	30.00

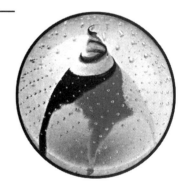

CT-853
SIROCCO

Designer:	Margot Thomson
Type:	Weight — Spherical
Colour:	See below
Edition:	1991
Status:	Closed
Series:	Unlimited — Modern Design
Original Issue Price:	£19.95, U.S. $75.00, Can. $110.00

Colourways	U.S. $	Can. $	U.K. £
1. Aqua	80.00	110.00	25.00
2. Magenta	80.00	110.00	25.00

CT-854
SNOW TRAIL BLUE

Designer:	Margot Thomson
Type:	Weight — Spherical
Edition:	1991
Status:	Closed
Series:	Unlimited — Modern Design
Original Issue Price:	£29.95, U.S. $99.50

Name	U.S. $	Can. $	U.K. £
Snow Trail Blue	100.00	140.00	30.00

CT-855
SPIN OFF

Designer:	Alastair MacIntosh
Type:	Weight — Spherical
Edition:	1991
Status:	Closed
Series:	Unlimited — Modern Design
Original Issue Price:	£29.95, U.S. $110.00

Name	U.S. $	Can. $	U.K. £
Spin Off	110.00	150.00	30.00

CT-856
STARLIGHT

Designer:	Colin Terris
Type:	Weight — Spherical
Colour:	See below
Edition:	1991
Status:	See below
Series:	Unlimited — Modern Design
Original Issue Price:	£19.95, U.S. $79.50

Colourways/Status	U.S. $	Can. $	U.K. £
1. Blue (Closed)	110.00	150.00	28.50
2. Sable (Active)	110.00	150.00	23.95

CT-857
STEELBLUE

Designer:	Alastair MacIntosh
Type:	Weight — Spherical
Edition:	1991
Status:	Active
Series:	Unlimited — Modern Design
Original Issue Price:	£23.95, U.S. $95.00

Name	U.S. $	Can. $	U.K. £
Steelblue	95.00	125.00	28.50

CT-858
WHITE HORSES

Designer:	Margot Thomson
Type:	Weight — Spherical
Edition:	1991
Status:	Closed
Series:	Unlimited — Modern Design
Original Issue Price:	£29.95, U.S. $110.00

Name	U.S. $	Can. $	U.K. £
White Horses	110.00	150.00	30.00

CT-859
DIZZY

Designer:	Margot Thomson
Type:	Weight — Spherical
Colour:	See below
Edition:	1991
Status:	Closed
Series:	Unlimited — Modern Design
Original Issue Price:	£19.95, U.S. $69.50

Colourways	U.S. $	Can. $	U.K. £
1. Green	70.00	100.00	20.00
2. Pink	70.00	100.00	20.00

CT-860
PIXIE

Designer:	Alastair MacIntosh
Type:	Weight — Spherical, miniature
Colour:	See below
Edition:	1991
Status:	Active
Series:	Medium and Miniature Size
Original Issue Price:	£13.95, U.S. $49.50

Colourways	U.S. $	Can. $	U.K. £
1. Blue	54.50	75.00	17.50
2. Pink	54.50	75.00	17.50
3. White	54.50	75.00	17.50

CT-861
MINI BUTTERFLY

Designer:	Allan Scott
Type:	Weight — Spherical
Edition:	1991
Status:	Closed
Series:	Millefiori Miniatures
Original Issue Price:	£29.95, U.S. $99.50

Name	U.S. $	Can. $	U.K. £
Mini Butterfly	100.00	140.00	30.00

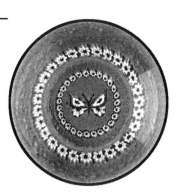

CT-862
MINI HEART

Designer: Allan Scott
Type: Weight — Spherical
Edition: 1991
Status: Closed
Series: Millefiori Miniatures
Original Issue Price: £29.95, U.S. $99.50

Name	U.S. $	Can. $	U.K. £
Mini Heart	100.00	140.00	30.00

CT-863
MINI ORCHID

Designer: Allan Scott
Type: Weight — Spherical
Edition: 1991
Status: Closed
Series: Millefiori Miniatures
Original Issue Price: £29.95, U.S. $99.50

Name	U.S. $	Can. $	U.K. £
Mini Orchid	100.00	140.00	30.00

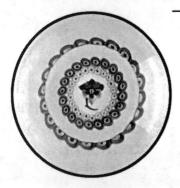

CT-864
MINI PANSY

Designer: Allan Scott
Type: Weight — Spherical
Edition: 1991
Status: Closed
Series: Millefiori Miniatures
Original Issue Price: £29.95, U.S. $99.50

Name	U.S. $	Can. $	U.K. £
Mini Pansy	100.00	140.00	30.00

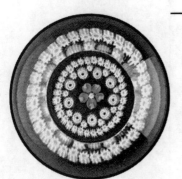

CT-865
MINI ROSE

Designer: Allan Scott
Type: Weight — Spherical
Edition: 1991
Status: Closed
Series: Millefiori Miniatures
Original Issue Price: £29.95, U.S. $99.50

Name	U.S. $	Can. $	U.K. £
Mini Rose	100.00	140.00	30.00

CT-866A
ALPHA

Designer:	Colin Terris
Type:	Weight — Spherical
Edition:	1992 in a limited edition of 150
Status:	Fully subscribed
Series:	Limited — Modern Design
Original Issue Price:	£215.00/set, U.S. $695.00/set

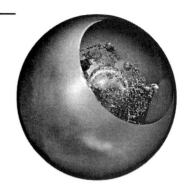

Name	U.S. $	Can. $	U.K. £
Alpha	350.00	500.00	175.00
Set	700.00	1,000.00	350.00

Note: CT-866A and B were issued and sold as a set.

CT-866B
OMEGA

Designer:	Colin Terris
Type:	Weight — Spherical
Edition:	1992 in a limited edition of 150
Status:	Fully subscribed
Series:	Limited — Modern Design
Original Issue Price:	£215.00/set, U.S. $695.00/set

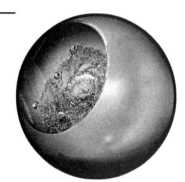

Name	U.S. $	Can. $	U.K. £
Omega	350.00	500.00	175.00

CT-867
ARGO

Designer:	Alastair MacIntosh
Type:	Weight — Spherical
Edition:	1992 in a limited edition of 650
Status:	Closed at No. 420
Series:	Limited — Modern Design
Original Issue Price:	£75.00, U.S. $250.00

Name	U.S. $	Can. $	U.K. £
Argo	250.00	350.00	85.00

CT-868
CASTILLION

Designer:	Alastair MacIntosh
Type:	Weight — Spherical
Edition:	1992 in a limited edition of 650
Status:	Closed at No. 391
Series:	Limited — Modern Design
Original Issue Price:	£85.00, U.S. $290.00

Name	U.S. $	Can. $	U.K. £
Castillion	290.00	400.00	85.00

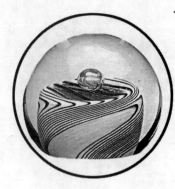

CT-869
CONTOURS

Designer:	Alastair MacIntosh
Type:	Weight — Spherical
Edition:	1992 in a limited edition of 750
Status:	Closed at No. 371
Series:	Limited — Modern Design
Original Issue Price:	£50.00, U.S. $175.00

Name	U.S. $	Can. $	U.K. £
Contours	175.00	250.00	50.00

CT-870
DARK SECRET

Designer:	Alastair MacIntosh
Type:	Weight — Spherical
Edition:	1992 in a limited edition of 750
Status:	Fully subscribed
Series:	Limited — Modern Design
Original Issue Price:	£45.00, U.S. $150.00

Name	U.S. $	Can. $	U.K. £
Dark Secret	150.00	200.00	45.00

CT-871
HARVEST TIME

Designer:	Helen MacDonald
Type:	Weight — Domed
Edition:	1992 in a limited edition of 100
Status:	Fully subscribed
Original Issue Price:	£100.00, U.S. $675.00

Name	U.S. $	Can. $	U.K. £
Harvest Time	675.00	975.00	250.00

CT-872
HYDROPONIC

Designer:	Colin Terris
Type:	Weight — Spherical
Edition:	1992 in a limited edition of 750
Status:	Fully subscribed
Series:	Limited — Modern Design
Original Issue Price:	£55.00, U.S. $190.00

Name	U.S. $	Can. $	U.K. £
Hydroponic	190.00	275.00	55.00

CT-873
IMPRESSIONS

Designer:	Alastair MacIntosh
Type:	Weight — Spherical
Edition:	1992 in a limited edition of 750
Status:	Closed at No. 371
Series:	Limited — Modern Design
Original Issue Price:	£65.00, U.S. $225.00

Name	U.S. $	Can. $	U.K. £
Impressions	225.00	325.00	65.00

CT-874
ISTANBUL

Designer:	Shona Spittal
Type:	Weight — Domed
Edition:	1992 in a limited edition of 650
Status:	Closed at No. 279
Series:	Limited — Modern Design
Original Issue Price:	£99.00, U.S. $350.00

Name	U.S. $	Can. $	U.K. £
Istanbul	350.00	500.00	100.00

CT-875
LILAC POOL

Designer:	Stuart Cumming
Type:	Weight — Spherical
Edition:	1992 in a limited edition of 750
Status:	Closed at No. 740
Series:	Limited — Modern Design
Original Issue Price:	£69.00, U.S. $230.00

Name	U.S. $	Can. $	U.K. £
Lilac Pool	230.00	325.00	75.00

CT-876
MEDITATION

Designer:	Margot Thomson
Type:	Weight — Domed
Edition:	1992 in a limited edition of 350
Status:	Fully subscribed
Series:	Limited — Modern Design
Original Issue Price:	£99.00, U.S. $350.00

Name	U.S. $	Can. $	U.K. £
Meditation	350.00	500.00	100.00

CT-877
MYSTIC ISLAND

Designer:	Colin Terris
Type:	Weight — Spherical
Edition:	1992 in a limited edition of 350
Status:	Fully subscribed
Series:	Limited — Modern Design
Original Issue Price:	£110.00, U.S. $350.00

Name	U.S. $	Can. $	U.K. £
Mystic Island	350.00	500.00	125.00

CT-878
NAVIGATOR

Designer:	Margot Thomson
Type:	Weight — Spherical
Edition:	1992 in a limited edition of 100
Status:	Fully subscribed
Series:	Limited — Modern Design
Original Issue Price:	£135.00, U.S. $450.00

Name	U.S. $	Can. $	U.K. £
Navigator	450.00	650.00	175.00

CT-879
ORIGIN

Designer:	Margot Thomson
Type:	Weight — Domed
Edition:	1992 in a limited edition of 750
Status:	Fully subscribed
Series:	Limited — Modern Design
Original Issue Price:	£50.00, U.S. $175.00

Name	U.S. $	Can. $	U.K. £
Origin	175.00	250.00	50.00

CT-880
PAINTED DESERT

Designer:	Margot Thomson
Type:	Weight — Spherical
Edition:	1992 in a limited edition of 750
Status:	Closed at No. 558
Series:	Limited — Modern Design
Original Issue Price:	£65.00, U.S. $225.00

Name	U.S. $	Can. $	U.K. £
Painted Desert	225.00	325.00	65.00

CT-881
PROPHECY

Designer:	Margot Thomson
Type:	Weight — Spherical
Edition:	1992 in a limited edition of 750
Status:	Fully subscribed
Series:	Limited — Modern Design
Original Issue Price:	£55.00, U.S. $190.00

Name	U.S. $	Can. $	U.K. £
Prophecy	190.00	275.00	55.00

CT-882
SCARAB

Designer:	Colin Terris
Type:	Weight — Spherical
Edition:	1992 in a limited edition of 750
Status:	Closed at No. 650
Series:	Limited — Modern Design
Original Issue Price:	£70.00, U.S. $250.00

Name	U.S. $	Can. $	U.K. £
Scarab	250.00	350.00	70.00

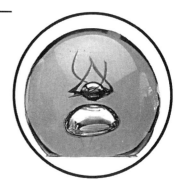

CT-883
SERGEANT MAJOR

Designer:	Sarah Peterson
Type:	Weight — Domed
Edition:	1992 in a limited edition of 650
Status:	Closed at No. 240
Series:	Limited — Modern Design
Original Issue Price:	£75.00, U.S. $250.00

Name	U.S. $	Can. $	U.K. £
Sergeant Major	250.00	350.00	75.00

CT-884
SPACE CRYSTAL

Designer:	Colin Terris
Type:	Weight — Spherical
Edition:	1992 in a limited edition of 50
Status:	Fully subscribed
Series:	Limited — Modern Design
Original Issue Price:	£175.00, U.S. $595.00

Name	U.S. $	Can. $	U.K. £
Space Crystal	595.00	850.00	225.00

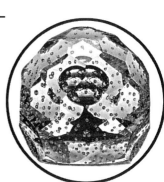

CT-885
SPACE LANDING

Designer:	Alastair MacIntosh
Type:	Weight — Spherical
Edition:	1992 in a limited edition of 750
Status:	Closed at No. 483
Series:	Limited — Modern Design
Original Issue Price:	£69.00, U.S. $250.00

Name	U.S. $	Can. $	U.K. £
Space Landing	250.00	350.00	70.00

CT-886
STAR ORCHID

Designer:	Colin Terris
Type:	Weight — Spherical
Edition:	1992 in a limited edition of 150
Status:	Fully subscribed
Series:	Limited — Modern Design
Original Issue Price:	£125.00, U.S. $425.00

Name	U.S. $	Can. $	U.K. £
Star Orchid	425.00	600.00	175.00

CT-887
SURVEILLANCE

Designer:	Alastair MacIntosh
Type:	Weight — Spherical
Edition:	1992 in a limited edition of 650
Status:	Closed at No. 645
Series:	Limited — Modern Design
Original Issue Price:	£79.00, U.S. $275.00

Name	U.S. $	Can. $	U.K. £
Surveillance	275.00	375.00	80.00

CT-888
TROPICAL POOL

Designer:	Helen MacDonald
Type:	Weight — Domed
Edition:	1992 in a limited edition of 100
Status:	Fully subscribed
Series:	Limited — Modern Design
Original Issue Price:	£200.00, U.S. $275.00

Name	U.S. $	Can. $	U.K. £
Tropical Pool	650.00	900.00	250.00

CT-889
DOG ROSE

Designer:	Margot Thomson
Type:	Weight — Spherical
Edition:	1992 in a limited edition of 100
Status:	Closed at No. 69
Series:	Whitefriars Collection
Original Issue Price:	£155.00, U.S. $525.00

Name	U.S. $	Can. $	U.K. £
Dog Rose	650.00	895.00	155.00

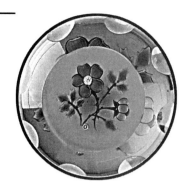

CT-890
FUCHSIA PERFUME BOTTLE

Designer:	Margot Thomson
Type:	Perfume bottle
Edition:	1992 in a limited edition of 100
Status:	Closed at No. 97
Series:	Whitefriars Collection
Original Issue Price:	£195.00, U.S. $675.00

Name	U.S. $	Can. $	U.K. £
Fuchsia Perfume Bottle	675.00	975.00	195.00

CT-891
HONEYSUCKLE

Designer:	Allan Scott
Type:	Weight — Spherical
Edition:	1992 in a limited edition of 100
Status:	Closed at No. 94
Series:	Whitefriars Collection
Original Issue Price:	£145.00, U.S. $495.00

Name	U.S. $	Can. $	U.K. £
Honeysuckle	495.00	700.00	145.00

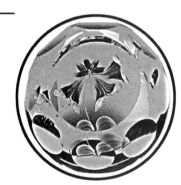

CT-892
JASMINE

Designer:	Margot Thomson
Type:	Weight — Spherical
Edition:	1992 in a limited edition of 100
Status:	Closed at No. 92
Series:	Whitefriars Collection
Original Issue Price:	£145.00, U.S. $495.00

Name	U.S. $	Can. $	U.K. £
Jasmine	495.00	700.00	145.00

CT-893
NARCISSUS

Designer:	Margot Thomson
Type:	Weight — Spherical
Edition:	1992 in a limited edition of 100
Status:	Closed at No. 95
Series:	Whitefriars Collection
Original Issue Price:	£155.00, U.S. $595.00

Name	U.S. $	Can. $	U.K. £
Narcissus	595.00	850.00	155.00

CT-894
NASTURTIUM

Designer:	Margot Thomson
Type:	Weight — Spherical
Edition:	1992 in a limited edition of 100
Status:	Closed at No. 73
Series:	Whitefriars Collection
Original Issue Price:	£145.00, U.S. $495.00

Name	U.S. $	Can. $	U.K. £
Nasturtium	495.00	700.00	145.00

CT-895
BUTTERFLY

Designer:	William Manson
Type:	Weight — Spherical
Cane:	WM (William Manson)
Edition:	1992 in a limited edition of 50
Status:	Fully subscribed
Series:	Traditional Collection
Original Issue Price:	£225.00, U.S. $775.00

Name	U.S. $	Can. $	U.K. £
Butterfly	800.00	1,100.00	225.00

CT-896
LIZARD

Designer:	William Manson
Type:	Weight — Spherical
Cane:	WM (William Manson)
Edition:	1992 in a limited edition of 50
Status:	Fully subscribed
Series:	Traditional Collection
Original Issue Price:	£225.00, U.S. $775.00

Name	U.S. $	Can. $	U.K. £
Lizard	800.00	1,100.00	225.00

CT-897
PRIMROSES

Designer:	William Manson
Type:	Weight — Spherical
Cane:	WM (William Manson)
Edition:	1992 in a limited edition of 250
Status:	Closed at No. 150
Series:	Traditional Collection
Original Issue Price:	£95.00, U.S. $325.00

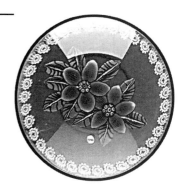

Name	U.S. $	Can. $	U.K. £
Primroses	325.00	450.00	95.00

CT-898
PUFFIN

Designer:	William Manson
Type:	Weight — Spherical
Cane:	WM (William Manson)
Edition:	1992 in a limited edition of 100
Status:	Fully subscribed
Series:	Traditional Collection
Original Issue Price:	£175.00, U.S. $595.00

Name	U.S. $	Can. $	U.K. £
Puffin	595.00	850.00	175.00

CT-899
ROSE GARLAND

Designer:	William Manson
Type:	Weight — Spherical
Cane:	WM (William Manson)
Edition:	1992 in a limited edition of 100
Status:	Closed at No. 95
Series:	Traditional Collection
Original Issue Price:	£175.00, U.S. $595.00

Name	U.S. $	Can. $	U.K. £
Rose Garland	595.00	850.00	175.00

CT-900
SERPENT

Designer:	William Manson
Type:	Weight — Spherical
Cane:	WM (William Manson)
Edition:	1992 in a limited edition of 50
Status:	Fully subscribed
Series:	Traditional Collection
Original Issue Price:	£195.00, U.S. $675.00

Name	U.S. $	Can. $	U.K. £
Serpent	800.00	1,100.00	195.00

CT-901
STRAWBERRY

Designer:	William Manson
Type:	Weight — Spherical
Cane:	WM (William Manson)
Edition:	1992 in a limited edition of 50
Status:	Fully subscribed
Series:	Traditional Collection
Original Issue Price:	£195.00, U.S. $675.00

Name	U.S. $	Can. $	U.K. £
Strawberry	800.00	1,100.00	195.00

CT-902
THISTLE

Designer:	William Manson
Type:	Weight — Spherical
Cane:	WM (William Manson)
Edition:	1992 in a limited edition of 100
Status:	Closed at No. 76
Series:	Traditional Collection
Original Issue Price:	£175.00, U.S. $595.00

Name	U.S. $	Can. $	U.K. £
Thistle	595.00	850.00	175.00

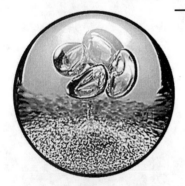

CT-903
WEATHERVANE

Designer:	Colin Terris
Type:	Weight — Spherical
Edition:	1992 in a limited edition of 1,617
Status:	Closed
Original Issue Price:	£75.00, U.S. $215.00

Name	U.S. $	Can. $	U.K. £
Weathervane	215.00	300.00	85.00

Note: This is the 1992 Collectors' Paperweight.

CT-904
CHECKPOINTS

Designer:	Alastair MacIntosh
Type:	Weight — Spherical
Edition:	1992
Status:	Closed
Series:	Unlimited
Original Issue Price:	£29.95, U.S. $99.50

Name	U.S. $	Can. $	U.K. £
Checkpoints	100.00	140.00	30.00

CT-905
DOUBLE MAGNUM 92

Designer:	Margot Thomson
Type:	Weight — Spherical, double magnum
Edition:	1992
Status:	Closed
Series:	Unlimited — Modern Design
Original Issue Price:	£175.00, U.S. $595.00

Name	U.S. $	Can. $	U.K. £
Double Magnum 92	595.00	850.00	200.00

CT-906
MOONFLOWER MAGENTA

Designer:	Colin Terris
Type:	Weight — Spherical
Edition:	1992
Status:	Active
Series:	Unlimited — Modern Design
Original Issue Price:	£29.95, U.S. $110.00

Name	U.S. $	Can. $	U.K. £
Moonflower Magenta	110.00	155.00	35.00

CT-907
RAZZAMATAZZ

Designer:	Alastair MacIntosh
Type:	Weight — Spherical
Colour:	See below
Edition:	1992
Status:	Closed
Series:	Unlimited — Modern Design
Original Issue Price:	£24.95, U.S. $87.50

Colourways	U.S. $	Can. $	U.K. £
1. Ruby	90.00	120.00	25.00
2. Sable	90.00	120.00	25.00

CT-908
RUFFLES

Designer:	Alastair MacIntosh
Type:	Weight — Spherical
Edition:	1992
Status:	Active
Series:	Unlimited — Modern Design
Original Issue Price:	£24.95, U.S. $87.50

Name	U.S. $	Can. $	U.K. £
Ruffles	95.00	130.00	29.50

CT-909
SILVER RAIN

Designer:	Alastair MacIntosh
Type:	Weight — Spherical
Edition:	1992
Status:	Closed
Series:	Unlimited — Modern Design
Original Issue Price:	£24.95, U.S. $87.50

Name	U.S. $	Can. $	U.K. £
Silver Rain	90.00	125.00	25.00

CT-910
MINI BUTTERFLY PERFUME BOTTLE

Designer:	Allan Scott
Type:	Perfume bottle
Edition:	1992
Status:	Closed
Series:	Millefiori Miniatures
Original Issue Price:	£49.95, U.S. $175.00

Name	U.S. $	Can. $	U.K. £
Mini Butterfly Perfume Bottle	175.00	250.00	50.00

CT-911
MINI HEART PERFUME BOTTLE

Designer:	Allan Scott
Type:	Perfume bottle
Edition:	1992
Status:	Closed
Series:	Romance
Original Issue Price:	£49.95, U.S. $175.00

Name	U.S. $	Can. $	U.K. £
Mini Heart Perfume Bottle	175.00	250.00	50.00

CT-912
MINI ROSE PERFUME BOTTLE

Designer:	Allan Scott
Type:	Perfume bottle
Edition:	1992
Status:	Closed
Series:	Millefiori Miniatures
Original Issue Price:	£49.95, U.S. $175.00

Name	U.S. $	Can. $	U.K. £
Mini Rose Perfume Bottle	175.00	250.00	50.00

CT-913
MINI THISTLE PERFUME BOTTLE

Designer:	Allan Scott	
Type:	Perfume bottle	
Edition:	1992	
Status:	Closed	
Series:	Millefiori Miniatures	
Original Issue Price:	£49.95, U.S. $175.00	

Name	U.S. $	Can. $	U.K. £
Mini Thistle Perfume Bottle	175.00	250.00	50.00

CT-914A
WINTER CELEBRATION — ONE

Designer:	Margot Thomson
Type:	Weight — Spherical
Edition:	1992 in a limited edition of 50
Status:	Fully subscribed
Series:	Limited — Modern Design
Original Issue Price:	£295.00/set, U.S. $995.00/set

Name	U.S. $	Can. $	U.K. £
Winter Celebration Weight 1	500.00	700.00	150.00
Set	1,000.00	1,400.00	300.00

Note: CT-914A and B were issued and sold as a set.

CT-914B
WINTER CELEBRATION — TWO

Designer:	Margot Thomson
Type:	Weight — Spherical
Edition:	1992 in a limited edition of 50
Status:	Fully subscribed
Series:	Limited — Modern Design
Original Issue Price:	£295.00/set, U.S. $995.00/set

Name	U.S. $	Can. $	U.K. £
Winter Celebration Weight 2	500.00	700.00	150.00

CT-915
TREE LIZARD

Designer:	William Manson
Type:	Weight — Spherical
Edition:	1992 in a limited edition of 50
Status:	Fully subscribed
Series:	Traditional Collection
Original Issue Price:	£225.00, U.S. $775.00

Name	U.S. $	Can. $	U.K. £
Tree Lizard	800.00	1,100.00	225.00

CT-916
DRAGONFLY and SNAIL

Designer:	William Manson
Type:	Weight — Spherical
Edition:	1992 in a limited edition of 50
Status:	Fully subscribed
Series:	Traditional Collection
Original Issue Price:	£195.00, U.S. $675.00

Name	U.S. $	Can. $	U.K. £
Dragonfly and Snail	800.00	1,100.00	200.00

CT-917
RASPBERRIES

Designer:	William Manson
Type:	Weight — Spherical
Edition:	1992 in a limited edition of 50
Status:	Fully subscribed
Series:	Traditional Collection
Original Issue Price:	£195.00, U.S. $675.00

Name	U.S. $	Can. $	U.K. £
Raspberries	800.00	1,100.00	200.00

CT-918
DESERT SPRING

Designer:	Alastair MacIntosh
Type:	Weight — Spherical
Edition:	1992
Status:	Active
Series:	Unlimited — Modern Design
Original Issue Price:	£19.95, U.S. $72.50

Name	U.S. $	Can. $	U.K. £
Desert Spring	72.50	90.00	21.50

CT-919
FASCINATION

Designer:	Alastair MacIntosh
Type:	Weight — Spherical
Edition:	1992
Status:	Active
Series:	Unlimited — Modern Design
Original Issue Price:	£24.95, U.S. $87.50

Name	U.S. $	Can. $	U.K. £
Fascination	95.00	130.00	29.50

CT-920
MOSAIC

Designer:	Alastair MacIntosh
Type:	Weight — Spherical
Edition:	1992
Status:	Closed
Series:	Unlimited — Modern Design
Original Issue Price:	£24.95, U.S. $87.50

Name	*U.S. $*	*Can. $*	*U.K. £*
Mosaic	90.00	120.00	25.00

CT-921
OBSESSION

Designer:	Alastair MacIntosh
Type:	Weight — Spherical
Edition:	1992
Status:	Closed
Series:	Unlimited — Modern Design
Original Issue Price:	£19.95, U.S. $72.50

Name	*U.S. $*	*Can. $*	*U.K. £*
Obsession	75.00	100.00	20.00

CT-922
SUNSET ORCHID

Designer:	Colin Terris
Type:	Weight — Domed
Edition:	1992 in a limited edition of 100
Status:	Fully subscribed
Series:	Limited — Modern Design
Original Issue Price:	£200.00, U.S. $675.00

Name	*U.S. $*	*Can. $*	*U.K. £*
Sunset Orchid	675.00	975.00	300.00

CT-923
ENCHANTED CASTLE

Designer:	Helen MacDonald and Alastair MacIntosh
Type:	Weight — Domed
Edition:	1992 in a limited edition of 100
Series:	Limited — Modern Design
Status:	Fully subscribed
Original Issue Price:	£200.00, U.S. $675.00

Name	*U.S. $*	*Can. $*	*U.K. £*
Enchanted Castle	675.00	975.00	250.00

242

CT-924
TIME TRAVELLER

Designer:	Colin Terris
Type:	Weight — Spherical
Edition:	1992 in a limited edition of 750
Status:	Closed at No. 741
Series:	Limited — Modern Design
Original Issue Price:	£49.00, U.S. $175.00

Name	U.S. $	Can. $	U.K. £
Time Traveller	175.00	250.00	50.00

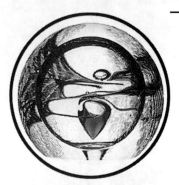

CT-925
CORAL ENCOUNTER

Designer:	Alastair MacIntosh
Type:	Weight — Spherical
Edition:	1992 in a limited edition of 750
Status:	Closed at No. 517
Series:	Limited — Modern Design
Original Issue Price:	£55.00, U.S. $190.00

Name	U.S. $	Can. $	U.K. £
Coral Encounter	190.00	275.00	55.00

CT-926
DOUBLE EXPOSURE

Designer:	Colin Terris
Type:	Weight — Spherical
Edition:	1992 in a limited edition of 50
Status:	Fully subscribed
Series:	Limited — Modern Design
Original Issue Price:	£175.00, U.S. $595.00

Name	U.S. $	Can. $	U.K. £
Double Exposure	650.00	895.00	400.00

CT-927
SANDFLOWER

Designer:	Colin Terris
Type:	Weight — Spherical
Edition:	1992 in a limited edition of 350
Status:	Closed at No. 284
Series:	Limited — Modern Design
Original Issue Price:	£99.00, U.S. $350.00

Name	U.S. $	Can. $	U.K. £
Sandflower	350.00	500.00	100.00

CT-928
GOLDEN RAINBOW

Designer:	Margot Thomson		
Type:	Weight — Spherical		
Edition:	1992 in a limited edition of 750		
Status:	Closed at No. 595		
Series:	Limited — Modern Design		
Original Issue Price:	£55.00, U.S. $190.00		

Name	U.S. $	Can. $	U.K. £
Golden Rainbow	190.00	275.00	55.00

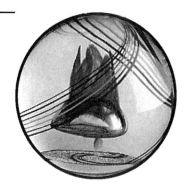

CT-929
INNOVATION

Designer:	Alastair MacIntosh		
Type:	Weight — Domed		
Edition:	1992 in a limited edition of 750		
Status:	Closed at No. 486		
Series:	Limited — Modern Design		
Original Issue Price:	£45.00, U.S. $150.00		

Name	U.S. $	Can. $	U.K. £
Innovation	150.00	200.00	45.00

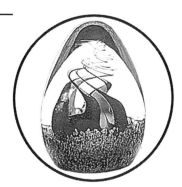

CT-930
ARCTIC CARNATION

Designer:	Alastair MacIntosh		
Type:	Weight — Domed		
Edition:	1993 in a limited edition of 650		
Status:	Fully subscribed		
Series:	Limited — Modern Design		
Original Issue Price:	£80.00, U.S. $275.00		

Name	U.S. $	Can. $	U.K. £
Arctic Carnation	275.00	375.00	90.00

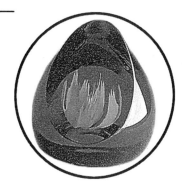

CT-931
BALLERINA

Designer:	Colin Terris		
Type:	Weight — Spherical		
Edition:	1993 in a limited edition of 50		
Status:	Fully subscribed		
Series:	Limited — Modern Design		
Original Issue Price:	£175.00, U.S. $595.00		

Name	U.S. $	Can. $	U.K. £
Ballerina	650.00	895.00	200.00

CT-932
BLUE ICE

Designer:	Colin Terris	
Type:	Weight — Spherical	
Edition:	1993 in a limited edition of 75	
Status:	Fully subscribed	
Series:	Limited — Modern Design	
Original Issue Price:	£150.00, U.S. $525.00	

Name	U.S. $	Can. $	U.K. £
Blue Ice	525.00	750.00	200.00

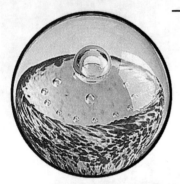

CT-933
CLOCKWORK

Designer:	Alastair MacIntosh	
Type:	Weight — Spherical	
Edition:	1993 in a limited edition of 750	
Status:	Closed at No. 153	
Series:	Limited — Modern Design	
Original Issue Price:	£45.00, U.S. $150.00	

Name	U.S. $	Can. $	U.K. £
Clockwork	200.00	300.00	45.00

CT-934
CORONA

Designer:	Alastair MacIntosh	
Type:	Weight — Spherical	
Edition:	1993 in a limited edition of 750	
Status:	Closed at No. 161	
Series:	Limited — Modern Design	
Original Issue Price:	£55.00, U.S. $195.00	

Name	U.S. $	Can. $	U.K. £
Corona	200.00	300.00	55.00

CT-935
CRESCENT MOON

Designer:	Colin Terris	
Type:	Weight — Spherical	
Edition:	1993 in a limited edition of 750	
Status:	Fully subscribed	
Series:	Limited — Modern Design	
Original Issue Price:	£50.00, U.S. $175.00	

Name	U.S. $	Can. $	U.K. £
Crescent Moon	175.00	250.00	60.00

CT-936
CYCLOID

Designer: Margot Thomson
Type: Weight — Spherical
Edition: 1993 in a limited edition of 750
Status: Closed at No. 470
Series: Limited — Modern Design
Original Issue Price: £50.00, U.S. $175.00

Name	U.S. $	Can. $	U.K. £
Cycloid	175.00	250.00	50.00

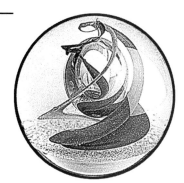

CT-937
DINNER PARTY

Designer: Alastair MacIntosh
Type: Weight — Spherical
Edition: 1993 in a limited edition of 750
Status: Closed at No. 197
Series: Limited — Modern Design
Original Issue Price: £60.00, U.S. $225.00

Name	U.S. $	Can. $	U.K. £
Dinner Party	225.00	325.00	60.00

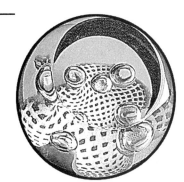

CT-938
DOUBLE CROSS

Designer: Margot Thomson
Type: Weight — Spherical
Edition: 1993 in a limited edition of 750
Status: Closed at No. 326
Series: Limited — Modern Design
Original Issue Price: £55.00, U.S. $210.00

Name	U.S. $	Can. $	U.K. £
Double Cross	210.00	300.00	55.00

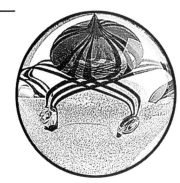

CT-939
DOUBLE MAGNUM 93

Designer: Margot Thomson
Type: Weight — Spherical, double magnum
Edition: 1993 in a limited edition of 150
Status: Closed at No. 101
Series: Limited — Modern Design
Original Issue Price: £175.00, U.S. $595.00

Name	U.S. $	Can. $	U.K. £
Double Magnum 93	595.00	850.00	200.00

CT-940
EXUBERANCE

Designer:	Alastair MacIntosh
Type:	Weight — Spherical
Edition:	1993 in a limited edition of 750
Status:	Closed at No. 436
Series:	Limited — Modern Design
Original Issue Price:	£55.00, U.S. 195.00

Name	U.S. $	Can. $	U.K. £
Exuberance	195.00	275.00	55.00

CT-941
FANTASY ORCHID

Designer:	Alastair MacIntosh
Type:	Weight — Domed
Edition:	1993 in a limited edition of 1,653
Status:	Closed
Original Issue Price:	£75.00, U.S. $215.00

Name	U.S. $	Can. $	U.K. £
Fantasy Orchid	215.00	300.00	85.00

Note: This is the 1993 Collectors' Paperweight.

CT-942
GLACIER

Designer:	Helen MacDonald and Alastair MacIntosh
Type:	Weight — Domed
Edition:	1993 in a limited edition of 100
Status:	Closed at No. 95
Series:	Limited — Modern Design
Original Issue Price:	£200.00, U.S. $695.00

Name	U.S. $	Can. $	U.K. £
Glacier	695.00	1,000.00	250.00

CT-943
GO-BETWEEN

Designer:	Margot Thomson
Type:	Weight — Spherical
Edition:	1993 in a limited edition of 750
Status:	Closed at No. 317
Series:	Limited — Modern Design
Original Issue Price:	£60.00, U.S. $225.00

Name	U.S. $	Can. $	U.K. £
Go-Between	225.00	325.00	60.00

CT-944
HIGH DIVE

Designer:	Alastair MacIntosh
Type:	Weight — Spherical
Edition:	1993 in a limited edition of 750
Status:	Closed at No. 327
Series:	Limited — Modern Design
Original Issue Price:	£55.00, U.S. $195.00

Name	U.S. $	Can. $	U.K. £
High Dive	195.00	275.00	55.00

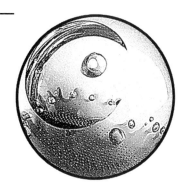

CT-945
HUMBUG

Designer:	Margot Thomson
Type:	Weight — Spherical
Edition:	1993 in a limited edition of 750
Status:	Closed at No. 490
Series:	Limited — Modern Design
Original Issue Price:	£60.00, U.S. $210.00

Name	U.S. $	Can. $	U.K. £
Humbug	210.00	300.00	60.00

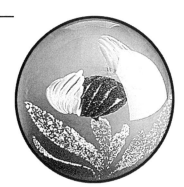

CT-946
INTERCEPTOR

Designer:	Colin Terris
Type:	Weight — Spherical
Edition:	1993 in a limited edition of 75
Status:	Fully subscribed
Series:	Limited — Modern Design
Original Issue Price:	£150.00, U.S. $525.00

Name	U.S. $	Can. $	U.K. £
Interceptor	600.00	850.00	375.00

CT-947
INTERMEZZO

Designer:	Colin Terris
Type:	Weight — Spherical
Edition:	1993 in a limited edition of 750
Status:	Closed at No. 411
Series:	Limited — Modern Design
Original Issue Price:	£50.00, U.S. $175.00

Name	U.S. $	Can. $	U.K. £
Intermezzo	175.00	250.00	50.00

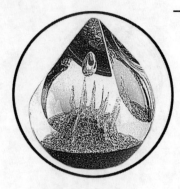

CT-948
ISLAND FANTASY

Designer:	Colin Terris
Type:	Weight — Domed, pyramid facets
Edition:	1993 in a limited edition of 350
Status:	Fully subscribed
Original Issue Price:	£99.00, U.S. $350.00

Name	U.S. $	Can. $	U.K. £
Island Fantasy	350.00	500.00	100.00

CT-949
LUNAR ORCHID

Designer:	Alastair MacIntosh
Type:	Weight — Spherical
Edition:	1993 in a limited edition of 750
Status:	Fully subscribed
Series:	Limited — Modern Design
Original Issue Price:	£50.00, U.S. $175.00

Name	U.S. $	Can. $	U.K. £
Lunar Orchid	175.00	250.00	50.00

CT-950
MATADOR

Designer:	Colin Terris
Type:	Weight — Spherical
Edition:	1993 in a limited edition of 750
Status:	Closed at No. 504
Series:	Limited — Modern Design
Original Issue Price:	£60.00, U.S. $225.00

Name	U.S. $	Can. $	U.K. £
Matador	225.00	325.00	60.00

CT-951
MAZE

Designer:	Alastair MacIntosh
Type:	Weight — Spherical
Edition:	1993 in a limited edition of 750
Status:	Closed at No. 535
Series:	Limited — Modern Design
Original Issue Price:	£45.00, U.S. $150.00

Name	U.S. $	Can. $	U.K. £
Maze	150.00	200.00	45.00

CT-952
MOON MOUNTAINS

Designer: Colin Terris
Type: Weight — Spherical
Edition: 1993 in a limited edition of 750
Status: Closed at No. 284
Series: Limited — Modern Design
Original Issue Price: £65.00, U.S. $230.00

Name	U.S. $	Can. $	U.K. £
Moon Mountains	230.00	325.00	65.00

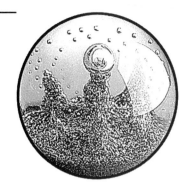

CT-953
NIMBUS

Designer: Margot Thomson
Type: Weight — Spherical
Edition: 1993 in a limited edition of 750
Status: Fully subscribed
Series: Limited — Modern Design
Original Issue Price: £39.95, U.S. $140.00

Name	U.S. $	Can. $	U.K. £
Nimbus	140.00	200.00	40.00

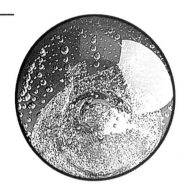

CT-954
NORDIC GLADE

Designer: Helen MacDonald and Alastair MacIntosh
Type: Weight — Domed
Edition: 1993 in a limited edition of 100
Status: Fully subscribed
Series: Limited — Modern Design
Original Issue Price: £200.00, U.S. $695.00

Name	U.S. $	Can. $	U.K. £
Nordic Glade	695.00	1,000.00	250.00

CT-955
OCEAN WAVE

Designer: Helen MacDonald and Alastair MacIntosh
Type: Weight — Domed
Edition: 1993 in a limited edition of 100
Status: Fully subscribed
Series: Limited — Modern Design
Original Issue Price: £200.00, U.S. $695.00

Name	U.S. $	Can. $	U.K. £
Ocean Wave	695.00	1,000.00	250.00

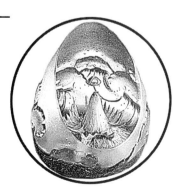

CT-956
PILGRIMAGE

Designer:	Colin Terris
Type:	Weight — Spherical
Edition:	1993 in a limited edition of 750
Status:	Closed at No. 202
Series:	Limited — Modern Design
Original Issue Price:	£65.00, U.S. $230.00

Name	U.S. $	Can. $	U.K. £
Pilgrimage	230.00	325.00	65.00

CT-957
PULSAR

Designer:	Colin Terris
Type:	Weight — Spherical
Edition:	1993 in a limited edition of 750
Status:	Closed at No. 612
Series:	Limited — Modern Design
Original Issue Price:	£55.00, U.S. $195.00

Name	U.S. $	Can. $	U.K. £
Pulsar	195.00	275.00	55.00

CT-958
SEA CRYSTAL

Designer:	Alastair MacIntosh
Type:	Weight — Spherical
Edition:	1993 in a limited edition of 75
Status:	Fully subscribed
Series:	Limited — Modern Design
Original Issue Price:	£150.00, U.S. $525.00

Name	U.S. $	Can. $	U.K. £
Sea Crystal	600.00	850.00	200.00

CT-959
SMOKE SIGNAL

Designer:	Colin Terris
Type:	Weight — Spherical
Edition:	1993 in a limited edition of 750
Status:	Fully subscribed
Series:	Limited — Modern Design
Original Issue Price:	£65.00, U.S. $230.00

Name	U.S. $	Can. $	U.K. £
Smoke Signal	230.00	325.00	65.00

CT-960
SOLSTICE

Designer:	Margot Thomson
Type:	Weight — Domed
Edition:	1993 in a limited edition of 350
Status:	Fully subscribed
Series:	Limited — Modern Design
Original Issue Price:	£99.00, U.S. $350.00

Name	U.S. $	Can. $	U.K. £
Solstice	350.00	500.00	100.00

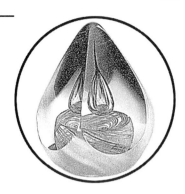

CT-961
SPINNING JENNY

Designer:	Margot Thomson
Type:	Weight — Spherical
Edition:	1993 in a limited edition of 350
Status:	Closed at No. 120
Series:	Limited — Modern Design
Original Issue Price:	£110.00, U.S. $395.00

Name	U.S. $	Can. $	U.K. £
Spinning Jenny	395.00	550.00	165.00

CT-962
THE DEEP

Designer:	Colin Terris
Type:	Weight — Spherical
Edition:	1993 in a limited edition of 100
Status:	Closed at No. 74
Original Issue Price:	£200.00, U.S. $695.00

Name	U.S. $	Can. $	U.K. £
The Deep	800.00	1,100.00	225.00

CT-963
THISTLEDOWN

Designer:	Colin Terris
Type:	Weight — Spherical
Edition:	1993 in a limited edition of 750
Status:	Closed at No. 343
Series:	Limited — Modern Design
Original Issue Price:	£55.00, U.S. $195.00

Name	U.S. $	Can. $	U.K. £
Thistledown	195.00	275.00	55.00

CT-964
5–4–3–2–1

Designer: Margot Thomson
Type: Weight — Domed
Edition: 1993 in a limited edition of 650
Status: Closed at No. 431
Series: Limited — Modern Design
Original Issue Price: £75.00, U.S. $275.00

Name	U.S. $	Can. $	U.K. £
5–4–3–2–1	275.00	375.00	75.00

CT-965
FIRENZE FLASK

Designer: Alastair MacIntosh
Type: Flask
Edition: 1993 in a limited edition of 50
Status: Closed at No. 42
Series: Limited — Modern Design
Original Issue Price: £195.00, U.S. $695.00

Name	U.S. $	Can. $	U.K. £
Firenze Flask	750.00	1,050.00	225.00

CT-966
MILANO FLASK

Designer: Alastair MacIntosh
Type: Flask
Edition: 1993 in a limited edition of 50
Status: Fully subscribed
Series: Limited — Modern Design
Original Issue Price: £195.00, U.S. $695.00

Name	U.S. $	Can. $	U.K. £
Milano Flask	750.00	1,050.00	225.00

CT-967
VERONA FLASK

Designer: Alastair MacIntosh
Type: Flask
Edition: 1993 in a limited edition of 50
Status: Closed at No. 46
Series: Limited — Modern Design
Original Issue Price: £175.00, U.S. $695.00

Name	U.S. $	Can. $	U.K. £
Verona Flask	750.00	1,050.00	225.00

CT-968A
MOONLIGHT PERFUME BOTTLE

Designer: Colin Terris
Type: Perfume bottle
Edition: 1993 in a limited edition of 75
Status: Closed at No. 72
Series: Limited — Modern Design
Original Issue Price: £195.00/set, U.S. $695.00/set

Name	U.S. $	Can. $	U.K. £
Moonlight Perfume Bottle	650.00	895.00	400.00
Set	975.00	1,345.00	600.00

Note: CT-968A and B were issued and sold as a set.

CT-968B
MOONLIGHT

Designer: Colin Terris
Type: Weight — Spherical
Edition: 1993 in a limited edition of 75
Status: Closed at No. 72
Series: Limited — Modern Design
Original Issue Price: £195.00/set, U.S. $695.00/set

Name	U.S. $	Can. $	U.K. £
Moonlight	325.00	450.00	200.00

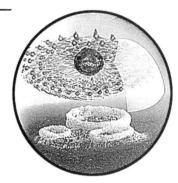

CT-969
BUTTERCUPS and DAISIES

Designer: Margot Thomson
Type: Weight — Spherical
Cane: white friar
Edition: 1993 in a limited edition of 100
Status: Closed at No. 70
Series: Whitefriars Collection
Original Issue Price: £155.00, U.S. $550.00

Name	U.S. $	Can. $	U.K. £
Buttercups and Daisies	550.00	775.00	155.00

CT-970
CYCLAMEN

Designer: Margot Thomson
Type: Weight — Spherical
Cane: white friar
Edition: 1993 in a limited edition of 100
Status: Fully subscribed
Series: Whitefriars Collection
Original Issue Price: £135.00, U.S. $525.00

Name	U.S. $	Can. $	U.K. £
Cyclamen	525.00	750.00	135.00

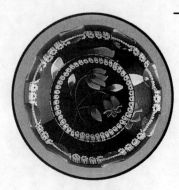

CT-971
HAREBELLS

Designer:	Margot Thomson
Type:	Weight — Spherical
Cane:	white friar
Edition:	1993 in a limited edition of 100
Status:	Closed at No. 53
Series:	Whitefriars Collection
Original Issue Price:	£145.00, U.S. $575.00

Name	*U.S. $*	*Can. $*	*U.K. £*
Harebells	575.00	825.00	145.00

CT-972
POPPIES PERFUME BOTTLE

Designer:	Margot Thomson
Type:	Perfume bottle
Cane:	white friar
Edition:	1993 in a limited edition of 100
Status:	Closed at No. 54
Series:	Whitefriars Collection
Original Issue Price:	£195.00, U.S. $695.00

Name	*U.S. $*	*Can. $*	*U.K. £*
Poppies Perfume Bottle	695.00	1,000.00	195.00

CT-973
REGAL LILY

Designer:	Margot Thomson
Type:	Weight — Spherical
Cane:	white friar
Edition:	1993 in a limited edition of 100
Status:	Closed at No. 70
Series:	Whitefriars Collection
Original Issue Price:	£135.00, U.S. $525.00

Name	*U.S. $*	*Can. $*	*U.K. £*
Regal Lily	525.00	750.00	135.00

CT-974A
SPRING CELEBRATION - ONE

Designer:	Margot Thomson
Type:	Weight — Spherical
Cane:	white friar
Edition:	1993 in a limited edition of 50
Status:	Fully subscribed
Series:	Whitefriars Collection
Original Issue Price:	£295.00/set, U.S. $1,150.00/set

Name	*U.S. $*	*Can. $*	*U.K. £*
Spring Celebration - One	575.00	825.00	150.00
Set	1,150.00	1,650.00	300.00

Note: CT-974A and B were issued and sold as a set.

CT-974B
SPRING CELEBRATION - TWO

Designer:	Margot Thomson
Type:	Weight — Spherical
Cane:	white friar
Edition:	1993 in a limited edition of 50
Status:	Fully subscribed
Series:	Whitefriars Collection
Original Issue Price:	£295.00/set, U.S. $1,150.00/set

Name	U.S. $	Can. $	U.K. £
Spring Celebration - Two	575.00	825.00	150.00

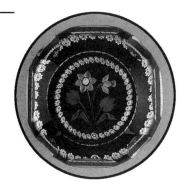

CT-975
SUMMER FLOWERS

Designer:	Margot Thomson
Type:	Weight — Spherical
Cane:	white friar
Edition:	1993 in a limited edition of 100
Status:	Closed at No. 73
Series:	Whitefriars Collection
Original Issue Price:	£195.00, U.S. $695.00

Name	U.S. $	Can. $	U.K. £
Summer Flowers	695.00	1,000.00	195.00

CT-976
WILD PANSY and STORKSBILL

Designer:	Margot Thomson
Type:	Weight — Spherical
Cane:	white friar
Edition:	1993 in a limited edition of 100
Status:	Closed at No. 97
Series:	Whitefriars Collection
Original Issue Price:	£135.00, U.S. $475.00

Name	U.S. $	Can. $	U.K. £
Wild Pansy and Storksbill	475.00	675.00	135.00

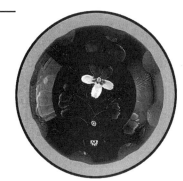

CT-977
CATERPILLAR

Designer:	William Manson
Type:	Weight — Spherical
Cane:	WM (William Manson)
Edition:	1993 in a limited edition of 50
Status:	Fully subscribed
Series:	Traditional Collection
Original Issue Price:	£195.00, U.S. $695.00

Name	U.S. $	Can. $	U.K. £
Caterpillar	800.00	1,100.00	195.00

CT-978
CHERRIES

Designer: William Manson
Type: Weight — Spherical
Cane: WM (William Manson)
Edition: 1993 in a limited edition of 50
Status: Fully subscribed
Series: Traditional Collection
Original Issue Price: £215.00, U.S. $750.00

Name	U.S. $	Can. $	U.K. £
Cherries	800.00	1,100.00	215.00

CT-979
COCKATOO

Designer: William Manson
Type: Weight — Spherical
Cane: WM (William Manson)
Edition: 1993 in a limited edition of 50
Status: Fully subscribed
Series: Traditional Collection
Original Issue Price: £195.00, U.S. $695.00

Name	U.S. $	Can. $	U.K. £
Cockatoo	800.00	1,100.00	195.00

CT-980
DOVES

Designer: William Manson
Type: Weight — Spherical
Cane: WM (William Manson)
Edition: 1993 in a limited edition of 50
Status: Fully subscribed
Series: Traditional Collection
Original Issue Price: £195.00, U.S. $695.00

Name	U.S. $	Can. $	U.K. £
Doves	800.00	1,100.00	195.00

CT-981
GRAPES

Designer: William Manson
Type: Weight — Spherical
Cane: WM (William Manson)
Edition: 1993 in a limited edition of 50
Status: Closed at No. 43
Series: Traditional Collection
Original Issue Price: £215.00, U.S. $750.00

Name	U.S. $	Can. $	U.K. £
Grapes	800.00	1,100.00	215.00

CT-982
SUMMER TRILOGY

Designer:	William Manson
Type:	Weight — Spherical
Cane:	WM (William Manson)
Edition:	1993 in a limited edition of 50
Status:	Fully subscribed
Series:	Traditional Collection

Original Issue Price: £195.00, U.S. $695.00

Name	U.S. $	Can. $	U.K. £
Summer Trilogy	800.00	1,100.00	195.00

CT-983
TUNA FISH

Designer:	William Manson
Type:	Weight — Spherical
Cane:	WM (William Manson)
Edition:	1993 in a limited edition of 50
Status:	Fully subscribed
Series:	Traditional Collection

Original Issue Price: £195.00, U.S. $695.00

Name	U.S. $	Can. $	U.K. £
Tuna Fish	800.00	1,100.00	195.00

CT-984
BLUE SPLASH

Designer:	Alastair MacIntosh
Type:	Weight — Spherical
Edition:	1993
Status:	Closed
Series:	Unlimited — Modern Design

Original Issue Price: £24.95, U.S. $87.50

Name	U.S. $	Can. $	U.K. £
Blue Splash	90.00	120.00	25.00

CT-985
CONGRATULATIONS

Designer:	Margot Thomson
Type:	Weight — Spherical
Colour:	See below
Edition:	1993
Status:	Active
Series:	Unlimited — Modern Design

Original Issue Price: £24.95, U.S. $87.50

Colourways	U.S. $	Can. $	U.K. £
1. Gold	95.00	130.00	30.00
2. Ruby	95.00	130.00	30.00
3. Silver	95.00	130.00	30.00

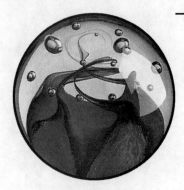

CT-986
DIABOLO

Designer:	Alastair MacIntosh
Type:	Weight — Spherical
Edition:	1993
Status:	Active
Series:	Unlimited — Modern Design
Original Issue Price:	£23.95, U.S. $79.50

Name	U.S. $	Can. $	U.K. £
Diabolo	95.00	125.00	28.50

CT-987
FOUNTAIN

Designer:	Colin Terris
Type:	Weight — Spherical
Edition:	1993
Status:	Active
Series:	Unlimited — Modern Design
Original Issue Price:	£29.95, U.S. $99.50

Name	U.S. $	Can. $	U.K. £
Fountain	110.00	150.00	34.50

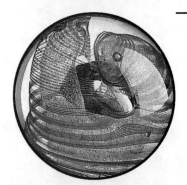

CT-988
ORIENTAL SILK

Designer:	Margot Thomson
Type:	Weight — Spherical
Edition:	1993
Status:	Active
Series:	Unlimited — Modern Design
Original Issue Price:	£23.95, U.S. $79.50

Name	U.S. $	Can. $	U.K. £
Oriental Silk	87.50	125.00	28.50

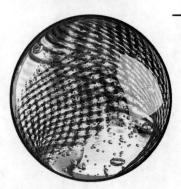

CT-989
TARTAN TWIST

Designer:	Alastair MacIntosh
Type:	Weight — Spherical
Edition:	1993
Status:	Closed
Series:	Unlimited — Modern Design
Original Issue Price:	£21.95, U.S. $79.50

Name	U.S. $	Can. $	U.K. £
Tartan Twist	80.00	110.00	25.00

CT-990
TWIRL

Designer:	Margot Thomson
Type:	Weight — Spherical, medium-sized
Colour:	See below
Edition:	1993
Status:	Active
Series:	Medium and Miniature Size
Original Issue Price:	£12.95, U.S. $45.00

Colourways	U.S. $	Can. $	U.K. £
1. Blue	52.50	75.00	16.50
2. Gold	52.50	75.00	16.50
3. Pink	52.50	75.00	16.50

CT-991
CLEMATIS

Designer:	Allan Scott
Type:	Weight — Spherical
Edition:	1993
Status:	Closed
Series:	Millefiori Miniatures
Original Issue Price:	£29.95, U.S. $115.00

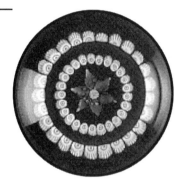

Name	U.S. $	Can. $	U.K. £
Clematis	115.00	160.00	30.00

CT-992
FUCHSIA

Designer:	Allan Scott
Type:	Weight — Spherical
Edition:	1993
Status:	Closed
Series:	Millefiori Miniatures
Original Issue Price:	£29.95, U.S. $115.00

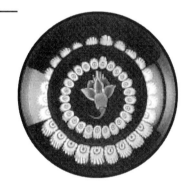

Name	U.S. $	Can. $	U.K. £
Fuchsia	115.00	160.00	30.00

CT-993
IRIS

Designer:	Allan Scott
Type:	Weight — Spherical
Edition:	1993
Status:	Closed
Series:	Millefiori Miniatures
Original Issue Price:	£29.95, U.S. $115.00

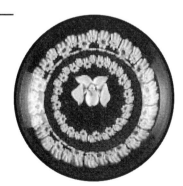

Name	U.S. $	Can. $	U.K. £
Iris	115.00	160.00	30.00

CT-994
CLEMATIS PERFUME BOTTLE

Designer: Allan Scott
Type: Perfume bottle
Edition: 1993
Status: Closed
Series: Millefiori Miniatures
Original Issue Price: £49.95, U.S. $175.00

Name	U.S. $	Can. $	U.K. £
Clematis Perfume Bottle	175.00	250.00	50.00

CT-995
FUCHSIA PERFUME BOTTLE

Designer: Allan Scott
Type: Perfume bottle
Edition: 1993
Status: Closed
Series: Millefiori Miniatures
Original Issue Price: £49.95, U.S. $175.00

Name	U.S. $	Can. $	U.K. £
Fuchsia Perfume Bottle	175.00	250.00	50.00

CT-996
IRIS PERFUME BOTTLE

Designer: Allan Scott
Type: Perfume bottle
Edition: 1993
Status: Closed
Series: Millefiori Miniatures
Original Issue Price: £49.95, U.S. $175.00

Name	U.S. $	Can. $	U.K. £
Iris Perfume Bottle	175.00	250.00	50.00

CT-997
BALMORAL INKWELL

Designer: Colin Terris
Type: Inkwell
Edition: 1993 in a limited edition of 50
Status: Closed at No. 30
Series: Limited — Modern Design
Original Issue Price: £295.00, U.S. $995.00

Name	U.S. $	Can. $	U.K. £
Balmoral Inkwell	1,200.00	1,700.00	300.00

CT-998
DUNVEGAN INKWELL

Designer: Colin Terris
Type: Inkwell
Edition: 1993 in a limited edition of 50
Status: Closed at No. 29
Series: Limited — Modern Design
Original Issue Price: £295.00, U.S. $995.00

Name	U.S. $	Can. $	U.K. £
Dunvegan Inkwell	1,200.00	1,700.00	300.00

CT-999
OCEAN PEARL

Designer: Alastair MacIntosh
Type: Weight — Spherical
Edition: 1993 in a limited edition of 50
Status: Fully subscribed
Series: Limited — Modern Design
Original Issue Price: £225.00, U.S. $695.00

Name	U.S. $	Can. $	U.K. £
Ocean Pearl	800.00	1,100.00	275.00

CT-1000
POLE STAR

Designer: Colin Terris
Type: Weight — Spherical
Edition: 1993 in a limited edition of 75
Status: Fully subscribed
Series: Limited — Modern Design
Original Issue Price: £185.00, U.S. $595.00

Name	U.S. $	Can. $	U.K. £
Pole Star	595.00	850.00	250.00

CT-1001
CELESTIAL CRYSTAL

Designer: Colin Terris
Type: Weight — Spherical
Edition: 1993 in a limited edition of 50
Series: Limited — Modern Design
Status: Fully subscribed
Original Issue Price: £225.00, U.S. $695.00

Name	U.S. $	Can. $	U.K. £
Celestial Crystal	725.00	1,000.00	275.00

CT-1002
EURYTHMIC

Designer: Margot Thomson
Type: Weight — Spherical
Edition: 1993 in a limited edition of 750
Status: Closed at No. 488
Series: Limited — Modern Design
Original Issue Price: £65.00, U.S. $225.00

Name	U.S. $	Can. $	U.K. £
Eurythmic	225.00	325.00	65.00

CT-1003
STRATOSPHERE

Designer: Colin Terris
Type: Weight — Spherical
Edition: 1993 in a limited edition of 75
Status: Fully subscribed
Series: Limited — Modern Design
Original Issue Price: £185.00, U.S. $595.00

Name	U.S. $	Can. $	U.K. £
Stratosphere	595.00	850.00	250.00

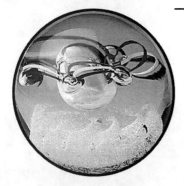

CT-1004
TRICOLOUR

Designer: Margot Thomson
Type: Weight — Spherical
Edition: 1993 in a limited edition of 750
Status: Closed at No. 318
Series: Limited — Modern Design
Original Issue Price: £60.00, U.S. $235.00

Name	U.S. $	Can. $	U.K. £
Tricolour	235.00	325.00	60.00

CT-1005
JACUZZI

Designer: Margot Thomson
Type: Weight — Spherical
Edition: 1993 in a limited edition of 650
Status: Closed at No. 287
Series: Limited — Modern Design
Original Issue Price: £65.00, U.S. $225.00

Name	U.S. $	Can. $	U.K. £
Jacuzzi	225.00	325.00	65.00

CT-1006
HYDROFOIL

Designer:	Margot Thomson
Type:	Weight — Spherical
Edition:	1993 in a limited edition of 750
Status:	Closed at No. 493
Series:	Limited — Modern Design
Original Issue Price:	£55.00, U.S. $190.00

Name	U.S. $	Can. $	U.K. £
Hydrofoil	190.00	275.00	55.00

CT-1007
EVEREST

Designer:	Alastair MacIntosh
Type:	Weight — Domed
Edition:	1993 in a limited edition of 750
Status:	Fully subscribed
Series:	Limited — Modern Design
Original Issue Price:	£60.00, U.S. $210.00

Name	U.S. $	Can. $	U.K. £
Everest	210.00	300.00	60.00

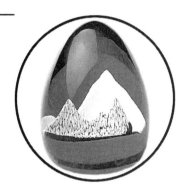

CT-1008
OCEAN ODYSSEY

Designer:	Margot Thomson
Type:	Weight — Teardrop
Edition:	1993 in a limited edition of 350
Status:	Closed at No. 285
Series:	Limited — Modern Design
Original Issue Price:	£99.00, U.S. $350.00

Name	U.S. $	Can. $	U.K. £
Ocean Odyssey	350.00	500.00	100.00

CT-1009
NIGHT VISION

Designer:	Margot Thomson
Type:	Weight — Spherical
Edition:	1993 in a limited edition of 150
Status:	Closed at No. 121
Series:	Limited — Modern Design
Original Issue Price:	£135.00, U.S. $525.00

Name	U.S. $	Can. $	U.K. £
Night Vision	525.00	750.00	175.00

CT-1010
SUNBURST

Designer:	Margot Thomson
Type:	Weight — Spherical
Edition:	1993 in a limited edition of 750
Status:	Closed at No. 395
Series:	Limited — Modern Design
Original Issue Price:	£50.00, U.S. $175.00

Name	U.S. $	Can. $	U.K. £
Sunburst	175.00	250.00	50.00

CT-1011
BLUETITS

Designer:	William Manson
Type:	Weight — Spherical
Edition:	1993 in a limited edition of 50
Status:	Fully subscribed
Series:	Traditional Collection
Original Issue Price:	£199.00, U.S. $695.00

Name	U.S. $	Can. $	U.K. £
Bluetits	800.00	1,100.00	200.00

CT-1012
BUTTERFLY and BLUEBELLS

Designer:	William Manson
Type:	Weight — Spherical
Edition:	1993 in a limited edition of 50
Status:	Closed at No. 38
Series:	Traditional Collection
Original Issue Price:	£199.00, U.S. $695.00

Name	U.S. $	Can. $	U.K. £
Butterfly and Bluebells	800.00	1,100.00	200.00

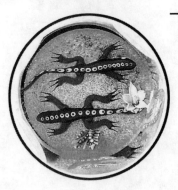

CT-1013
DOUBLE SALAMANDER

Designer:	William Manson
Type:	Weight — Spherical
Edition:	1993 in a limited edition of 25
Status:	Fully subscribed
Series:	Traditional Collection
Original Issue Price:	£395.00, U.S. $1,375.00

Name	U.S. $	Can. $	U.K. £
Double Salamander	1,650.00	2,250.00	400.00

CT-1014
WATERLILIES and DRAGONFLY

Designer:	William Manson
Type:	Weight — Spherical
Edition:	1993 in a limited edition of 50
Status:	Closed at No. 42
Series:	Traditional Collection
Original Issue Price:	£215.00, U.S. $750.00

Name	U.S. $	Can. $	U.K. £
Waterlilies and Dragonfly	750.00	1,000.00	215.00

CT-1015
HUMMING BIRD

Designer:	William Manson
Type:	Weight — Spherical
Edition:	1993 in a limited edition of 50
Status:	Fully subscribed
Series:	Traditional Collection
Original Issue Price:	£199.00, U.S. $695.00

Name	U.S. $	Can. $	U.K. £
Humming Bird	750.00	1,000.00	200.00

CT-1016
TADPOLES

Designer:	William Manson
Type:	Weight — Spherical
Edition:	1993 in a limited edition of 50
Status:	Fully subscribed
Series:	Traditional Collection
Original Issue Price:	£215.00, U.S. $750.00

Name	U.S. $	Can. $	U.K. £
Tadpoles	750.00	1,000.00	215.00

CT-1017
RED ROSES

Designer:	William Manson
Type:	Weight — Spherical
Edition:	1993 in a limited edition of 50
Status:	Fully subscribed
Series:	Traditional Collection
Original Issue Price:	£215.00, U.S. $750.00

Name	U.S. $	Can. $	U.K. £
Red Roses	750.00	1,000.00	215.00

CT-1018
BUTTERFLY

Designer: William Manson
Type: Weight — Spherical
Edition: 1993 in a limited edition of 150
Status: Closed at No. 141
Series: Traditional Collection
Original Issue Price: £60.00, U.S. $210.00

Name	U.S. $	Can. $	U.K. £
Butterfly	210.00	300.00	60.00

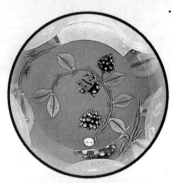

CT-1019
LADYBIRD

Designer: William Manson
Type: Weight — Spherical
Edition: 1993 in a limited edition of 150
Status: Fully subscribed
Series: Traditional Collection
Original Issue Price: £60.00, U.S. $210.00

Name	U.S. $	Can. $	U.K. £
Ladybird	210.00	300.00	60.00

CT-1020
WATERLILY

Designer: William Manson
Type: Weight — Spherical
Edition: 1993 in a limited edition of 150
Status: Closed at No. 138
Series: Traditional Collection
Original Issue Price: £60.00, U.S. $210.00

Name	U.S. $	Can. $	U.K. £
Waterlily	210.00	300.00	60.00

CT-1021
WOODLAND FLOWERS

Designer: William Manson
Type: Weight — Spherical
Edition: 1993 in a limited edition of 150
Status: Fully subscribed
Series: Traditional Collection
Original Issue Price: £60.00, U.S. $210.00

Name	U.S. $	Can. $	U.K. £
Woodland Flowers	210.00	300.00	60.00

CT-1022
MIDNIGHT ORCHIDS

Designer:	Colin Terris and Allan Scott
Type:	Weight — Spherical, quadruple overlay
Edition:	1993 in a limited edition of 25
Status:	Fully subscribed
Series:	Whitefriars Collection
Original Issue Price:	£495.00, U.S. $1,725.00

Name	U.S. $	Can. $	U.K. £
Midnight Orchids	2,000.00	2,900.00	650.00

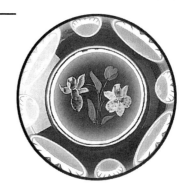

CT-1023A
SUMMER CELEBRATION — ONE

Designer:	Margot Thomson
Type:	Weight — Spherical
Edition:	1993 in a limited edition of 50
Status:	Fully subscribed
Series:	Whitefriars Collection
Original Issue Price:	£299.00/set, U.S. $1,150.00/set

Name	U.S. $	Can. $	U.K. £
Summer Celebration - One	575.00	825.00	150.00
Set	1,150.00	1,650.00	300.00

Note: CT-1023A and B were issued and sold as a set.

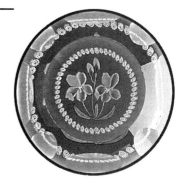

CT-1023B
SUMMER CELEBRATION — TWO

Designer:	Margot Thomson
Type:	Weight — Spherical
Edition:	1993 in a limited edition of 50
Status:	Fully subscribed
Series:	Whitefriars Collection
Original Issue Price:	£299.00/set, U.S. $1,150.00/set

Name	U.S. $	Can. $	U.K. £
Summer Celebration - Two	575.00	825.00	150.00

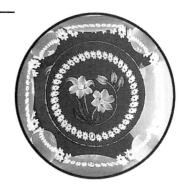

CT-1024
MYRIAD RED

Designer:	Caithness Studios
Type:	Weight — Spherical
Edition:	1993
Status:	Closed
Original Issue Price:	£29.95, U.S. $110.00

Name	U.S. $	Can. $	U.K. £
Myriad Red	110.00	145.00	30.00

CT-1025
MOONFLOWER RED

Designer: Colin Terris
Type: Weight — Spherical
Edition: 1993
Status: Closed
Series: Unlimited — Modern Design
Original Issue Price: £31.95, U.S. $99.50

Name	U.S. $	Can. $	U.K. £
Moonflower Red	100.00	140.00	35.00

CT-1026
PARALLEL LINES

Designer: Margot Thomson
Type: Weight — Spherical
Edition: 1993
Status: Closed
Series: Unlimited — Modern Design
Original Issue Price: £29.95, U.S. $99.50

Name	U.S. $	Can. $	U.K. £
Parallel Lines	100.00	140.00	30.00

CT-1027
FESTIVAL

Designer: Margot Thomson
Type: Weight — Spherical
Edition: 1993
Status: Closed
Series: Unlimited — Modern Design
Original Issue Price: £16.95, U.S. $58.50

Name	U.S. $	Can. $	U.K. £
Festival	60.00	80.00	18.00

CT-1028
LEVITATION

Designer: Alastair MacIntosh
Type: Weight — Spherical
Edition: 1994 in a limited edition of 750
Status: Closed at No. 251
Series: Limited — Modern Design
Original Issue Price: £70.00, U.S. $225.00

Name	U.S. $	Can. $	U.K. £
Levitation	225.00	325.00	70.00

CT-1029
AUTUMN DREAM

Designer:	Colin Terris
Type:	Weight — Domed
Edition:	1994 in a limited edition of 650
Status:	Closed at No. 420
Series:	Limited — Modern Design
Original Issue Price:	£85.00, U.S. $275.00

Name	U.S. $	Can. $	U.K. £
Autumn Dream	275.00	375.00	85.00

CT-1030
GAUCHO

Designer:	Margot Thomson
Type:	Weight — Teardrop
Edition:	1994 in a limited edition of 650
Status:	Closed at No. 437
Series:	Limited — Modern Design
Original Issue Price:	£75.00, U.S. $250.00

Name	U.S. $	Can. $	U.K. £
Gaucho	250.00	350.00	75.00

CT-1031
DOUBLE MAGNUM 94

Designer:	Margot Thomson
Type:	Weight — Spherical, double magnum
Edition:	1994 in a limited edition of 150
Status:	Closed at No. 86
Series:	Limited — Modern Design
Original Issue Price:	£195.00, U.S. $595.00

Name	U.S. $	Can. $	U.K. £
Double Magnum 94	650.00	895.00	200.00

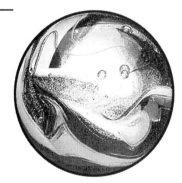

CT-1032
IMAGES

Designer:	Colin Terris
Type:	Weight — Spherical
Edition:	1994 in a limited edition of 50
Status:	Fully subscribed
Series:	Limited — Modern Design
Original Issue Price:	£235.00, U.S. $750.00

Name	U.S. $	Can. $	U.K. £
Images	800.00	1,100.00	325.00

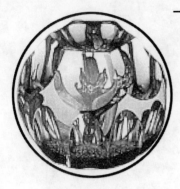

CT-1033
SERENADE

Designer: Colin Terris
Type: Weight — Spherical
Edition: 1994 in a limited edition of 50
Status: Fully subscribed
Series: Limited — Modern Design
Original Issue Price: £235.00, U.S. $750.00

Name	U.S. $	Can. $	U.K. £
Serenade	800.00	1,100.00	250.00

CT-1034
SEVENTH HEAVEN

Designer: Alastair MacIntosh
Type: Weight — Domed
Edition: 1994 in a limited edition of 150
Status: Fully subscribed
Series: Limited — Modern Design
Original Issue Price: £150.00, U.S. $495.00

Name	U.S. $	Can. $	U.K. £
Seventh Heaven	495.00	700.00	200.00

CT-1035
SWAN FLIGHT

Designer: Margot Thomson
Type: Weight — Domed
Edition: 1994 in a limited edition of 75
Status: Fully subscribed
Original Issue Price: £195.00, U.S. $650.00

Name	U.S. $	Can. $	U.K. £
Swan Flight	650.00	895.00	225.00

CT-1036
PINK CHIFFON

Designer: Alastair MacIntosh
Type: Weight — Spherical, magnum size
Edition: 1994 in a limited edition of 250
Status: Closed at No. 87
Series: Limited — Modern Design
Original Issue Price: £125.00, U.S. $395.00

Name	U.S. $	Can. $	U.K. £
Pink Chiffon	400.00	550.00	125.00

CT-1037
PASSION

Designer:	Colin Terris
Type:	Weight — Spherical
Edition:	1994 in a limited edition of 50
Status:	Fully subscribed
Series:	Limited — Modern Design
Original Issue Price:	£250.00, U.S. $750.00

Name	U.S. $	Can. $	U.K. £
Passion	800.00	1,100.00	275.00

CT-1038
STAR CONQUEST

Designer:	Alastair MacIntosh
Type:	Weight — Spherical
Edition:	1994 in a limited edition of 750
Status:	Closed at No. 428
Original Issue Price:	£70.00, U.S. $230.00

Name	U.S. $	Can. $	U.K. £
Star Conquest	230.00	325.00	70.00

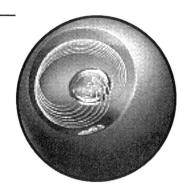

CT-1039
STORM WATCH

Designer:	Helen MacDonald and Alastair MacIntosh
Type:	Weight — Domed
Edition:	1994 in a limited edition of 100
Status:	Fully subscribed
Original Issue Price:	£235.00, U.S. $750.00

Name	U.S. $	Can. $	U.K. £
Storm Watch	750.00	1,050.00	250.00

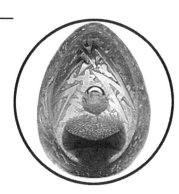

CT-1040
DRUID

Designer:	Alastair MacIntosh
Type:	Weight — Domed
Edition:	1994 in a limited edition of 650
Status:	Closed at No. 568
Series:	Limited — Modern Design
Original Issue Price:	£85.00, U.S. $295.00

Name	U.S. $	Can. $	U.K. £
Druid	300.00	450.00	90.00

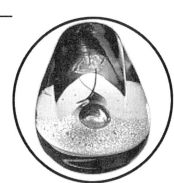

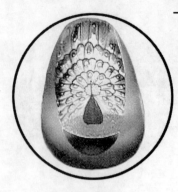

CT-1041
PEACOCK

Designer:	Helen MacDonald
Type:	Weight — Domed
Edition:	1994 in a limited edition of 100
Status:	Fully subscribed
Original Issue Price:	£235.00, U.S. $750.00

Name	U.S. $	Can. $	U.K. £
Peacock	750.00	1,050.00	235.00

CT-1042
BIRDS OF PARADISE

Designer:	Helen MacDonald
Type:	Weight — Domed
Edition:	1994 in a limited edition of 100
Status:	Fully subscribed
Series:	Limited — Modern Design
Original Issue Price:	£235.00, U.S. $750.00

Name	U.S. $	Can. $	U.K. £
Birds of Paradise	750.00	1,050.00	235.00

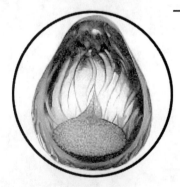

CT-1043
FIREFLAME

Designer:	Helen MacDonald and Alastair MacIntosh
Type:	Weight — Domed
Edition:	1994 in a limited edition of 100
Status:	Fully subscribed
Series:	Limited — Modern Design
Original Issue Price:	£235.00, U.S. $750.00

Name	U.S. $	Can. $	U.K. £
Fireflame	750.00	1,050.00	235.00

CT-1044
DIVINE LIGHT

Designer:	Margot Thomson
Type:	Weight — Spherical
Edition:	1994 in a limited edition of 750
Status:	Closed at No. 429
Series:	Limited — Modern Design
Original Issue Price:	£70.00, U.S. $225.00

Name	U.S. $	Can. $	U.K. £
Divine Light	225.00	325.00	70.00

CT-1045
OVERSEER

Designer:	Margot Thomson
Type:	Weight — Spherical
Edition:	1994 in a limited edition of 750
Status:	Closed at No. 527
Series:	Limited — Modern Design
Original Issue Price:	£40.00, U.S. $140.00

Name	U.S. $	Can. $	U.K. £
Overseer	145.00	200.00	40.00

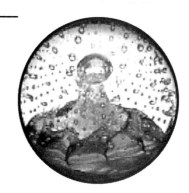

CT-1046
BLUE SAIL

Designer:	Alastair MacIntosh
Type:	Weight — Spherical
Edition:	1994 in a limited edition of 750
Status:	Fully subscribed
Series:	Limited — Modern Design
Original Issue Price:	£50.00, U.S. $150.00

Name	U.S. $	Can. $	U.K. £
Blue Sail	150.00	200.00	50.00

CT-1047
ACCORD

Designer:	Margot Thomson
Type:	Weight — Spherical
Edition:	1994 in a limited edition of 750
Status:	Closed at No. 564
Series:	Limited — Modern Design
Original Issue Price:	£70.00, U.S. $225.00

Name	U.S. $	Can. $	U.K. £
Accord	225.00	325.00	70.00

CT-1048
MAYPOLE

Designer:	Margot Thomson
Type:	Weight — Domed
Edition:	1994 in a limited edition of 750
Status:	Closed at No. 472
Series:	Limited — Modern Design
Original Issue Price:	£55.00, U.S. $175.00

Name	U.S. $	Can. $	U.K. £
Maypole	175.00	275.00	55.00

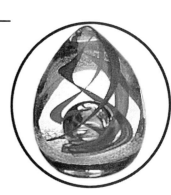

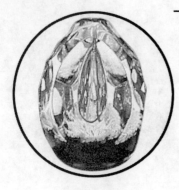

CT-1049
TRANSATLANTIC

Designer:	Margot Thomson
Type:	Weight — Domed
Edition:	1994 in a limited edition of 150
Status:	Closed at No. 124
Series:	Limited — Modern Design
Original Issue Price:	£150.00, U.S. $550.00

Name	U.S. $	Can. $	U.K. £
Transatlantic	550.00	775.00	150.00

CT-1050
MOONRISE

Designer:	Margot Thomson
Type:	Weight — Domed
Edition:	1994 in a limited edition of 750
Status:	Closed at No. 404
Series:	Limited — Modern Design
Original Issue Price:	£65.00, U.S. $225.00

Name	U.S. $	Can. $	U.K. £
Moonrise	225.00	325.00	65.00

CT-1051
THE HEALER

Designer:	Colin Terris
Type:	Weight — Spherical
Edition:	1994 in a limited edition of 750
Status:	Closed at No. 486
Series:	Limited — Modern Design
Original Issue Price:	£70.00, U.S. $225.00

Name	U.S. $	Can. $	U.K. £
The Healer	225.00	325.00	70.00

CT-1052
SUBMARINER

Designer:	Colin Terris
Type:	Weight — Spherical
Edition:	1994 in a limited edition of 750
Status:	Closed at No. 678
Series:	Limited — Modern Design
Original Issue Price:	£65.00, U.S. $225.00

Name	U.S. $	Can. $	U.K. £
Submariner	225.00	325.00	65.00

CT-1053
MELODY

Designer:	Margot Thomson
Type:	Weight — Spherical
Edition:	1994 in a limited edition of 650
Status:	Closed at No. 558
Series:	Limited — Modern Design
Original Issue Price:	£75.00, U.S. $250.00

Name	U.S. $	Can. $	U.K. £
Melody	250.00	350.00	75.00

CT-1054
RING O' ROSES

Designer:	Margot Thomson
Type:	Weight — Spherical
Edition:	1994 in a limited edition of 750
Status:	Closed at No. 530
Series:	Limited — Modern Design
Original Issue Price:	£65.00, U.S. $225.00

Name	U.S. $	Can. $	U.K. £
Ring o' Roses	225.00	325.00	65.00

CT-1055
ENDEARMENT

Designer:	Colin Terris
Type:	Weight — Spherical
Edition:	1994 in a limited edition of 75
Status:	Fully subscribed
Series:	Limited — Modern Design
Original Issue Price:	£175.00, U.S. $575.00

Name	U.S. $	Can. $	U.K. £
Endearment	575.00	825.00	175.00

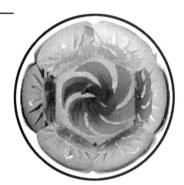

CT-1056
REVERENCE

Designer:	Colin Terris
Type:	Weight — Spherical
Edition:	1994 in a limited edition of 75
Status:	Fully subscribed
Series:	Limited — Modern Design
Original Issue Price:	£175.00, U.S. $550.00

Name	U.S. $	Can. $	U.K. £
Reverence	550.00	775.00	175.00

CT-1057
HARLEQUIN DOUBLE

Designer:	Paul Ysart derivative
Type:	Weight — Domed
Cane:	94
Edition:	1994 in a limited edition of 500
Status:	Closed at No. 437
Series:	Classic Collection
Original Issue Price:	£55.00, U.S. $175.00

Name	U.S. $	Can. $	U.K. £
Harlequin Double	175.00	250.00	55.00

Note: Weights CT-1057 through 1061 were issued to commemorate the 25th anniversary of the Caithness Glass paperweight collection.

CT-1058
HARLEQUIN SINGLE

Designer:	Paul Ysart derivative
Type:	Weight — Spherical
Cane:	94
Edition:	1994 in a limited edition of 500
Status:	Closed at No. 403
Series:	Classic Collection
Original Issue Price:	£45.00, U.S. $150.00

Name	U.S. $	Can. $	U.K. £
Harlequin Single	150.00	200.00	45.00

CT-1059
FLOWER IN THE RAIN

Designer:	Colin Terris
Type:	Weight — Spherical
Cane:	94
Edition:	1994 in a limited edition of 500
Status:	Closed at No. 409
Series:	Classic Collection
Original Issue Price:	£60.00, U.S. $185.00

Name	U.S. $	Can. $	U.K. £
Flower in the Rain	185.00	250.00	60.00

CT-1060
SILVER CORAL

Designer:	Colin Terris
Type:	Weight — Spherical
Cane:	94
Edition:	1994 in a limited edition of 500
Status:	Closed at No. 282
Series:	Classic Collection
Original Issue Price:	£65.00, U.S. $210.00

Name	U.S. $	Can. $	U.K. £
Silver Coral	210.00	300.00	65.00

CT-1061
SILVER MOONFLOWER

Designer: Colin Terris
Type: Weight — Spherical, magnum size
Cane: 94
Edition: 1994 in a limited edition of 350
Status: Fully subscribed
Series: Classic Collection
Original Issue Price: £65.00, U.S. $225.00

Name	U.S. $	Can. $	U.K. £
Silver Moonflower	225.00	325.00	65.00

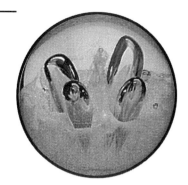

CT-1062
JUBILEE ORCHID

Designer: Colin Terris
Type: Weight — Spherical
Edition: 1994 in a limited edition of 1,883
Status: Closed at 1,883
Original Issue Price: £99.00, U.S. $275.00

Name	U.S. $	Can. $	U.K. £
Jubilee Orchid	275.00	375.00	125.00

Note: This is the 1994 Collectors' Paperweight.

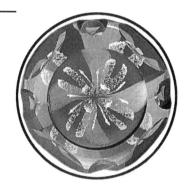

CT-1063
WOOD ANEMONES

Designer: Margot Thomson
Type: Weight — Spherical
Edition: 1994 in a limited edition of 50
Status: Closed at No. 39
Series: Whitefriars Collection
Original Issue Price: £165.00, U.S. $595.00

Name	U.S. $	Can. $	U.K. £
Wood Anemones	650.00	895.00	165.00

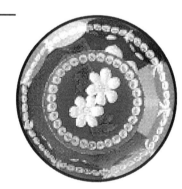

CT-1064
LILY OF THE VALLEY

Designer: Margot Thomson
Type: Weight — Spherical
Edition: 1994 in a limited edition of 50
Status: Fully subscribed
Series: Whitefriars Collection
Original Issue Price: £175.00, U.S. $650.00

Name	U.S. $	Can. $	U.K. £
Lily of the Valley	650.00	895.00	175.00

CT-1065
CHRISTMAS ROSE

Designer:	Margot Thomson
Type:	Weight — Spherical
Edition:	1994 in a limited edition of 50
Status:	Closed at No. 45
Series:	Whitefriars Collection

Original Issue Price: £165.00, U.S. $595.00

Name	U.S. $	Can. $	U.K. £
Christmas Rose	600.00	850.00	165.00

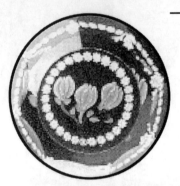

CT-1066
MAGNOLIA

Designer:	Margot Thomson
Type:	Weight — Spherical
Edition:	1994 in a limited edition of 50
Status:	Fully subscribed
Series:	Whitefriars Collection

Original Issue Price: £150.00, U.S. $575.00

Name	U.S. $	Can. $	U.K. £
Magnolia	600.00	850.00	150.00

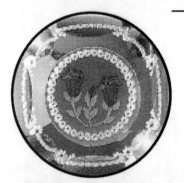

CT-1067A
AUTUMN CELEBRATION — ONE

Designer:	Margot Thomson
Type:	Weight — Spherical
Edition:	1994 in a limited edition of 50
Status:	Fully subscribed
Series:	Whitefriars Collection

Original Issue Price: £325.00/set, U.S. $1,150.00/set

Name	U.S. $	Can. $	U.K. £
Autumn Celebration - One	575.00	800.00	165.00
Set	1,150.00	1,600.00	330.00

Note: CT-1067A and B were issued and sold as a set.

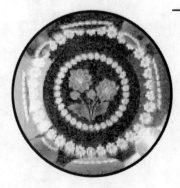

CT-1067B
AUTUMN CELEBRATION — TWO

Designer:	Margot Thomson
Type:	Weight — Spherical
Edition:	1994 in a limited edition of 50
Status:	Fully subscribed
Series:	Whitefriars Collection

Original Issue Price: £325.00/set, U.S. $1,150.00/set

Name	U.S. $	Can. $	U.K. £
Autumn Celebration -Two	575.00	800.00	165.00

CT-1068
PANSIES

Designer:	Margot Thomson
Type:	Weight — Spherical
Edition:	1994 in a limited edition of 50
Status:	Fully subscribed
Series:	Whitefriars Collection

Original Issue Price: £215.00, U.S. $750.00

Name	U.S. $	Can. $	U.K. £
Pansies	750.00	1,050.00	215.00

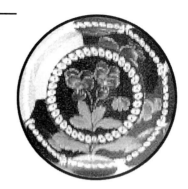

CT-1069
PERIWINKLES

Designer:	Margot Thomson
Type:	Weight — Spherical
Edition:	1994 in a limited edition of 50
Status:	Closed at No. 46
Series:	Whitefriars Collection

Original Issue Price: £175.00, U.S. $650.00

Name	U.S. $	Can. $	U.K. £
Periwinkles	650.00	925.00	175.00

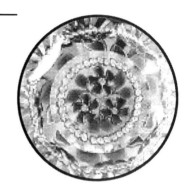

CT-1070
WINTER FLOWERS

Designer:	Margot Thomson
Type:	Weight — Spherical
Edition:	1994 in a limited edition of 50
Status:	Closed at No. 44
Series:	Whitefriars Collection

Original Issue Price: £215.00, U.S. $750.00

Name	U.S. $	Can. $	U.K. £
Winter Flowers	750.00	1,050.00	215.00

CT-1071
CHERRY BLOSSOM PERFUME BOTTLE

Designer:	Margot Thomson
Type:	Perfume bottle
Edition:	1994 in a limited edition of 50
Status:	Closed at No. 30
Series:	Whitefriars Collection

Original Issue Price: £215.00, U.S. $775.00

Name	U.S. $	Can. $	U.K. £
Cherry Blossom Perfume Bottle	800.00	1,100.00	215.00

CT-1072A
CARNATION PERFUME BOTTLE

Designer: Margot Thomson
Type: Perfume bottle
Edition: 1994 in a limited edition of 50
Status: Closed at No. 38
Series: Whitefriars Collection
Original Issue Price: £395.00/set, U.S. $1,375.00/set

Name	U.S. $	Can. $	U.K. £
Carnation Perfume Bottle	1,000.00	1,450.00	395.00
Set	1,400.00	2,030.00	695.00

Note: CT-1072A and B were issued and sold as a set.

CT-1072B
CARNATION

Designer: Margot Thomson
Type: Weight — Spherical
Edition: 1994 in a limited edition of 50
Status: Closed at No. 38
Series: Whitefriars Collection
Original Issue Price: £395.00/set, U.S. $1,375.00/set

Name	U.S. $	Can. $	U.K. £
Carnation	400.00	580.00	300.00

CT-1073
WOODLAND GLADE

Designer: Colin Terris and Allan Scott
Type: Weight — Spherical, quadruple overlay
Edition: 1994 in a limited edition of 25
Status: Fully subscribed
Series: Whitefriars Collection
Original Issue Price: £595.00, U.S. $2,100.00

Name	U.S. $	Can. $	U.K. £
Woodland Glade	2,100.00	3,000.00	595.00

CT-1074
ZEBRA FISH

Designer: William Manson
Type: Weight — Spherical
Edition: 1994 in a limited edition of 50
Status: Closed at No. 39
Series: Traditional Collection
Original Issue Price: £215.00, U.S. $775.00

Name	U.S. $	Can. $	U.K. £
Zebra Fish	800.00	1,100.00	215.00

CT-1075
BUTTERFLY GARLAND

Designer: William Manson
Type: Weight — Spherical
Edition: 1994 in a limited edition of 50
Status: Closed at No. 41
Series: Traditional Collection
Original Issue Price: £215.00, U.S. $695.00

Name	U.S. $	Can. $	U.K. £
Butterfly Garland	800.00	1,100.00	215.00

CT-1076
LADYBIRD and BUTTERFLY

Designer: William Manson
Type: Weight — Spherical
Edition: 1994 in a limited edition of 50
Status: Closed at No. 44
Series: Traditional Collection
Original Issue Price: £215.00, U.S. $750.00

Name	U.S. $	Can. $	U.K. £
Ladybird and Butterfly	800.00	1,100.00	215.00

CT-1077
WATERHEN

Designer: William Manson
Type: Weight — Spherical
Edition: 1994 in a limited edition of 50
Status: Closed at No. 34
Series: Traditional Collection
Original Issue Price: £215.00, U.S. $775.00

Name	U.S. $	Can. $	U.K. £
Waterhen	800.00	1,100.00	215.00

CT-1078
SPINOSAURUS

Designer: William Manson
Type: Weight — Spherical
Edition: 1994 in a limited edition of 50
Status: Closed at No. 45
Series: Traditional Collection
Original Issue Price: £275.00, U.S. $995.00

Name	U.S. $	Can. $	U.K. £
Spinosaurus	995.00	1,400.00	275.00

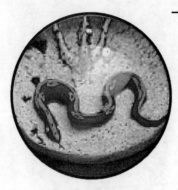

CT-1079
SIDEWINDER

Designer:	William Manson
Type:	Weight — Spherical
Edition:	1994 in a limited edition of 50
Status:	Closed at No. 38
Series:	Traditional Collection
Original Issue Price:	£275.00, U.S. $995.00

Name	U.S. $	Can. $	U.K. £
Sidewinder	995.00	1,400.00	275.00

CT-1080
PILOT FISH

Designer:	William Manson
Type:	Weight — Spherical
Edition:	1994 in a limited edition of 50
Status:	Closed at No. 42
Series:	Traditional Collection
Original Issue Price:	£235.00, U.S. $850.00

Name	U.S. $	Can. $	U.K. £
Pilot Fish	950.00	1,350.00	235.00

CT-1081
MORNING GLORY

Designer:	William Manson
Type:	Weight — Spherical
Edition:	1994 in a limited edition of 50
Status:	Fully subscribed
Series:	Traditional Collection
Original Issue Price:	£225.00, U.S. $750.00

Name	U.S. $	Can. $	U.K. £
Morning Glory	750.00	1,050.00	225.00

CT-1082
FOSSIL

Designer:	William Manson
Type:	Weight — Spherical
Edition:	1994 in a limited edition of 50
Status:	Closed at No. 33
Series:	Traditional Collection
Original Issue Price:	£225.00, U.S. $775.00

Name	U.S. $	Can. $	U.K. £
Fossil	925.00	1,275.00	225.00

CT-1083
HUMMING BIRD

Designer:	William Manson
Type:	Weight — Spherical
Edition:	1994 in a limited edition of 50
Status:	Fully subscribed
Series:	Traditional Collection
Original Issue Price:	£215.00, U.S. $775.00

Name	U.S. $	Can. $	U.K. £
Humming Bird	775.00	1,100.00	215.00

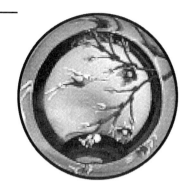

CT-1084
FROG

Designer:	William Manson
Type:	Weight — Spherical
Edition:	1994 in a limited edition of 50
Status:	Closed at No. 47
Series:	Traditional Collection
Original Issue Price:	£225.00, U.S. $825.00

Name	U.S. $	Can. $	U.K. £
Frog	825.00	1,150.00	225.00

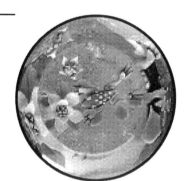

CT-1085
BUTTERCUPS

Designer:	William Manson
Type:	Weight — Spherical, medium-sized
Edition:	1994 in a limited edition of 150
Status:	Closed at No. 138
Series:	Traditional Collection — Medium Sized
Original Issue Price:	£65.00, U.S. $210.00

Name	U.S. $	Can. $	U.K. £
Buttercups	210.00	300.00	65.00

CT-1086
RED ROSE

Designer:	William Manson
Type:	Weight — Spherical, medium-sized
Edition:	1994 in a limited edition of 150
Status:	Fully subscribed
Series:	Traditional Collection — Medium Sized
Original Issue Price:	£65.00, U.S. $210.00

Name	U.S. $	Can. $	U.K. £
Red Rose	210.00	300.00	65.00

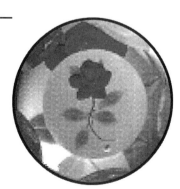

CT-1087
YELLOW ROSE

Designer:	William Manson
Type:	Weight — Spherical, medium-sized
Edition:	1994 in a limited edition of 150
Status:	Fully subscribed
Series:	Traditional Collection — Medium Sized

Original Issue Price: £65.00, U.S. $210.00

Name	U.S. $	Can. $	U.K. £
Yellow Rose	210.00	300.00	65.00

CT-1088
PANSY

Designer:	William Manson
Type:	Weight — Spherical, medium-sized
Edition:	1994 in a limited edition of 150
Status:	Closed at No. 142
Series:	Traditional Collection — Medium Sized

Original Issue Price: £65.00, U.S. $210.00

Name	U.S. $	Can. $	U.K. £
Pansy	210.00	300.00	65.00

CT-1089
FEATHERS

Designer:	Alastair MacIntosh
Type:	Weight — Spherical
Edition:	1994
Status:	Closed
Series:	Unlimited — Modern Design

Original Issue Price: £26.95, U.S. $87.50

Name	U.S. $	Can. $	U.K. £
Feathers	90.00	120.00	30.00

CT-1090
GULF STREAM

Designer:	Alastair MacIntosh
Type:	Weight — Spherical
Edition:	1994
Status:	Closed
Series:	Unlimited — Modern Design

Original Issue Price: £28.95, U.S. $99.50

Name	U.S. $	Can. $	U.K. £
Gulf Stream	100.00	140.00	30.00

CT-1091
INNER CIRCLE

Designer: Alastair MacIntosh
Type: Weight — Spherical
Edition: 1994
Status: Closed
Series: Unlimited — Modern Design
Original Issue Price: £32.95, U.S. $115.00

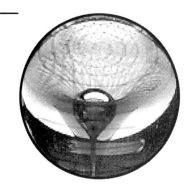

Name	U.S. $	Can. $	U.K. £
Inner Circle	115.00	160.00	35.00

CT-1092
MOONFLOWER RAINBOW

Designer: Colin Terris
Type: Weight — Spherical
Colour: Blue, green, white and fuchsia
Edition: 1994
Status: Closed
Series: Unlimited — Modern Design
Original Issue Price: £32.95, U.S. $99.50

Name	U.S. $	Can. $	U.K. £
Moonflower Rainbow	100.00	140.00	35.00

CT-1093
SPARKLE

Designer: Colin Terris
Type: Weight — Spherical
Colour: See below
Edition: 1994
Status: Active
Series: Unlimited — Modern Design
Original Issue Price: £26.95, U.S. $87.50

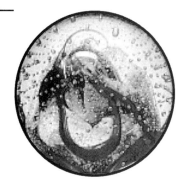

Colourways	U.S. $	Can. $	U.K. £
1. Blue	95.00	130.00	30.00
2. Purple	95.00	130.00	30.00

CT-1094
JUBILEE 94 DOUBLE MAGNUM

Designer: Colin Terris
Type: Weight — Spherical, double magnum
Edition: 1994 in a limited edition of 25
Status: Fully subscribed
Series: Limited — Modern Design
Original Issue Price: £850.00, U.S. $2,750.00

Name	U.S. $	Can. $	U.K. £
Jubilee 94 Double Magnum	3,000.00	4,000.00	1,100.00

Note: This paperweight was issued to commemorate the 25th anniversary of the Caithness Glass paperweight collection.

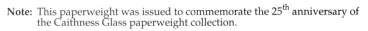

CT-1095
FAIRY TALE

Designer:	Alastair MacIntosh
Type:	Weight — Domed
Edition:	1994 in a limited edition of 650
Status:	Fully subscribed
Series:	Limited — Modern Design
Original Issue Price:	£75.00, U.S. $225.00

Name	U.S. $	Can. $	U.K. £
Fairy Tale	225.00	325.00	75.00

CT-1096
LILY POND

Designer:	Helen MacDonald
Type:	Weight — Domed
Edition:	1994 in a limited edition of 100
Status:	Closed at No. 93
Series:	Limited — Modern Design
Original Issue Price:	£235.00, U.S. $695.00

Name	U.S. $	Can. $	U.K. £
Lily Pond	695.00	1,000.00	275.00

CT-1097
AZTEC

Designer:	Alastair MacIntosh
Type:	Weight — Spherical
Edition:	1994 in a limited edition of 500
Status:	Closed at No. 135
Series:	Limited — Modern Design
Original Issue Price:	£85.00, U.S. $250.00

Name	U.S. $	Can. $	U.K. £
Aztec	250.00	350.00	85.00

CT-1098
BLOSSOM

Designer:	Colin Terris
Type:	Weight — Spherical
Edition:	1994 in a limited edition of 75
Status:	Fully subscribed
Series:	Limited — Modern Design
Original Issue Price:	£175.00, U.S. $495.00

Name	U.S. $	Can. $	U.K. £
Blossom	500.00	725.00	175.00

CT-1099
GOLDEN SUNRISE

Designer:	Alan Scrimgeour		
Type:	Weight — Spherical		
Edition:	1994 in a limited edition of 750		
Status:	Closed at No. 465		
Series:	Limited — Modern Design		
Original Issue Price:	£65.00, U.S. $195.00		

Name	U.S. $	Can. $	U.K. £
Golden Sunrise	195.00	275.00	65.00

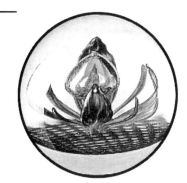

CT-1100
BLACK MAGIC

Designer:	Alastair MacIntosh		
Type:	Weight — Spherical		
Edition:	1994 in a limited edition of 750		
Status:	Closed at No. 541		
Series:	Limited — Modern Design		
Original Issue Price:	£50.00, U.S. $165.00		

Name	U.S. $	Can. $	U.K. £
Black Magic	165.00	225.00	50.00

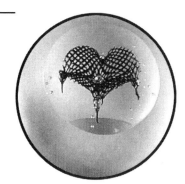

CT-1101
L'AMOUR

Designer:	Colin Terris		
Type:	Weight — Spherical		
Edition:	1994 in a limited edition of 50		
Status:	Fully subscribed		
Series:	Limited — Modern Design		
Original Issue Price:	£250.00, U.S. $750.00		

Name	U.S. $	Can. $	U.K. £
L'amour	800.00	1,100.00	275.00

CT-1102
MONET TRIBUTE

Designer:	Colin Terris		
Type:	Weight — Spherical, double overlay		
Edition:	1994 in a limited edition of 50		
Status:	Fully subscribed		
Series:	Limited — Modern Design		
Original Issue Price:	£350.00, U.S. $1,000.00		

Name	U.S. $	Can. $	U.K. £
Monet Tribute	1,100.00	1,600.00	375.00

Note: This paperweight was issued to honour the Monet exhibit at the Art Institute of Chicago.

CT-1103
FROSTY MORNING

Designer: John Spittal
Type: Weight — Domed
Edition: 1994 in a limited edition of 350
Status: Fully subscribed
Series: Limited — Modern Design
Original Issue Price: £99.00, U.S. $295.00

Name	U.S. $	Can. $	U.K. £
Frosty Morning	295.00	425.00	100.00

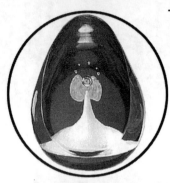

CT-1104
GUARDIAN ANGEL

Designer: Helen MacDonald
Type: Weight — Domed
Edition: 1994 in a limited edition of 500
Status: Closed at No. 465
Series: Limited — Modern Design
Original Issue Price: £90.00, U.S. $250.00

Name	U.S. $	Can. $	U.K. £
Guardian Angel	250.00	350.00	90.00

CT-1105
SHIFTING SANDS

Designer: Helen MacDonald
Type: Weight — Domed
Edition: 1994 in a limited edition of 650
Status: Fully subscribed
Series: Limited — Modern Design
Original Issue Price: £70.00, U.S. $210.00

Name	U.S. $	Can. $	U.K. £
Shifting Sands	210.00	300.00	70.00

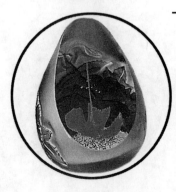

CT-1106
SCARLET HIBISCUS

Designer: Helen MacDonald and Alastair MacIntosh
Type: Weight — Domed
Edition: 1994 in a limited edition of 100
Status: Closed at No. 93
Series: Limited — Modern Design
Original Issue Price: £245.00, U.S. $695.00

Name	U.S. $	Can. $	U.K. £
Scarlet Hibiscus	695.00	1,000.00	275.00

CT-1107
ARCTIC AWAKENING

Designer: Colin Terris
Type: Weight — Domed, quadruple overlay
Edition: 1994 in a limited edition of 25
Status: Fully subscribed
Series: Limited — Modern Design
Original Issue Price: £495.00, U.S. $1,500.00

Name	U.S. $	Can. $	U.K. £
Arctic Awakening	1,500.00	2,000.00	795.00

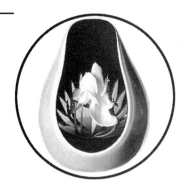

CT-1108
SUMMER GLADE

Designer: Helen MacDonald and Alastair MacIntosh
Type: Weight — Domed
Edition: 1994 in a limited edition of 100
Status: Closed at No. 77
Series: Limited — Modern Design
Original Issue Price: £245.00, U.S. $695.00

Name	U.S. $	Can. $	U.K. £
Summer Glade	700.00	1,000.00	275.00

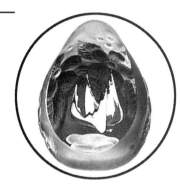

CT-1109
AZALEA

Designer: Colin Terris and Allan Scott
Type: Weight — Spherical, triple overlay
Edition: 1994 in a limited edition of 25
Status: Fully subscribed
Series: Whitefriars Collection
Original Issue Price: £595.00, U.S. $1,750.00

Name	U.S. $	Can. $	U.K. £
Azalea	1,750.00	2,500.00	650.00

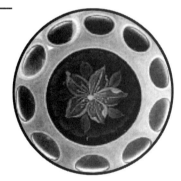

CT-1110
AZURE BOUQUET

Designer: Allan Scott
Type: Weight — Spherical
Edition: 1994 in a limited edition of 50
Status: Closed at No. 35
Series: Whitefriars Collection
Original Issue Price: £175.00, U.S. $595.00

Name	U.S. $	Can. $	U.K. £
Azure Bouquet	600.00	850.00	175.00

CT-1111
BUTTERFLY BOUQUET

Designer: Allan Scott
Type: Weight — Spherical
Edition: 1994 in a limited edition of 50
Status: Fully subscribed
Series: Whitefriars Collection
Original Issue Price: £165.00, U.S. $495.00

Name	U.S. $	Can. $	U.K. £
Butterfly Bouquet	500.00	700.00	165.00

CT-1112
CINQUEFOIL

Designer: Allan Scott
Type: Weight — Spherical
Edition: 1994 in a limited edition of 50
Status: Closed at No. 41
Series: Whitefriars Collection
Original Issue Price: £175.00, U.S. $595.00

Name	U.S. $	Can. $	U.K. £
Cinquefoil	595.00	850.00	175.00

CT-1113
HIBISCUS

Designer: Allan Scott
Type: Weight — Spherical
Edition: 1994 in a limited edition of 50
Status: Closed at No. 45
Series: Whitefriars Collection
Original Issue Price: £215.00, U.S. $750.00

Name	U.S. $	Can. $	U.K. £
Hibiscus	750.00	1,050.00	215.00

CT-1114
SUMMER POSY

Designer: Allan Scott
Type: Weight — Spherical
Edition: 1994 in a limited edition of 50
Status: Fully subscribed
Series: Whitefriars Collection
Original Issue Price: £185.00, U.S. $650.00

Name	U.S. $	Can. $	U.K. £
Summer Posy	650.00	925.00	185.00

CT-1115
FLORAL GARDEN

Designer:	William Manson
Type:	Weight — Spherical
Edition:	1994 in a limited edition of 50
Status:	Closed at No. 34
Series:	Traditional Collection
Original Issue Price:	£250.00, U.S. $695.00

Name	U.S. $	Can. $	U.K. £
Floral Garden	800.00	1,100.00	250.00

CT-1116
LILIUM

Designer:	William Manson
Type:	Weight — Spherical
Edition:	1994 in a limited edition of 50
Status:	Closed at No. 30
Series:	Traditional Collection
Original Issue Price:	£235.00, U.S. $795.00

Name	U.S. $	Can. $	U.K. £
Lilium	795.00	1,150.00	235.00

CT-1117
LORIKEET

Designer:	William Manson
Type:	Weight — Spherical
Edition:	1994 in a limited edition of 50
Status:	Closed at No. 31
Series:	Traditional Collection
Original Issue Price:	£225.00, U.S. $750.00

Name	U.S. $	Can. $	U.K. £
Lorikeet	750.00	1,050.00	225.00

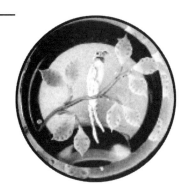

CT-1118
SEASCAPE

Designer:	William Manson
Type:	Weight — Spherical
Edition:	1994 in a limited edition of 50
Status:	Fully subscribed
Series:	Traditional Collection
Original Issue Price:	£275.00, U.S. $825.00

Name	U.S. $	Can. $	U.K. £
Seascape	875.00	1,225.00	275.00

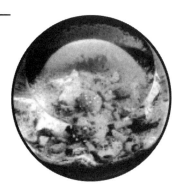

CT-1119
SNOWMAN

Designer:	William Manson
Type:	Weight — Spherical
Edition:	1994 in a limited edition of 50
Status:	Fully subscribed
Series:	Traditional Collection
Original Issue Price:	£250.00, U.S. $750.00

Name	U.S. $	Can. $	U.K. £
Snowman	750.00	1,000.00	250.00

CT-1120
STINGRAY

Designer:	William Manson
Type:	Weight — Spherical
Edition:	1994 in a limited edition of 50
Status:	Fully subscribed
Series:	Traditional Collection
Original Issue Price:	£275.00, U.S. $895.00

Name	U.S. $	Can. $	U.K. £
Stingray	895.00	1,250.00	275.00

CT-1121
SUNFLOWER

Designer:	William Manson
Type:	Weight — Spherical
Edition:	1994 in a limited edition of 50
Status:	Closed at No. 33
Series:	Traditional Collection
Original Issue Price:	£215.00, U.S. $750.00

Name	U.S. $	Can. $	U.K. £
Sunflower	750.00	1,000.00	215.00

CT-1122
MINI BUTTERFLY and ORANGE FLOWER

Designer:	Allan Scott
Type:	Weight — Spherical
Edition:	1994 in a limited edition of 150
Status:	Closed at No. 102
Series:	Traditional Collection — Nature Study
Original Issue Price:	£70.00, U.S. $210.00

Name	U.S. $	Can. $	U.K. £
Mini Butterfly and Orange Flower	210.00	300.00	70.00

CT-1123
MINI BUTTERFLY and YELLOW FLOWER

Designer: Allan Scott
Type: Weight — Spherical
Edition: 1994 in a limited edition of 150
Status: Closed at No. 95
Series: Traditional Collection — Nature Study
Original Issue Price: £70.00, U.S. $210.00

Name	U.S. $	Can. $	U.K. £
Mini Butterfly and Yellow Flower	210.00	300.00	70.00

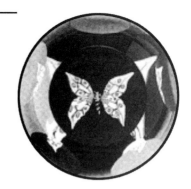

CT-1124
ORANGE BUTTERFLY

Designer: Allan Scott
Type: Weight — Spherical
Edition: 1994 in a limited edition of 50
Status: Fully subscribed
Series: Traditional Collection — Nature Study
Original Issue Price: £125.00, U.S. $375.00

Name	U.S. $	Can. $	U.K. £
Orange Butterfly	375.00	525.00	125.00

CT-1125
YELLOW BUTTERFLY

Designer: Allan Scott
Type: Weight — Spherical
Edition: 1994 in a limited edition of 50
Status: Fully subscribed
Series: Traditional Collection — Nature Study
Original Issue Price: £125.00, U.S. $375.00

Name	U.S. $	Can. $	U.K. £
Yellow Butterfly	400.00	550.00	125.00

CT-1126
YELLOW BUTTERFLY — LATTICINO BASE

Designer: Allan Scott
Type: Weight — Spherical
Edition: 1994 in a limited edition of 50
Status: Fully subscribed
Series: Traditional Collection — Nature Study
Original Issue Price: £99.00, U.S. $295.00

Name	U.S. $	Can. $	U.K. £
Yellow Butterfly — Latticino Base	295.00	400.00	100.00

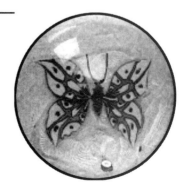

CT-1127
CHERRY BLOSSOM

Designer: William Manson
Type: Weight — Spherical
Edition: 1994 in a limited edition of 150
Status: Closed at No. 123
Series: Traditional Collection
Original Issue Price: £70.00, U.S. $210.00

Name	U.S. $	Can. $	U.K. £
Cherry Blossom	210.00	300.00	70.00

CT-1128
GRAPES

Designer: William Manson
Type: Weight — Spherical
Edition: 1994 in a limited edition of 150
Status: Closed at No. 87
Series: Traditional Collection
Original Issue Price: £70.00, U.S. $210.00

Name	U.S. $	Can. $	U.K. £
Grapes	210.00	300.00	70.00

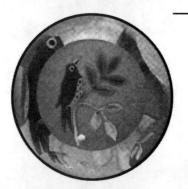

CT-1129
SONGBIRD

Designer: William Manson
Type: Weight — Spherical
Edition: 1994 in a limited edition of 150
Status: Closed at No. 110
Series: Traditional Collection
Original Issue Price: £70.00, U.S. $210.00

Name	U.S. $	Can. $	U.K. £
Songbird	210.00	300.00	70.00

CT-1130
STRAWBERRY

Designer: William Manson
Type: Weight — Spherical
Edition: 1994 in a limited edition of 150
Status: Closed at No. 125
Series: Traditional Collection
Original Issue Price: £70.00, U.S. $210.00

Name	U.S. $	Can. $	U.K. £
Strawberry	210.00	300.00	70.00

CT-1131
ASCENSION

Designer:	Alastair MacIntosh
Type:	Weight — Domed
Edition:	1994
Status:	Active
Series:	Unlimited — Modern Design
Original Issue Price:	£28.50, U.S. $87.50

Name	U.S. $	Can. $	U.K. £
Ascension	99.50	125.00	31.00

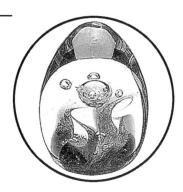

CT-1132
ESCAPADE

Designer:	David Nicoll
Type:	Weight — Spherical
Edition:	1994
Status:	Closed
Series:	Unlimited — Modern Design
Original Issue Price:	£29.50, U.S. $95.00

Name	U.S. $	Can. $	U.K. £
Escapade	95.00	130.00	30.00

CT-1133
FLOWER OF SCOTLAND

Designer:	Alastair MacIntosh
Type:	Weight — Spherical
Edition:	1994
Status:	Active
Series:	Unlimited — Modern Design
Original Issue Price:	£33.50, U.S. $95.00

Name	U.S. $	Can. $	U.K. £
Flower of Scotland	110.00	145.00	35.00

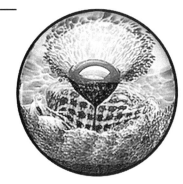

CT-1134
OCEAN BREEZE

Designer:	Alastair MacIntosh
Type:	Weight — Spherical
Edition:	1994
Status:	Active
Series:	Unlimited — Modern Design
Original Issue Price:	£30.00, U.S. $87.50

Name	U.S. $	Can. $	U.K. £
Ocean Breeze	99.50	140.00	31.50

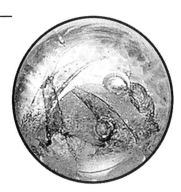

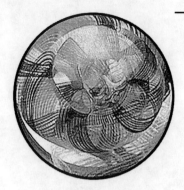

CT-1135
SORCERER

Designer:	Alastair MacIntosh
Type:	Weight — Spherical
Edition:	1994
Status:	Active
Series:	Unlimited — Modern Design
Original Issue Price:	£26.50, U.S. $75.00

Name	U.S. $	Can. $	U.K. £
Sorcerer	87.50	125.00	27.50

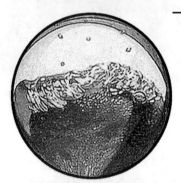

CT-1136
WAVECREST

Designer:	Alastair MacIntosh
Type:	Weight — Spherical
Edition:	1994
Status:	Active
Series:	Unlimited — Modern Design
Original Issue Price:	£29.50, U.S. $87.50

Name	U.S. $	Can. $	U.K. £
Wavecrest	95.00	130.00	30.00

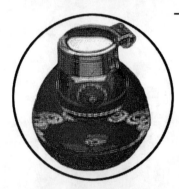

CT-1137
THISTLE INKWELL

Designer:	Allan Scott
Type:	Inkwell
Edition:	1994
Status:	Closed
Series:	Millefiori Miniatures
Original Issue Price:	£55.00, U.S. $175.00

Name	U.S. $	Can. $	U.K. £
Thistle Inkwell	175.00	250.00	55.00

CT-1138
ROSE INKWELL

Designer:	Allan Scott
Type:	Inkwell
Edition:	1994
Status:	Closed
Series:	Millefiori Miniatures
Original Issue Price:	£55.00, U.S. $175.00

Name	U.S. $	Can. $	U.K. £
Rose Inkwell	175.00	250.00	55.00

CT-1139
FUCHSIA INKWELL

Designer:	Allan Scott
Type:	Inkwell
Edition:	1994
Status:	Closed
Series:	Millefiori Miniatures
Original Issue Price:	£55.00, U.S. $175.00

Name	U.S. $	Can. $	U.K. £
Fuchsia Inkwell	175.00	250.00	55.00

CT-1140
HEART INKWELL

Designer:	Allan Scott
Type:	Inkwell
Edition:	1994
Status:	Closed
Series:	Millefiori Miniatures
Original Issue Price:	£55.00, U.S. $175.00

Name	U.S. $	Can. $	U.K. £
Heart Inkwell	175.00	250.00	55.00

CT-1141
LUNAR TOUCHDOWN

Designer:	Colin Terris
Type:	Weight — Domed
Edition:	1994 in a limited edition of 50
Status:	Fully subscribed
Series:	Limited — Modern Design
Original Issue Price:	£250.00, U.S. $675.00

Name	U.S. $	Can. $	U.K. £
Lunar Touchdown	800.00	1,100.00	350.00

Note: CT-1141, 1142 and 1143 were issued to commemorate the 25th anniversary of the 1969 lunar landing.

CT-1142
THE EAGLE HAS LANDED

Designer:	Colin Terris
Type:	Weight — Spherical
Edition:	1994 in a limited edition of 500
Status:	Closed at No. 336
Series:	Limited — Modern Design
Original Issue Price:	£65.00, U.S. $190.00

Name	U.S. $	Can. $	U.K. £
The Eagle Has Landed	190.00	275.00	65.00

CT-1143
MISSION APOLLO XI

Designer: Colin Terris
Type: Weight — Domed
Edition: 1994 in a limited edition of 750
Status: Closed at No. 242
Original Issue Price: £39.95, U.S. $99.50

Name	U.S. $	Can. $	U.K. £
Mission Apollo XI	100.00	140.00	40.00

CT-1144
PAPER CHASE

Designer: Alastair MacIntosh
Type: Weight — Spherical
Edition: 1995 in a limited edition of 750
Status: Closed at No. 692
Series: Limited — Modern Design
Original Issue Price: £40.00, U.S. $140.00

Name	U.S. $	Can. $	U.K. £
Paper Chase	140.00	200.00	40.00

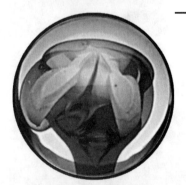

CT-1145
ORGANZA

Designer: Colin Terris
Type: Weight — Spherical
Edition: 1995 in a limited edition of 650
Status: Closed at No. 411
Series: Limited — Modern Design
Original Issue Price: £65.00, U.S. $225.00

Name	U.S. $	Can. $	U.K. £
Organza	225.00	325.00	65.00

CT-1146
EMERALD VISION

Designer: Philip Chaplain
Type: Weight — Spherical
Edition: 1995 in a limited edition of 750
Status: Fully subscribed
Series: Limited — Modern Design
Original Issue Price: £45.00, U.S. $150.00

Name	U.S. $	Can. $	U.K. £
Emerald Vision	150.00	200.00	45.00

CT-1147
SUPERSONIC

Designer:	Alastair MacIntosh
Type:	Weight — Spherical
Edition:	1995 in a limited edition of 750
Status:	Closed at No. 739
Series:	Limited — Modern Design
Original Issue Price:	£40.00, U.S. $140.00

Name	U.S. $	Can. $	U.K. £
Supersonic	140.00	200.00	40.00

CT-1148
AMORE

Designer:	Colin Terris
Type:	Weight — Spherical
Edition:	1995 in a limited edition of 50
Status:	Fully subscribed
Series:	Limited — Modern Design
Original Issue Price:	£275.00, U.S. $775.00

Name	U.S. $	Can. $	U.K. £
Amore	775.00	1,225.00	300.00

CT-1149
DEBUT

Designer:	Helen MacDonald
Type:	Weight — Domed
Edition:	1995 in a limited edition of 50
Status:	Fully subscribed
Series:	Limited — Modern Design
Original Issue Price:	£275.00, U.S. $850.00

Name	U.S. $	Can. $	U.K. £
Debut	850.00	1,225.00	275.00

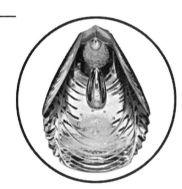

CT-1150
COMMUNICATION

Designer:	Philip Chaplain
Type:	Weight — Spherical
Edition:	1995 in a limited edition of 750
Status:	Fully subscribed
Series:	Limited — Modern Design
Original Issue Price:	£45.00, U.S. $150.00

Name	U.S. $	Can. $	U.K. £
Communication	150.00	200.00	45.00

CT-1151
VOGUE

Designer:	Colin Terris
Type:	Weight — Spherical
Edition:	1995 in a limited edition of 650
Status:	Fully subscribed
Series:	Limited — Modern Design
Original Issue Price:	£65.00, U.S. $225.00

Name	U.S. $	Can. $	U.K. £
Vogue	225.00	325.00	65.00

CT-1152
INDIGO

Designer:	Alastair MacIntosh
Type:	Weight — Spherical
Edition:	1995 in a limited edition of 650
Status:	Fully subscribed
Series:	Limited — Modern Design
Original Issue Price:	£65.00, U.S. $225.00

Name	U.S. $	Can. $	U.K. £
Indigo	225.00	325.00	65.00

CT-1153
WATCHTOWER

Designer:	Philip Chaplain
Type:	Weight — Spherical
Edition:	1995 in a limited edition of 750
Status:	Closed at No. 730
Series:	Limited — Modern Design
Original Issue Price:	£50.00, U.S. $165.00

Name	U.S. $	Can. $	U.K. £
Watchtower	165.00	225.00	50.00

CT-1154
DREAM MAKER

Designer:	Philip Chaplain
Type:	Weight — Domed
Edition:	1995 in a limited edition of 750
Status:	Fully subscribed
Series:	Limited — Modern Design
Original Issue Price:	£50.00, U.S. $165.00

Name	U.S. $	Can. $	U.K. £
Dream Maker	165.00	225.00	50.00

CT-1155
SIENA FLASK

Designer: Alastair MacIntosh
Type: Flask
Edition: 1995 in a limited edition of 50
Status: Closed at No. 41
Series: Limited — Modern Design
Original Issue Price: £195.00, U.S. $595.00

Name	U.S. $	Can. $	U.K. £
Siena Flask	595.00	850.00	200.00

CT-1156
TORINO FLASK

Designer: Alastair MacIntosh
Type: Flask
Edition: 1995 in a limited edition of 50
Status: Closed at No. 34
Series: Limited — Modern Design
Original Issue Price: £175.00, U.S. $550.00

Name	U.S. $	Can. $	U.K. £
Torino Flask	550.00	775.00	200.00

CT-1157
SORRENTO FLASK

Designer: Alastair MacIntosh
Type: Flask
Edition: 1995 in a limited edition of 50
Status: Closed at No. 43
Series: Limited — Modern Design
Original Issue Price: £195.00, U.S. $595.00

Name	U.S. $	Can. $	U.K. £
Sorrento Flask	595.00	850.00	200.00

CT-1158A
MERCURY

Designer: Colin Terris
Type: Weight — Spherical
Edition: 1995 in a limited edition of 350
Status: Closed at No. 232
Series: Planets, Set One (1995)
Original Issue Price: £395.00/set, U.S. $1,250.00/set

Name	U.S. $	Can. $	U.K. £
Mercury	325.00	450.00	100.00
Set	1,300.00	1,800.00	400.00

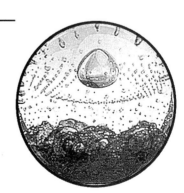

Note: CT-1158A, B, C and D were issued and sold as a set and are a new design interpretation of the 1969 original.

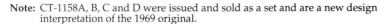

CT-1158B
VENUS

Designer:	Colin Terris
Type:	Weight — Spherical
Edition:	1995 in a limited edition of 350
Status:	Closed at No. 232
Series:	Planets, Set One (1995)
Original Issue Price:	£395.00/set, U.S. $1,250.00/set

Name	U.S. $	Can. $	U.K. £
Venus	325.00	450.00	100.00

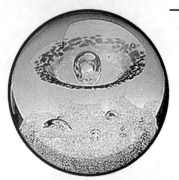

CT-1158C
SATURN

Designer:	Colin Terris
Type:	Weight — Spherical
Edition:	1995 in a limited edition of 350
Status:	Closed at No. 232
Series:	Planets, Set One (1995)
Original Issue Price:	£395.00/set, U.S. $1,250.00/set

Name	U.S. $	Can. $	U.K. £
Saturn	325.00	450.00	100.00

CT-1158D
MARS

Designer:	Colin Terris
Type:	Weight — Spherical
Edition:	1995 in a limited edition of 350
Status:	Closed at No. 232
Series:	Planets, Set One (1995)
Original Issue Price:	£395.00/set, U.S. $1,250.00/set

Name	U.S. $	Can. $	U.K. £
Mars	325.00	450.00	100.00

CT-1159
FUSION

Designer:	Alastair MacIntosh
Type:	Weight — Spherical
Edition:	1995 in a limited edition of 50
Status:	Fully subscribed
Series:	Limited — Modern Design
Original Issue Price:	£250.00, U.S. $750.00

Name	U.S. $	Can. $	U.K. £
Fusion	750.00	1,000.00	250.00

CT-1160
FINESSE

Designer:	Colin Terris
Type:	Weight — Spherical
Edition:	1995 in a limited edition of 75
Status:	Fully subscribed
Series:	Limited — Modern Design
Original Issue Price:	£175.00, U.S. $550.00

Name	U.S. $	Can. $	U.K. £
Finesse	550.00	775.00	175.00

CT-1161
FORCEFIELD

Designer:	Alastair MacIntosh
Type:	Weight — Spherical
Edition:	1995 in a limited edition of 50
Status:	Fully subscribed
Series:	Limited — Modern Design
Original Issue Price:	£250.00, U.S. $750.00

Name	U.S. $	Can. $	U.K. £
Forcefield	800.00	1,100.00	300.00

CT-1162
DOUBLE MAGNUM '95

Designer:	Colin Terris
Type:	Weight — Spherical, double magnum
Edition:	1995 in a limited edition of 150
Status:	Closed at No. 48
Series:	Limited — Modern Design
Original Issue Price:	£195.00, U.S. $595.00

Name	U.S. $	Can. $	U.K. £
Double Magnum '95	650.00	895.00	200.00

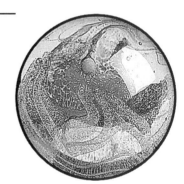

CT-1163
TYROLEAN SUMMER

Designer:	Alastair MacIntosh
Type:	Weight — Domed
Edition:	1995 in a limited edition of 500
Status:	Closed at No. 475
Series:	Limited — Modern Design
Original Issue Price:	£75.00, U.S. $250.00

Name	U.S. $	Can. $	U.K. £
Tyrolean Summer	250.00	350.00	75.00

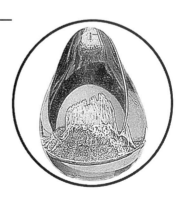

CT-1164
PARADISE

Designer:	Alastair MacIntosh
Type:	Weight — Domed
Edition:	1995 in a limited edition of 350
Status:	Fully subscribed
Series:	Limited — Modern Design
Original Issue Price:	£99.00, U.S. $310.00

Name	U.S. $	Can. $	U.K. £
Paradise	310.00	425.00	100.00

CT-1165
CARIBBEAN SUNRISE

Designer:	Colin Terris
Type:	Weight — Domed, quadruple overlay
Edition:	1995 in a limited edition of 25
Status:	Fully subscribed
Series:	Limited — Modern Design
Original Issue Price:	£495.00, U.S. $1,750.00

Name	U.S. $	Can. $	U.K. £
Caribbean Sunrise	1,750.00	2,500.00	795.00

CT-1166
CATCHING RAINDROPS

Designer:	Colin Terris
Type:	Weight — Spherical
Edition:	1995 in a limited edition of 650
Status:	Closed at No. 622
Series:	Limited — Modern Design
Original Issue Price:	£65.00, U.S. $225.00

Name	U.S. $	Can. $	U.K. £
Catching Raindrops	225.00	325.00	65.00

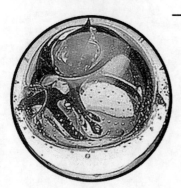

CT-1167
COCOON

Designer:	Colin Terris
Type:	Weight — Spherical
Edition:	1995 in a limited edition of 750
Status:	Closed at No. 357
Series:	Limited — Modern Design
Original Issue Price:	£60.00, U.S. $195.00

Name	U.S. $	Can. $	U.K. £
Cocoon	195.00	275.00	60.00

CT-1168
TREBLE CHANCE

Designer: Helen MacDonald
Type: Weight — Spherical
Edition: 1995 in a limited edition of 100
Status: Closed at No. 76
Series: Limited — Modern Design
Original Issue Price: £150.00, U.S. $475.00

Name	U.S. $	Can. $	U.K. £
Treble Chance	475.00	675.00	150.00

CT-1169
EASTERN PROMISE

Designer: Colin Terris
Type: Weight — Spherical
Edition: 1995 in a limited edition of 75
Status: Closed at No. 68
Series: Limited — Modern Design
Original Issue Price: £175.00, U.S. $550.00

Name	U.S. $	Can. $	U.K. £
Eastern Promise	550.00	775.00	175.00

CT-1170
TROPICAL FANTASY

Designer: Colin Terris
Type: Weight — Spherical
Edition: 1995 in a limited edition of 75
Status: Fully subscribed
Series: Limited — Modern Design
Original Issue Price: £195.00, U.S. $595.00

Name	U.S. $	Can. $	U.K. £
Tropical Fantasy	650.00	895.00	195.00

CT-1171
ALLEY CAT

Designer: Helen MacDonald
Type: Weight — Domed
Edition: 1995 in a limited edition of 100
Status: Fully subscribed
Series: Limited — Modern Design
Original Issue Price: £235.00, U.S. $725.00

Name	U.S. $	Can. $	U.K. £
Alley Cat	725.00	1,050.00	300.00

CT-1172
SMALL WORLD

Designer: Helen MacDonald
Type: Weight — Spherical
Edition: 1995 in a limited edition of 75
Status: Fully subscribed
Original Issue Price: £250.00, U.S. $750.00

Name	U.S. $	Can. $	U.K. £
Small World	750.00	1,000.00	275.00

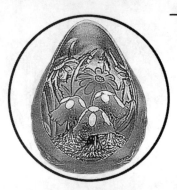

CT-1173
FAIRY LAND

Designer: Helen MacDonald
Type: Weight — Domed
Edition: 1995 in a limited edition of 100
Status: Fully subscribed
Series: Limited — Modern Design
Original Issue Price: £235.00, U.S. $750.00

Name	U.S. $	Can. $	U.K. £
Fairy Land	750.00	1,000.00	275.00

CT-1174
TROPICAL VISION

Designer: Helen MacDonald
Type: Weight — Domed
Edition: 1995 in a limited edition of 100
Status: Fully subscribed
Series: Limited — Modern Design
Original Issue Price: £235.00, U.S. $725.00

Name	U.S. $	Can. $	U.K. £
Tropical Vision	725.00	1,000.00	275.00

CT-1175
ORIENTAL DAWN

Designer: Helen MacDonald
Type: Weight — Domed
Edition: 1995 in a limited edition of 100
Status: Closed at No. 72
Series: Limited — Modern Design
Original Issue Price: £235.00, U.S. $725.00

Name	U.S. $	Can. $	U.K. £
Oriental Dawn	725.00	1,000.00	275.00

CT-1176
FANDANGO

Designer:	Colin Terris
Type:	Weight — Spherical, magnum size
Edition:	1995 in a limited edition of 250
Status:	Closed at No. 90
Series:	Limited — Modern Design
Original Issue Price:	£125.00, U.S. $395.00

Name	U.S. $	Can. $	U.K. £
Fandango	395.00	550.00	125.00

CT-1177
COVENANT

Designer:	Helen MacDonald
Type:	Weight — Spherical
Edition:	1995 in a limited edition of 75
Status:	Fully subscribed
Series:	Limited — Modern Design
Original Issue Price:	£195.00, U.S. $595.00

Name	U.S. $	Can. $	U.K. £
Covenant	600.00	850.00	235.00

CT-1178
DOUBLE VISION

Designer:	Alastair MacIntosh
Type:	Weight — Spherical
Edition:	1995 in a limited edition of 50
Status:	Fully subscribed
Series:	Limited — Modern Design
Original Issue Price:	£225.00, U.S. $775.00

Name	U.S. $	Can. $	U.K. £
Double Vision	775.00	1,100.00	225.00

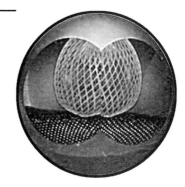

CT-1179
LASER

Designer:	Philip Chaplain
Type:	Weight — Spherical
Edition:	1995 in a limited edition of 750
Status:	Closed at No. 453
Series:	Limited — Modern Design
Original Issue Price:	£60.00, U.S. $195.00

Name	U.S. $	Can. $	U.K. £
Laser	195.00	275.00	60.00

CT-1180
JACK IN THE BOX

Designer: Margot Thomson
Type: Weight — Domed
Edition: 1995 in a limited edition of 1,618
Status: Closed at No. 1,618
Original Issue Price: £80.00, U.S. $215.00

Name	U.S. $	Can. $	U.K. £
Jack in the Box	215.00	300.00	85.00

Note: This is the 1995 Collectors' Paperweight.

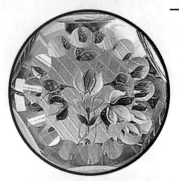

CT-1181
ORCHID SPRAY

Designer: Allan Scott
Type: Weight — Spherical
Edition: 1995 in a limited edition of 50
Status: Fully subscribed
Series: Whitefriars Collection
Original Issue Price: £225.00, U.S. $695.00

Name	U.S. $	Can. $	U.K. £
Orchid Spray	700.00	1,000.00	225.00

CT-1182
FRITILLARIA

Designer: Margot Thomson
Type: Weight — Spherical
Edition: 1995 in a limited edition of 50
Status: Closed at No. 32
Series: Whitefriars Collection
Original Issue Price: £175.00, U.S. $595.00

Name	U.S. $	Can. $	U.K. £
Fritillaria	600.00	950.00	175.00

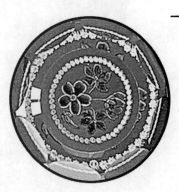

CT-1183
GERANIUM

Designer: Margot Thomson
Type: Weight — Spherical
Edition: 1995 in a limited edition of 50
Status: Closed at No. 39
Series: Whitefriars Collection
Original Issue Price: £175.00, U.S. $595.00

Name	U.S. $	Can. $	U.K. £
Geranium	600.00	850.00	175.00

CT-1184
MARIGOLDS

Designer: Margot Thomson
Type: Weight — Spherical
Edition: 1995 in a limited edition of 50
Status: Fully subscribed
Series: Whitefriars Collection
Original Issue Price: £185.00, U.S. $575.00

Name	U.S. $	Can. $	U.K. £
Marigolds	575.00	825.00	185.00

CT-1185
PANSY PERFUME BOTTLE

Designer: Margot Thomson
Type: Perfume bottle
Edition: 1995 in a limited edition of 50
Status: Closed at No. 36
Series: Whitefriars Collection
Original Issue Price: £225.00, U.S. $750.00

Name	U.S. $	Can. $	U.K. £
Pansy Perfume Bottle	750.00	1,050.00	225.00

CT-1186
RHODODENDRON

Designer: Margot Thomson
Type: Weight — Spherical
Edition: 1995 in a limited edition of 50
Status: Closed at No. 45
Series: Whitefriars Collection
Original Issue Price: £215.00, U.S. $750.00

Name	U.S. $	Can. $	U.K. £
Rhododendron	750.00	1,050.00	215.00

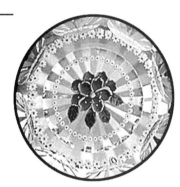

CT-1187
IRIS BOUQUET

Designer: Colin Terris & Allan Scott
Type: Weight — Spherical, quadruple overlay
Edition: 1995 in a limited edition of 25
Status: Fully subscribed
Series: Whitefriars Collection
Original Issue Price: £595.00, U.S. $1,900.00

Name	U.S. $	Can. $	U.K. £
Iris Bouquet	2,000.00	2,800.00	800.00

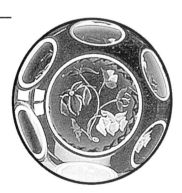

CT-1188
MECONOPSIS

Designer:	Margot Thomson
Type:	Weight — Spherical
Edition:	1995 in a limited edition of 50
Status:	Closed at No. 45
Series:	Whitefriars Collection
Original Issue Price:	£175.00, U.S. $595.00

Name	U.S. $	Can. $	U.K. £
Meconopsis	600.00	850.00	175.00

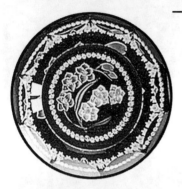

CT-1189
FREESIAS

Designer:	Margot Thomson
Type:	Weight — Spherical
Edition:	1995 in a limited edition of 50
Status:	Closed at No. 39
Series:	Whitefriars Collection
Original Issue Price:	£225.00, U.S. $750.00

Name	U.S. $	Can. $	U.K. £
Freesias	750.00	1,050.00	225.00

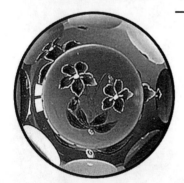

CT-1190
CAPE PRIMROSE

Designer:	Margot Thomson
Type:	Weight — Spherical
Edition:	1995 in a limited edition of 50
Status:	Closed at No. 32
Series:	Whitefriars Collection
Original Issue Price:	£165.00, U.S. $595.00

Name	U.S. $	Can. $	U.K. £
Cape Primrose	600.00	895.00	165.00

CT-1191A
COSMOS PERFUME BOTTLE

Designer:	Margot Thomson
Type:	Perfume bottle
Edition:	1995 in a limited edition of 50
Status:	Fully subscribed
Series:	Whitefriars Collection
Original Issue Price:	£395.00/set, U.S. $1,350.00/set

Name	U.S. $	Can. $	U.K. £
Cosmos Perfume Bottle	1,000.00	1,450.00	500.00
Set	1,400.00	2,030.00	800.00

Note: CT-1191A and B were issued and sold as a set.

CT-1191B
COSMOS

Designer:	Margot Thomson
Type:	Weight — Spherical
Edition:	1995 in a limited edition of 50
Status:	Fully subscribed
Series:	Whitefriars Collection
Original Issue Price:	£395.00/set, U.S. $1,350.00/set

Name	U.S. $	Can. $	U.K. £
Cosmos	400.00	580.00	300.00

CT-1192
YELLOW ROSE

Designer:	William Manson
Type:	Weight — Spherical
Edition:	1995 in a limited edition of 50
Status:	Closed at No. 43
Series:	Traditional Collection
Original Issue Price:	£250.00, U.S. $775.00

Name	U.S. $	Can. $	U.K. £
Yellow Rose	775.00	1,100.00	250.00

CT-1193
BUMBLEBEE and BLUEBELLS

Designer:	William Manson
Type:	Weight — Spherical
Edition:	1995 in a limited edition of 50
Status:	Closed at No. 41
Series:	Traditional Collection
Original Issue Price:	£250.00, U.S. $775.00

Name	U.S. $	Can. $	U.K. £
Bumblebee and Bluebells	775.00	1,100.00	250.00

CT-1194
HEDGEHOG

Designer:	William Manson
Type:	Weight — Spherical
Edition:	1995 in a limited edition of 50
Status:	Closed at No. 41
Series:	Traditional Collection
Original Issue Price:	£250.00, U.S. $775.00

Name	U.S. $	Can. $	U.K. £
Hedgehog	775.00	1,100.00	250.00

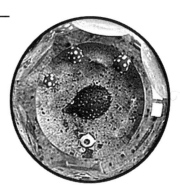

CT-1195
TURTLE

Designer: William Manson
Type: Weight — Spherical
Edition: 1995 in a limited edition of 50
Status: Closed at No. 37
Series: Traditional Collection
Original Issue Price: £275.00, U.S. $850.00

Name	U.S. $	Can. $	U.K. £
Turtle	850.00	1,200.00	275.00

CT-1196
PYTHON

Designer: William Manson
Type: Weight — Spherical
Edition: 1995 in a limited edition of 50
Status: Closed at No. 35
Series: Traditional Collection
Original Issue Price: £295.00, U.S. $895.00

Name	U.S. $	Can. $	U.K. £
Python	900.00	1,300.00	295.00

CT-1197
CORAL REEF

Designer: William Manson
Type: Weight — Spherical
Edition: 1995 in a limited edition of 50
Status: Closed at No. 38
Series: Traditional Collection
Original Issue Price: £225.00, U.S. $695.00

Name	U.S. $	Can. $	U.K. £
Coral Reef	700.00	1,000.00	225.00

CT-1198
SEAHORSE

Designer: William Manson
Type: Weight — Spherical
Edition: 1995 in a limited edition of 50
Status: Fully subscribed
Series: Traditional Collection
Original Issue Price: £275.00, U.S. $850.00

Name	U.S. $	Can. $	U.K. £
Seahorse	850.00	1,200.00	275.00

CT-1199
BLUE LAGOON

Designer: William Manson
Type: Weight — Spherical
Edition: 1995 in a limited edition of 50
Status: Fully subscribed
Series: Traditional Collection
Original Issue Price: £225.00, U.S. $695.00

Name	U.S. $	Can. $	U.K. £
Blue Lagoon	700.00	1,000.00	225.00

CT-1200
IGUANA

Designer: William Manson
Type: Weight — Spherical
Edition: 1995 in a limited edition of 50
Status: Closed at No. 31
Series: Traditional Collection
Original Issue Price: £295.00, U.S. $895.00

Name	U.S. $	Can. $	U.K. £
Iguana	800.00	1,350.00	300.00

CT-1201
KILLER WHALE

Designer: William Manson
Type: Weight — Spherical
Edition: 1995 in a limited edition of 50
Status: Closed at No. 41
Series: Traditional Collection
Original Issue Price: £225.00, U.S. $695.00

Name	U.S. $	Can. $	U.K. £
Killer Whale	700.00	1,000.00	225.00

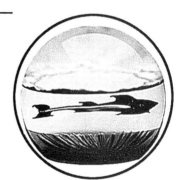

CT-1202
MARGUERITE

Designer: William Manson
Type: Weight — Spherical, medium-sized
Edition: 1995 in a limited edition of 150
Status: Fully subscribed
Series: Traditional Collection — Medium Sized
Original Issue Price: £75.00, U.S. $225.00

Name	U.S. $	Can. $	U.K. £
Marguerite	225.00	325.00	75.00

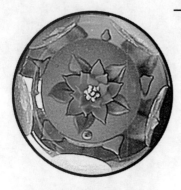

CT-1203
POINSETTIA

Designer:	William Manson
Type:	Weight — Spherical, medium-sized
Edition:	1995 in a limited edition of 150
Status:	Closed at No. 132
Series:	Traditional Collection — Medium Sized
Original Issue Price:	£75.00, U.S. $225.00

Name	U.S. $	Can. $	U.K. £
Poinsettia	225.00	325.00	75.00

CT-1204
DAHLIA

Designer:	William Manson
Type:	Weight — Spherical, medium-sized
Edition:	1995 in a limited edition of 150
Status:	Closed at No. 124
Series:	Traditional Collection — Medium Sized
Original Issue Price:	£75.00, U.S. $225.00

Name	U.S. $	Can. $	U.K. £
Dahlia	225.00	325.00	75.00

CT-1205
LILIUM

Designer:	William Manson
Type:	Weight — Spherical, medium-sized
Edition:	1995 in a limited edition of 150
Status:	Closed at No. 134
Series:	Traditional Collection — Medium Sized
Original Issue Price:	£75.00, U.S. $225.00

Name	U.S. $	Can. $	U.K. £
Lilium	225.00	325.00	75.00

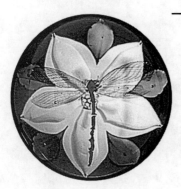

CT-1206
DRAGONFLY — WHITE FLOWER

Designer:	Allan Scott
Type:	Weight — Spherical
Edition:	1995 in a limited edition of 50
Status:	Fully subscribed
Series:	Traditional Collection — Nature Study
Original Issue Price:	£125.00, U.S. $395.00

Name	U.S. $	Can. $	U.K. £
Dragonfly — White Flower	400.00	550.00	125.00

CT-1207
DRAGONFLY — BLUE FLOWER

Designer:	Allan Scott
Type:	Weight — Spherical
Edition:	1995 in a limited edition of 50
Status:	Fully subscribed
Series:	Traditional Collection — Nature Study
Original Issue Price:	£125.00, U.S. $395.00

Name	U.S. $	Can. $	U.K. £
Dragonfly — Blue Flower	400.00	550.00	125.00

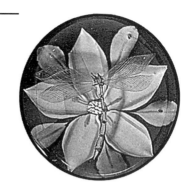

CT-1208
DRAGONFLY — LATTICINO BASE

Designer:	Allan Scott
Type:	Weight — Spherical
Edition:	1995 in a limited edition of 50
Status:	Fully subscribed
Series:	Traditional Collection — Nature Study
Original Issue Price:	£99.00, U.S. $325.00

Name	U.S. $	Can. $	U.K. £
Dragonfly — Latticino Base	325.00	450.00	100.00

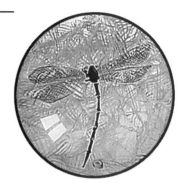

CT-1209
MINI DRAGONFLY — BLUE BASE

Designer:	Allan Scott
Type:	Weight — Spherical
Edition:	1995 in a limited edition of 150
Status:	Closed at No. 100
Series:	Traditional Collection — Nature Study
Original Issue Price:	£70.00, U.S. $225.00

Name	U.S. $	Can. $	U.K. £
Mini Dragonfly — Blue Base	225.00	325.00	70.00

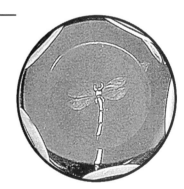

CT-1210
MINI DRAGONFLY — GOLD BASE

Designer:	Allan Scott
Type:	Weight — Spherical
Edition:	1995 in a limited edition of 150
Status:	Closed at No. 87
Series:	Traditional Collection — Nature Study
Original Issue Price:	£70.00, U.S. $225.00

Name	U.S. $	Can. $	U.K. £
Mini Dragonfly — Gold Base	250.00	350.00	70.00

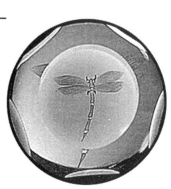

CT-1211
SCIMITAR

Designer: Margot Thomson
Type: Weight — Spherical
Edition: 1995
Status: Active
Series: Unlimited — Modern Design
Original Issue Price: £28.50, U.S. $95.00

Name	U.S. $	Can. $	U.K. £
Scimitar	95.00	130.00	30.00

CT-1212
SARACEN

Designer: Alastair MacIntosh
Type: Weight — Teardrop
Edition: 1995
Status: Active
Series: Unlimited — Modern Design
Original Issue Price: £27.00, U.S. $87.50

Name	U.S. $	Can. $	U.K. £
Saracen	95.00	125.00	29.50

CT-1213
BRUSHSTROKES

Designer: Alastair MacIntosh
Type: Weight — Spherical
Edition: 1995
Status: Closed
Series: Unlimited — Modern Design
Original Issue Price: £28.50, U.S. $95.00

Name	U.S. $	Can. $	U.K. £
Brushstrokes	95.00	130.00	30.00

CT-1214
CAULDRON RAINBOW

Designer: Colin Terris
Type: Weight — Spherical
Colour: White, blue, green and yellow
Edition: 1995
Status: Closed
Series: Unlimited — Modern Design
Original Issue Price: £28.50, U.S. $95.00

Name	U.S. $	Can. $	U.K. £
Cauldron Rainbow	95.00	130.00	30.00

CT-1215
MAY DANCE MAGENTA

Designer: Colin Terris
Type: Weight — Spherical
Edition: 1995
Status: Active
Series: Unlimited — Modern Design
Original Issue Price: £33.00, U.S. $115.00

Name	U.S. $	Can. $	U.K. £
May Dance Magenta	115.00	150.00	34.00

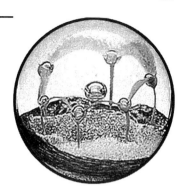

CT-1216
SEA GEM

Designer: Stuart Cumming
Type: Weight — Spherical, medium-sized
Colour: See below
Edition: 1995
Status: Active
Series: Medium and Miniature Size
Original Issue Price: £17.95, U.S. $62.50

Colourways	U.S. $	Can. $	U.K. £
1. Azure	62.50	85.00	19.00
2. Jade	62.50	85.00	19.00
3. Magenta	62.50	85.00	19.00
4. Rose	62.50	85.00	19.00

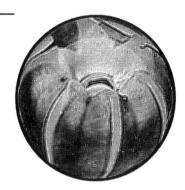

CT-1217
ETERNITY

Designer: Colin Terris
Type: Weight — Spherical
Colour: See below
Edition: 1995
Status: See below
Series: Romance
Original Issue Price: £32.50, U.S. $99.50

Colourways/Status	U.S. $	Can. $	U.K. £
1. Cobalt (Active)	110.00	145.00	33.50
2. Gold (Closed)	110.00	145.00	35.00

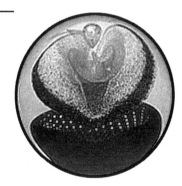

CT-1218
ROMANCE

Designer:	Alastair MacIntosh
Type:	Weight — Spherical
Edition:	1995
Status:	Active
Series:	Romance
Original Issue Price:	£32.50, U.S. $95.00

Name	U.S. $	Can. $	U.K. £
Romance	110.00	150.00	33.50

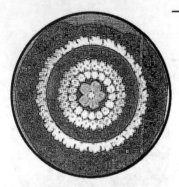

CT-1219
RED ROSE

Designer:	Allan Scott
Type:	Weight — Spherical
Edition:	1995
Status:	Closed
Series:	Romance
Original Issue Price:	£34.50, U.S. $115.00

Name	U.S. $	Can. $	U.K. £
Red Rose	115.00	160.00	35.00

CT-1220
RED ROSE PERFUME BOTTLE

Designer:	Allan Scott
Type:	Perfume bottle
Edition:	1995
Status:	Closed
Series:	Romance
Original Issue Price:	£57.70, U.S. $175.00

Name	U.S. $	Can. $	U.K. £
Red Rose Perfume Bottle	175.00	250.00	60.00

CT-1221
TWO'S COMPANY

Designer:	Alastair MacIntosh
Type:	Weight — Spherical
Edition:	1995 in a limited edition of 750
Status:	Closed at No. 586
Series:	Limited — Modern Design
Original Issue Price:	£50.00, U.S. $150.00

Name	U.S. $	Can. $	U.K. £
Two's Company	150.00	200.00	50.00

CT-1222
ROYALE

Designer:	Helen MacDonald
Type:	Weight — Domed
Edition:	1995 in a limited edition of 650
Status:	Closed at No. 469
Series:	Limited — Modern Design

Original Issue Price: £75.00, U.S. $230.00

Name	U.S. $	Can. $	U.K. £
Royale	230.00	325.00	75.00

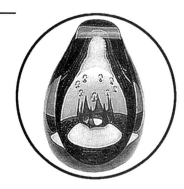

CT-1223
PHARAOH

Designer:	Philip Chaplain
Type:	Weight — Spherical
Edition:	1995 in a limited edition of 750
Status:	Closed at No. 549
Series:	Limited — Modern Design

Original Issue Price: £55.00, U.S. $165.00

Name	U.S. $	Can. $	U.K. £
Pharaoh	165.00	225.00	55.00

CT-1224
COLUMBINE

Designer:	Helen MacDonald
Type:	Weight — Spherical
Edition:	1995 in a limited edition of 50
Status:	Fully subscribed
Series:	Limited — Modern Design

Original Issue Price: £250.00, U.S. $775.00

Name	U.S. $	Can. $	U.K. £
Columbine	800.00	1,100.00	275.00

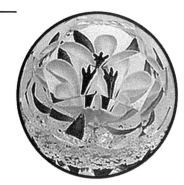

CT-1225
SOOTHSAYER

Designer:	Philip Chaplain
Type:	Weight — Spherical
Edition:	1995 in a limited edition of 750
Status:	Closed at No. 414
Series:	Limited — Modern Design

Original Issue Price: £45.00, U.S. $140.00

Name	U.S. $	Can. $	U.K. £
Soothsayer	140.00	200.00	45.00

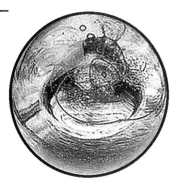

CT-1226
JOSEPH

Designer:	Helen MacDonald
Type:	Weight — Spherical
Edition:	1995 in a limited edition of 75
Status:	Fully subscribed
Series:	Limited — Modern Design
Original Issue Price:	£195.00, U.S. $675.00

Name	U.S. $	Can. $	U.K. £
Joseph	675.00	975.00	400.00

CT-1227
SAQQARA

Designer:	Helen MacDonald
Type:	Weight — Domed
Edition:	1995 in a limited edition of 50
Status:	Closed at No. 41
Series:	Limited — Modern Design
Original Issue Price:	£225.00, U.S. $695.00

Name	U.S. $	Can. $	U.K. £
Saqqara	700.00	1,000.00	250.00

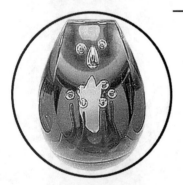

CT-1228
SNOW DANCE

Designer:	Margot Thomson
Type:	Weight — Domed
Edition:	1995 in a limited edition of 350
Status:	Closed at No. 252
Series:	Limited — Modern Design
Original Issue Price:	£99.00, U.S. $300.00

Name	U.S. $	Can. $	U.K. £
Snow Dance	300.00	425.00	100.00

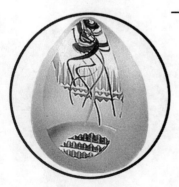

CT-1229
NEW HORIZONS

Designer:	Alastair MacIntosh
Type:	Weight — Domed
Edition:	1995 in a limited edition of 100
Status:	Fully subscribed
Series:	Limited — Modern Design
Original Issue Price:	£150.00, U.S. $450.00

Name	U.S. $	Can. $	U.K. £
New Horizons	450.00	650.00	160.00

CT-1230
THREE TENORS

Designer: Helen MacDonald
Type: Weight — Domed
Edition: 1995 in a limited edition of 100
Status: Fully subscribed
Series: Limited — Modern Design
Original Issue Price: £235.00, U.S. $725.00

Name	U.S. $	Can. $	U.K. £
Three Tenors	725.00	1,000.00	275.00

Note: This paperweight was issued to commemorate the concerts given by José Carreras, Plácido Domingo and Luciano Pavarotti.

CT-1231
SPELLCASTER

Designer: Alastair MacIntosh
Type: Weight — Domed
Edition: 1995 in a limited edition of 650
Status: Fully subscribed
Series: Limited — Modern Design
Original Issue Price: £70.00, U.S. $250.00

Name	U.S. $	Can. $	U.K. £
Spellcaster	250.00	350.00	70.00

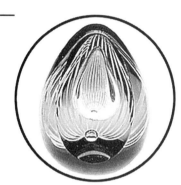

CT-1232
MEPHISTOPHELES

Designer: Philip Chaplain
Type: Weight — Domed
Edition: 1995 in a limited edition of 650
Status: Closed at No. 562
Series: Limited — Modern Design
Original Issue Price: £80.00, U.S. $250.00

Name	U.S. $	Can. $	U.K. £
Mephistopheles	250.00	350.00	80.00

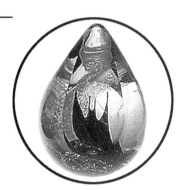

CT-1233
DAHLIA

Designer: Helen MacDonald
Type: Weight — Spherical
Edition: 1995 in a limited edition of 50
Status: Fully subscribed
Series: Limited — Modern Design
Original Issue Price: £275.00, U.S. $850.00

Name	U.S. $	Can. $	U.K. £
Dahlia	850.00	1,200.00	300.00

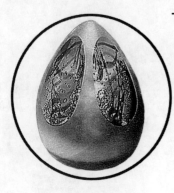

CT-1234
WISHING WELL

Designer: Philip Chaplain
Type: Weight — Domed
Edition: 1995 in a limited edition of 75
Status: Fully subscribed
Series: Limited — Modern Design
Original Issue Price: £175.00, U.S. $550.00

Name	U.S. $	Can. $	U.K. £
Wishing Well	550.00	775.00	175.00

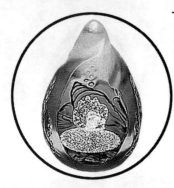

CT-1235
MERMAID'S SECRET

Designer: Helen MacDonald
Type: Weight — Domed
Edition: 1995 in a limited edition of 100
Status: Fully subscribed
Series: Limited — Modern Design
Original Issue Price: £235.00, U.S. $725.00

Name	U.S. $	Can. $	U.K. £
Mermaid's Secret	725.00	1,050.00	275.00

CT-1236
ADORATION

Designer: Colin Terris
Type: Weight — Spherical
Edition: 1995 in a limited edition of 50
Status: Fully subscribed
Series: Limited — Modern Design
Original Issue Price: £250.00, U.S. $775.00

Name	U.S. $	Can. $	U.K. £
Adoration	800.00	1,100.00	275.00

CT-1237
OMPHALOS

Designer: Philip Chaplain
Type: Weight — Domed
Edition: 1995 in a limited edition of 350
Status: Fully subscribed
Series: Limited — Modern Design
Original Issue Price: £85.00, U.S. $260.00

Name	U.S. $	Can. $	U.K. £
Omphalos	260.00	375.00	85.00

CT-1238
LOVEBIRDS

Designer:	Helen MacDonald
Type:	Weight — Spherical, footed
Edition:	1995 in a limited edition of 15
Status:	Fully subscribed
Original Issue Price:	£795.00, U.S. $2,500.00

Name	U.S. $	Can. $	U.K. £
Lovebirds	2,500.00	3,500.00	900.00

CT-1239
DOG TOOTH VIOLET

Designer:	Margot Thomson
Type:	Weight — Spherical
Edition:	1995 in a limited edition of 50
Status:	Closed at No. 33
Series:	Whitefriars Collection
Original Issue Price:	£175.00, U.S. $550.00

Name	U.S. $	Can. $	U.K. £
Dog Tooth Violet	550.00	895.00	175.00

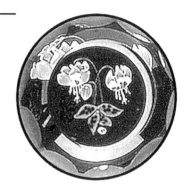

CT-1240
ROSE OF SHARON

Designer:	Margot Thomson
Type:	Weight — Spherical
Edition:	1995 in a limited edition of 50
Status:	Closed at No. 35
Series:	Whitefriars Collection
Original Issue Price:	£165.00, U.S. $495.00

Name	U.S. $	Can. $	U.K. £
Rose of Sharon	500.00	700.00	165.00

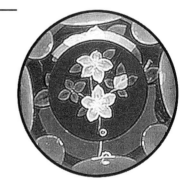

CT-1241
MALLOW

Designer:	Margot Thomson
Type:	Weight — Spherical
Edition:	1994 in a limited edition of 50
Status:	Closed at No. 39
Series:	Whitefriars Collection
Original Issue Price:	£175.00, U.S. $550.00

Name	U.S. $	Can. $	U.K. £
Mallow	550.00	800.00	175.00

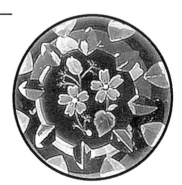

CT-1242
PINK RHODODENDRON

Designer:	Allan Scott and Margot Thomson
Type:	Weight — Spherical
Edition:	1994 in a limited edition of 25
Status:	Fully subscribed
Series:	Whitefriars Collection
Original Issue Price:	£495.00, U.S. $1,525.00

Name	U.S. $	Can. $	U.K. £
Pink Rhododendron	1,525.00	2,250.00	500.00

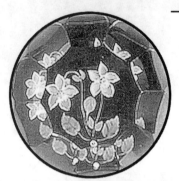

CT-1243
SWEET VIOLET

Designer:	Margot Thomson
Type:	Weight — Spherical
Edition:	1994 in a limited edition of 50
Status:	Closed at No. 49
Series:	Whitefriars Collection
Original Issue Price:	£175.00, U.S. $550.00

Name	U.S. $	Can. $	U.K. £
Sweet Violet	550.00	775.00	175.00

CT-1244A
SCARLET PIMPERNEL PERFUME BOTTLE

Designer:	Margot Thomson
Type:	Perfume bottle
Edition:	1995 in a limited edition of 50
Status:	Fully subscribed
Series:	Whitefriars Collection
Original Issue Price:	£395.00/set, U.S. $1,200.00/set

Name	U.S. $	Can. $	U.K. £
Scarlet Pimpernel Perfume Bottle	800.00	1,100.00	500.00
Set	1,275.00	1,775.00	800.00

Note: CT-1244A and B were issued and sold as a set.

CT-1244B
SCARLET PIMPERNEL

Designer:	Margot Thomson
Type:	Weight — Spherical
Edition:	1995 in a limited edition of 50
Status:	Fully subscribed
Series:	Whitefriars Collection
Original Issue Price:	£395.00/set, U.S. $1,200.00/set

Name	U.S. $	Can. $	U.K. £
Scarlet Pimpernel	475.00	675.00	300.00

CT-1245
SNAIL and BLOSSOM

Designer: William Manson
Type: Weight — Spherical
Edition: 1995 in a limited edition of 50
Status: Closed at No. 39
Series: Traditional Collection
Original Issue Price: £295.00, U.S. $895.00

Name	U.S. $	Can. $	U.K. £
Snail and Blossom	900.00	1,250.00	295.00

CT-1246
CATERPILLAR and CHERRY BLOSSOM

Designer: William Manson
Type: Weight — Spherical
Edition: 1995 in a limited edition of 50
Status: Closed at No. 38
Series: Traditional Collection
Original Issue Price: £295.00, U.S. $895.00

Name	U.S. $	Can. $	U.K. £
Caterpillar and Cherry Blossom	900.00	1,250.00	295.00

CT-1247
SUNSET FLIGHT

Designer: William Manson
Type: Weight — Spherical
Edition: 1995 in a limited edition of 50
Status: Closed at No. 42
Series: Traditional Collection
Original Issue Price: £250.00, U.S. $775.00

Name	U.S. $	Can. $	U.K. £
Sunset Flight	775.00	1,100.00	250.00

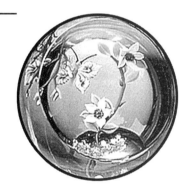

CT-1248
TROPICAL PARAKEET

Designer: William Manson
Type: Weight — Spherical
Edition: 1995 in a limited edition of 50
Status: Closed at No. 48
Series: Traditional Collection
Original Issue Price: £275.00, U.S. $850.00

Name	U.S. $	Can. $	U.K. £
Tropical Parakeet	850.00	1,200.00	275.00

CT-1249
AFRICAN CHAMELEON

Designer: William Manson
Type: Weight — Spherical
Edition: 1995 in a limited edition of 50
Status: Closed at No. 43
Series: Traditional Collection
Original Issue Price: £295.00, U.S. $895.00

Name	U.S. $	Can. $	U.K. £
African Chameleon	900.00	1,300.00	295.00

CT-1250
GOLD ROSE

Designer: William Manson
Type: Weight — Spherical, medium-sized
Edition: 1995 in a limited edition of 150
Status: Closed at No. 112
Series: Traditional Collection — Medium Sized
Original Issue Price: £75.00, U.S. $230.00

Name	U.S. $	Can. $	U.K. £
Gold Rose	230.00	325.00	75.00

CT-1251
PINK ROSE

Designer: William Manson
Type: Weight — Spherical, medium-sized
Edition: 1995 in a limited edition of 150
Status: Closed at No. 136
Series: Traditional Collection — Medium Sized
Original Issue Price: £75.00, U.S. $230.00

Name	U.S. $	Can. $	U.K. £
Pink Rose	230.00	325.00	75.00

CT-1252
PANSY

Designer: William Manson
Type: Weight — Spherical, medium-sized
Edition: 1995 in a limited edition of 150
Status: Closed at No. 135
Series: Traditional Collection — Medium Sized
Original Issue Price: £75.00, U.S. $230.00

Name	U.S. $	Can. $	U.K. £
Pansy	230.00	325.00	75.00

CT-1253
DELPHINIUM and LADYBIRD

Designer:	William Manson
Type:	Weight — Spherical, medium-sized
Edition:	1995 in a limited edition of 150
Status:	Closed at No. 90
Series:	Traditional Collection — Medium Sized
Original Issue Price:	£75.00, U.S. $230.00

Name	U.S. $	Can. $	U.K. £
Delphinium and Ladybird	230.00	325.00	75.00

CT-1254
BUTTERFLY — PURPLE FLOWER

Designer:	Allan Scott
Type:	Weight — Spherical
Edition:	1995 in a limited edition of 50
Status:	Closed at No. 41
Series:	Traditional Collection — Nature Study
Original Issue Price:	£195.00, U.S. $595.00

Name	U.S. $	Can. $	U.K. £
Butterfly — Purple Flower	600.00	850.00	195.00

CT-1255
BUTTERFLY — YELLOW FLOWER

Designer:	Allan Scott
Type:	Weight — Spherical
Edition:	1995 in a limited edition of 50
Status:	Closed at No. 46
Series:	Traditional Collection — Nature Study
Original Issue Price:	£195.00, U.S. $595.00

Name	U.S. $	Can. $	U.K. £
Butterfly — Yellow Flower	600.00	850.00	195.00

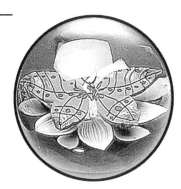

CT-1256
BUTTERFLY — LATTICINO BASE

Designer:	Allan Scott
Type:	Weight — Spherical
Edition:	1995 in a limited edition of 50
Status:	Closed at No. 35
Series:	Traditional Collection — Nature Study
Original Issue Price:	£175.00, U.S. $550.00

Name	U.S. $	Can. $	U.K. £
Butterfly — Latticino Base	550.00	800.00	175.00

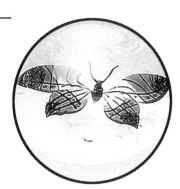

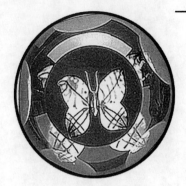

CT-1257
YELLOW BUTTERFLY — MINIATURE

Designer: Allan Scott
Type: Weight — Spherical
Edition: 1995 in a limited edition of 150
Status: Closed at No. 58
Series: Traditional Collection — Nature Study
Original Issue Price: £99.00, U.S. $295.00

Name	U.S. $	Can. $	U.K. £
Yellow Butterfly — Miniature	300.00	400.00	100.00

CT-1258
RED BUTTERFLY — MINIATURE

Designer: Allan Scott
Type: Weight — Spherical
Edition: 1995 in a limited edition of 150
Status: Closed at No. 62
Series: Traditional Collection — Nature Study
Original Issue Price: £99.00, U.S. $295.00

Name	U.S. $	Can. $	U.K. £
Red Butterfly — Miniature	300.00	400.00	100.00

CT-1259
CAPRICORN

Designer: Philip Chaplain
Type: Weight — Spherical
Edition: 1995
Status: Closed
Series: Zodiac Collection
Original Issue Price: £29.50, U.S. $95.00

Name	U.S. $	Can. $	U.K. £
Capricorn	95.00	130.00	30.00

CT-1260
AQUARIUS

Designer: Philip Chaplain
Type: Weight — Spherical
Edition: 1995
Status: Closed
Series: Zodiac Collection
Original Issue Price: £29.50, U.S. $95.00

Name	U.S. $	Can. $	U.K. £
Aquarius	95.00	130.00	30.00

CT-1261
PISCES

Designer: Philip Chaplain
Type: Weight — Spherical
Edition: 1995
Status: Closed
Series: Zodiac Collection
Original Issue Price: £29.50, U.S. $95.00

Name	U.S. $	Can. $	U.K. £
Pisces	95.00	130.00	30.00

CT-1262
ARIES

Designer: Philip Chaplain
Type: Weight — Spherical
Edition: 1995
Status: Closed
Series: Zodiac Collection
Original Issue Price: £29.50, U.S. $95.00

Name	U.S. $	Can. $	U.K. £
Aries	95.00	130.00	30.00

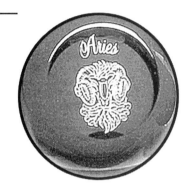

CT-1263
TAURUS

Designer: Philip Chaplain
Type: Weight — Spherical
Edition: 1995
Status: Closed
Series: Zodiac Collection
Original Issue Price: £29.50, U.S. $95.00

Name	U.S. $	Can. $	U.K. £
Taurus	95.00	130.00	30.00

CT-1264
GEMINI

Designer: Philip Chaplain
Type: Weight — Spherical
Edition: 1995
Status: Closed
Series: Zodiac Collection
Original Issue Price: £29.50, U.S. $95.00

Name	U.S. $	Can. $	U.K. £
Gemini	95.00	130.00	30.00

CT-1265
CANCER

Designer: Philip Chaplain
Type: Weight — Spherical
Edition: 1995
Status: Closed
Series: Zodiac Collection
Original Issue Price: £29.50, U.S. $95.00

Name	U.S. $	Can. $	U.K. £
Cancer	95.00	130.00	30.00

CT-1266
LEO

Designer: Philip Chaplain
Type: Weight — Spherical
Edition: 1995
Status: Closed
Series: Zodiac Collection
Original Issue Price: £29.50, U.S. $95.00

Name	U.S. $	Can. $	U.K. £
Leo	95.00	130.00	30.00

CT-1267
VIRGO

Designer: Philip Chaplain
Type: Weight — Spherical
Edition: 1995
Status: Closed
Series: Zodiac Collection
Original Issue Price: £29.50, U.S. $95.00

Name	U.S. $	Can. $	U.K. £
Virgo	95.00	130.00	30.00

CT-1268
LIBRA

Designer: Philip Chaplain
Type: Weight — Spherical
Edition: 1995
Status: Closed
Series: Zodiac Collection
Original Issue Price: £29.50, U.S. $95.00

Name	U.S. $	Can. $	U.K. £
Libra	95.00	130.00	30.00

CT-1269
SCORPIO

Designer:	Philip Chaplain
Type:	Weight — Spherical
Edition:	1995
Status:	Closed
Series:	Zodiac Collection
Original Issue Price:	£29.50, U.S. $95.00

Name	*U.S. $*	*Can. $*	*U.K. £*
Scorpio	95.00	130.00	30.00

CT-1270
SAGITTARIUS

Designer:	Philip Chaplain
Type:	Weight — Spherical
Edition:	1995
Status:	Closed
Series:	Zodiac Collection
Original Issue Price:	£29.50, U.S. $95.00

Name	*U.S. $*	*Can. $*	*U.K. £*
Sagittarius	95.00	130.00	30.00

CT-1271
GLAMIS ROSE PERFUME BOTTLE

Designer:	Colin Terris
Type:	Perfume bottle
Edition:	1995 in a limited edition of 95
Status:	Fully subscribed
Original Issue Price:	£295.00, U.S. $850.00

Name	*U.S. $*	*Can. $*	*U.K. £*
Glamis Rose Perfume Bottle	850.00	1,200.00	300.00

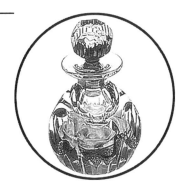

Note: This perfume bottle and weights CT-1272 and 1273 were issued to commemorate HM The Queen Mother's 95th birthday.

CT-1272
GLAMIS ROSE

Designer:	Allan Scott
Type:	Weight — Spherical
Edition:	1995 in a limited edition of 95
Status:	Fully subscribed
Original Issue Price:	£195.00, U.S. $575.00

Name	*U.S. $*	*Can. $*	*U.K. £*
Glamis Rose	575.00	825.00	195.00

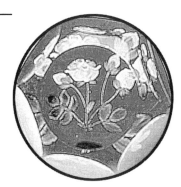

CT-1273
CASTLE OF MEY

Designer: Caithness Engraving Studios
Type: Weight — Spherical
Edition: 1995 in a limited edition of 750
Status: Closed at No. 84
Original Issue Price: £39.50, U.S. $115.00

Name	U.S. $	Can. $	U.K. £
Castle of Mey	115.00	175.00	40.00

CT-1274
VICTORY IN EUROPE

Designer: Philip Chaplain
Type: Weight — Spherical
Edition: 1995 in a limited edition of 500
Status: Closed at No. 140
Original Issue Price: £85.00, U.S. $250.00

Name	U.S. $	Can. $	U.K. £
Victory in Europe	250.00	350.00	85.00

Note: This paperweight was issued to celebrate the 50th anniversary of the Allied Forces' victory in Europe.

CT-1275
OSIRIS

Designer: Philip Chaplain
Type: Weight — Domed
Edition: 1996 in a limited edition of 350
Status: Closed at No. 338
Series: Limited — Modern Design
Original Issue Price: £85.00, U.S. $275.00

Name	U.S. $	Can. $	U.K. £
Osiris	275.00	375.00	85.00

CT-1276
WILDCARD

Designer: Philip Chaplain
Type: Weight — Spherical
Edition: 1996 in a limited edition of 750
Status: Fully subscribed
Series: Limited — Modern Design
Original Issue Price: £45.00, U.S. $150.00

Name	U.S. $	Can. $	U.K. £
Wildcard	150.00	200.00	45.00

CT-1277
REACTOR

Designer:	Philip Chaplain	
Type:	Weight — Spherical	
Edition:	1996 in a limited edition of 750	
Status:	Fully subscribed	
Series:	Limited — Modern Design	
Original Issue Price:	£45.00, U.S. $150.00	

Name	U.S. $	Can. $	U.K. £
Reactor	150.00	200.00	45.00

CT-1278
RIVER DANCERS

Designer:	Helen MacDonald	
Type:	Weight — Domed	
Edition:	1996 in a limited edition of 100	
Status:	Fully subscribed	
Series:	Limited — Modern Design	
Original Issue Price:	£235.00, U.S. $725.00	

Name	U.S. $	Can. $	U.K. £
River Dancers	725.00	1,050.00	300.00

CT-1279
SPACE ENCOUNTER

Designer:	Helen MacDonald	
Type:	Weight — Spherical	
Edition:	1996 in a limited edition of 75	
Status:	Fully subscribed	
Series:	Limited — Modern Design	
Original Issue Price:	£175.00, U.S. $525.00	

Name	U.S. $	Can. $	U.K. £
Space Encounter	525.00	750.00	175.00

CT-1280
NOAH'S ARK

Designer:	Helen MacDonald	
Type:	Weight — Teardrop	
Edition:	1996 in a limited edition of 100	
Status:	Fully subscribed	
Series:	Limited — Modern Design	
Original Issue Price:	£235.00, U.S. $795.00	

Name	U.S. $	Can. $	U.K. £
Noah's Ark	800.00	1,175.00	275.00

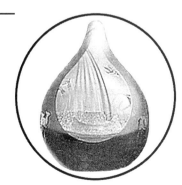

CT-1281
JUGGLER

Designer:	Margot Thomson
Type:	Weight — Spherical
Edition:	1996 in a limited edition of 750
Status:	Closed at No. 717
Series:	Limited — Modern Design
Original Issue Price:	£40.00, U.S. $150.00

Name	U.S. $	Can. $	U.K. £
Juggler	150.00	200.00	40.00

CT-1282
CHANNEL CROSSING

Designer:	Margot Thomson
Type:	Weight — Domed
Edition:	1996 in a limited edition of 650
Status:	Fully subscribed
Series:	Limited — Modern Design
Original Issue Price:	£70.00, U.S. $235.00

Name	U.S. $	Can. $	U.K. £
Channel Crossing	235.00	325.00	70.00

CT-1283
OCEANIC

Designer:	John Spittal
Type:	Weight — Pyramidal
Edition:	1996 in a limited edition of 50
Status:	Fully subscribed
Series:	Limited — Modern Design
Original Issue Price:	£295.00, U.S. $895.00

Name	U.S. $	Can. $	U.K. £
Oceanic	900.00	1,300.00	300.00

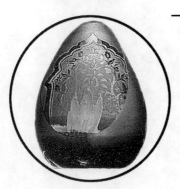

CT-1284
FAR PAVILION

Designer:	Helen MacDonald
Type:	Weight — Domed
Edition:	1996 in a limited edition of 100
Status:	Closed at No. 82
Series:	Limited — Modern Design
Original Issue Price:	£235.00, U.S. $725.00

Name	U.S. $	Can. $	U.K. £
Far Pavilion	725.00	1,050.00	235.00

CT-1285
VIVALDI

Designer:	Margot Thomson
Type:	Weight — Teardrop
Edition:	1996 in a limited edition of 750
Status:	Fully subscribed
Series:	Limited — Modern Design
Original Issue Price:	£60.00, U.S. $225.00

Name	U.S. $	Can. $	U.K. £
Vivaldi	225.00	325.00	60.00

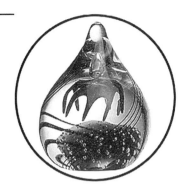

CT-1286
CAPTOR

Designer:	Alastair MacIntosh
Type:	Weight — Spherical
Edition:	1996 in a limited edition of 750
Status:	Closed at No. 654
Series:	Limited — Modern Design
Original Issue Price:	£50.00, U.S. $150.00

Name	U.S. $	Can. $	U.K. £
Captor	150.00	200.00	50.00

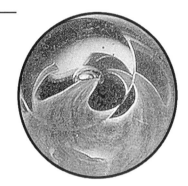

CT-1287
ALL THE FUN OF THE FAIR

Designer:	Helen MacDonald
Type:	Weight — Cylindrical
Edition:	1996 in a limited edition of 25
Status:	Fully subscribed
Series:	Limited — Modern Design
Original Issue Price:	£495.00, U.S. $1,500.00

Name	U.S. $	Can. $	U.K. £
All the Fun of the Fair	1,500.00	2,000.00	500.00

CT-1288
SING FOR YOUR SUPPER

Designer:	Helen MacDonald
Type:	Weight — Sculptural
Edition:	1996 in a limited edition of 15
Status:	Fully subscribed
Series:	Limited — Modern Design
Original Issue Price:	£795.00, U.S. $2,500.00

Name	U.S. $	Can. $	U.K. £
Sing for your Supper	2,500.00	3,500.00	800.00

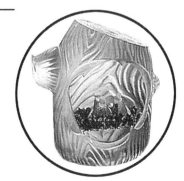

CT-1289
PINK ANEMONE

Designer:	Helen MacDonald
Type:	Weight — Spherical
Edition:	1996 in a limited edition of 50
Status:	Fully subscribed
Series:	Limited — Modern Design
Original Issue Price:	£250.00, U.S. $750.00

Name	U.S. $	Can. $	U.K. £
Pink Anemone	750.00	1,000.00	250.00

CT-1290
CORNFLOWER

Designer:	Helen MacDonald
Type:	Weight — Spherical
Edition:	1996 in a limited edition of 50
Status:	Fully subscribed
Series:	Limited — Modern Design
Original Issue Price:	£275.00, U.S. $825.00

Name	U.S. $	Can. $	U.K. £
Cornflower	825.00	1,150.00	275.00

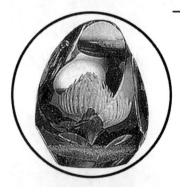

CT-1291
PROTEA

Designer:	Jeneo Lewis
Type:	Weight — Domed
Edition:	1996 in a limited edition of 50
Status:	Fully subscribed
Series:	Limited — Modern Design
Original Issue Price:	£225.00, U.S. $695.00

Name	U.S. $	Can. $	U.K. £
Protea	700.00	1,000.00	225.00

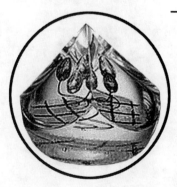

CT-1292
CHECKERS

Designer:	Helen MacDonald
Type:	Weight — Pyramid facets
Edition:	1996 in a limited edition of 350
Status:	Closed at No. 294
Series:	Limited — Modern Design
Original Issue Price:	£85.00, U.S. $275.00

Name	U.S. $	Can. $	U.K. £
Checkers	275.00	375.00	85.00

CT-1293
HALL OF MIRRORS

Designer: Shona Spittal
Type: Weight — Spherical
Edition: 1996 in a limited edition of 75
Status: Fully subscribed
Series: Limited — Modern Design
Original Issue Price: £195.00, U.S. $595.00

Name	U.S. $	Can. $	U.K. £
Hall of Mirrors	600.00	850.00	200.00

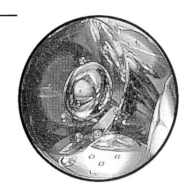

CT-1294
PINPOINT

Designer: Alastair MacIntosh
Type: Weight — Pyramid
Edition: 1996 in a limited edition of 50
Status: Fully subscribed
Series: Limited — Modern Design
Original Issue Price: £225.00, U.S. $695.00

Name	U.S. $	Can. $	U.K. £
Pinpoint	700.00	1,000.00	230.00

CT-1295
DEVIL'S ADVOCATE

Designer: Philip Chaplain
Type: Weight — Domed
Edition: 1996 in a limited edition of 150
Status: Fully subscribed
Series: Limited — Modern Design
Original Issue Price: £110.00, U.S. $330.00

Name	U.S. $	Can. $	U.K. £
Devil's Advocate	330.00	475.00	110.00

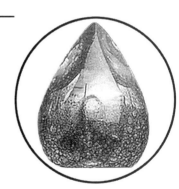

CT-1296
ABYSS

Designer: Philip Chaplain
Type: Weight — Domed
Edition: 1996 in a limited edition of 650
Status: Fully subscribed
Series: Limited — Modern Design
Original Issue Price: £65.00, U.S. $195.00

Name	U.S. $	Can. $	U.K. £
Abyss	195.00	275.00	65.00

CT-1297
SNOWY OWL

Designer:	Alastair MacIntosh		
Type:	Weight — Spherical		
Edition:	1996 in a limited edition of 650		
Status:	Fully subscribed		
Series:	Limited — Modern Design		
Original Issue Price:	£75.00, U.S. $225.00		

Name	U.S. $	Can. $	U.K. £
Snowy Owl	225.00	325.00	75.00

CT-1298
SPOOKY HANDS

Designer:	Philip Chaplain		
Type:	Weight — Spherical		
Edition:	1996 in a limited edition of 650		
Status:	Closed at No. 605		
Series:	Limited — Modern Design		
Original Issue Price:	£65.00, U.S. $195.00		

Name	U.S. $	Can. $	U.K. £
Spooky Hands	200.00	275.00	75.00

CT-1299
ENCHANTMENT

Designer:	Colin Terris		
Type:	Weight — Spherical, magnum size		
Edition:	1996 in a limited edition of 75		
Status:	Fully subscribed		
Series:	Limited — Modern Design		
Original Issue Price:	£350.00, U.S. $1,050.00		

Name	U.S. $	Can. $	U.K. £
Enchantment	1,050.00	1,500.00	425.00

CT-1300
MOSES

Designer:	Helen MacDonald		
Type:	Weight — Spherical		
Edition:	1996 in a limited edition of 75		
Status:	Fully subscribed		
Series:	Limited — Modern Design		
Original Issue Price:	£195.00, U.S. $595.00		

Name	U.S. $	Can. $	U.K. £
Moses	600.00	850.00	225.00

CT-1301
INCA GOLD

Designer:	Alastair MacIntosh
Type:	Weight — Domed
Edition:	1996 in a limited edition of 150
Status:	Fully subscribed
Series:	Limited — Modern Design
Original Issue Price:	£110.00, U.S. $330.00

Name	U.S. $	Can. $	U.K. £
Inca Gold	330.00	475.00	110.00

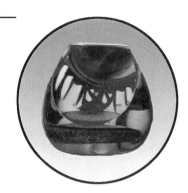

CT-1302A
NIGHT

Designer:	Colin Terris
Type:	Weight — Spherical
Edition:	1996 in a limited edition of 250
Status:	Fully subscribed
Series:	Limited — Modern Design
Original Issue Price:	£195.00/set, U.S. $595.00/set

Name	U.S. $	Can. $	U.K. £
Night	297.50	425.00	100.00
Set	595.00	850.00	200.00

Note: CT-1302A and B were issued and sold as a set.

CT-1302B
DAY

Designer:	Colin Terris
Type:	Weight — Spherical
Edition:	1996 in a limited edition of 250
Status:	Fully subscribed
Series:	Limited — Modern Design
Original Issue Price:	£195.00/set, U.S. $595.00/set

Name	U.S. $	Can. $	U.K. £
Day	297.50	425.00	100.00

CT-1303
DOUBLE MAGNUM '96

Designer:	Franco Toffolo
Type:	Weight — Spherical, double magnum
Edition:	1996 in a limited edition of 150
Status:	Closed at No. 126
Series:	Limited — Modern Design
Original Issue Price:	£195.00, U.S. $595.00

Name	U.S. $	Can. $	U.K. £
Double Magnum '96	600.00	850.00	200.00

CT-1304
TROPICANA

Designer:	Helen MacDonald	
Type:	Weight — Spherical	
Edition:	1996 in a limited edition of 1,765	
Status:	Closed at No. 1,765	
Original Issue Price:	£80.00, U.S. $215.00	

Name	U.S. $	Can. $	U.K. £
Tropicana	215.00	300.00	85.00

Note: This is the 1996 Collectors' Paperweight.

CT-1305
TWILIGHT ZONE

Designer:	Philip Chaplain	
Type:	Weight — Spherical	
Edition:	1996 in a limited edition of 750	
Status:	Closed at No. 441	
Series:	Limited — Modern Design	
Original Issue Price:	£55.00, U.S. $165.00	

Name	U.S. $	Can. $	U.K. £
Twilight Zone	165.00	225.00	55.00

CT-1306
SALOMÉ

Designer:	Alastair MacIntosh	
Type:	Weight — Spherical	
Edition:	1996 in a limited edition of 350	
Status:	Fully subscribed	
Series:	Limited — Modern Design	
Original Issue Price:	£85.00, U.S. $275.00	

Name	U.S. $	Can. $	U.K. £
Salomé	275.00	375.00	85.00

CT-1307
FOLLOW MY LEADER

Designer:	Colin Terris and William Manson	
Type:	Weight — Spherical	
Edition:	1996 in a limited edition of 50	
Status:	Fully subscribed	
Series:	Traditional Collection	
Original Issue Price:	£275.00, U.S. $850.00	

Name	U.S. $	Can. $	U.K. £
Follow My Leader	850.00	1,200.00	275.00

Millennium Collection

The Millennium collection introduces Caithness paperweights to the new millennium. This range of weights will offer everyone something to remember the celebrations of the Year 2000.

CT-1765
Millennium Carnival

CT-1767
Millennium Dancer

CT-1770
Millennium Liberty

CT-1774
Millennium Pebble

CT-1778
Millennium Fantasy

CT-1781
Millennium Fiesta

Collectors Society Collection

First issued in 1977 the Collectors Society Collection now has 22 weights in the series. For a complete listing please refer to page xi of the introduction.

CT-1180
Jack in the Box
1995 Weight

CT-941
Fantasy Orchid
1993 Weight

CT-373
Solitaire
1984 Weight

CT-1783
Millennium Vision
1999 Weight

Designers' Collections

Colin Terris

Introduced in 1997 the Colin Terris "Collection" has grown from the Designer Collection to include the Rose and Water Lily Collections. Over thirty weights now comprise these series.

CT-1470
Pink Beauty

CT-1615
Patriot

CT-1617
Faerie Dance

Alastair MacIntosh

At present seven weights make up the Alastair MacIntosh collection illustrating his distinctive style.

CT-1725
Dizzy Lizzy

CT-1726
Magic Castle

CT-1727
Propulsion

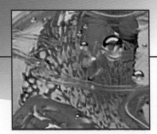

Double Magnum Collection

The 155mm giants of the paperweight world. Starting in 1983 and continuing into 1999 Caithness released a double magnum weight each year. These large weights make an outstanding display.

CT-522
Double Magnum Crimson

CT-780
Double Magnum Jade

CT-1094
Jubilee 94 Double Magnum

Egg Collection

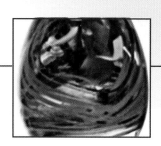

First launched in 1998 the "Collectable Eggs" series features intricate patterns and eyecatching colours. Issued in limited and unlimited editions over thirty weights are now in the collection.

CT-1610
Colour Pool - Green

CT-1653
Azurina

CT-1654
Eggstravaganza

CT-1655
Wavedancers

CT-1731
Daffodil

CT-1738
Sumatra

Perfume Bottle Collection

Perfume bottles combine the art of paperweights with the collectability of the perfume container. The wide range of bottles from the modern to the traditional will appeal to all collectors.

CT-119A
Sea Lace

CT-120
Blue Petal

CT-571
Poinsettia

CT-890
Fuchsia

CT-1191A
Cosmos

CT-1185
Pansy

Royalty Collection

The Royalty collection began in 1974 with the issue of CT-28 "Crown", which commemorates the marriage of Princess Anne and Captain Mark Phillips. Since then 43 weights have been released commemorating numerous royal events from birthdays to jubilees to marriages.

CT-148
Henry VIII

CT-238
Royal Wedding
Issued to commemorate the
marriage of Prince Charles
and Lady Diana Spencer

CT-287
Royal Birthday Tribute
Issued to commemorate the
birth of HRH Prince William

CT-1271
Glamis Rose Perfume Bottle
Issued to commemorate
HM The Queen Mother's
95th birthday

CT-1378
*HM Queen Elizabeth II
70TH Birthday Crown*
Issued to commemorate
HM The Queen's 70th birthday

CT-1473
Royal Golden Wedding Crown
Issued to commemorate
HM The Queen's
50th Wedding Anniversary

Collection Sets

The first weights produced by Caithness were the Planets in 1969. Since then dozens of collector sets have been issued both in limited and unlimited editions. One of the largest sets is the Traditional Nature Study collection.

Planets

CT-1A
Mars

Seasons

CT-46D
Winter

Nature Study

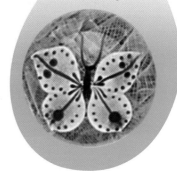

CT-1364
Purple Butterfly - Latticino Base

Elements

CT-21C
Fire

Sea Birds

CT-49
Cormorant

Water Lily

CT-1595
Traditional Pool

CT-1308
TEDDY BEAR

Designer:	William Manson
Type:	Weight — Spherical
Edition:	1996 in a limited edition of 50
Status:	Fully subscribed
Series:	Traditional Collection
Original Issue Price:	£295.00, U.S. $895.00

Name	U.S. $	Can. $	U.K. £
Teddy Bear	900.00	1,250.00	295.00

CT-1309
DAMSEL FLY

Designer:	William Manson
Type:	Weight — Spherical, faceted
Edition:	1996 in a limited edition of 50
Status:	Closed at No. 37
Series:	Traditional Collection
Original Issue Price:	£350.00, U.S. $1,075.00

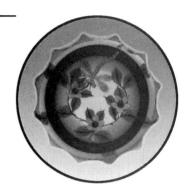

Name	U.S. $	Can. $	U.K. £
Damsel Fly	1,100.00	1,550.00	350.00

CT-1310
LAGOON LIFE

Designer:	William Manson
Type:	Weight — Spherical
Edition:	1996 in a limited edition of 50
Status:	Fully subscribed
Series:	Traditional Collection
Original Issue Price:	£295.00, U.S. $895.00

Name	U.S. $	Can. $	U.K. £
Lagoon Life	900.00	1,250.00	295.00

CT-1311
OCEAN ENCOUNTER

Designer:	William Manson
Type:	Weight — Spherical
Edition:	1996 in a limited edition of 50
Status:	Closed at No. 36
Series:	Traditional Collection
Original Issue Price:	£295.00, U.S. $895.00

Name	U.S. $	Can. $	U.K. £
Ocean Encounter	900.00	1,250.00	300.00

CT-1312
EGRET

Designer:	William Manson	
Type:	Weight — Spherical	
Edition:	1996 in a limited edition of 50	
Status:	Closed at No. 47	
Series:	Traditional Collection	
Original Issue Price:	£275.00, U.S. $850.00	

Name	U.S. $	Can. $	U.K. £
Egret	850.00	1,200.00	275.00

CT-1313
NEPTUNE'S KINGDOM

Designer:	William Manson	
Type:	Weight — Spherical, magnum size	
Edition:	1996 in a limited edition of 10	
Status:	Fully subscribed	
Series:	Traditional Collection	
Original Issue Price:	£795.00, U.S. $2,500.00	

Name	U.S. $	Can. $	U.K. £
Neptune's Kingdom	2,500.00	3,500.00	800.00

CT-1314
ORCHID

Designer:	William Manson	
Type:	Weight — Spherical	
Edition:	1996 in a limited edition of 150	
Status:	Fully subscribed	
Series:	Traditional Collection	
Original Issue Price:	£75.00, U.S. $230.00	

Name	U.S. $	Can. $	U.K. £
Orchid	230.00	325.00	75.00

CT-1315
GOLDEN SPLENDOUR

Designer:	William Manson	
Type:	Weight — Spherical	
Edition:	1996 in a limited edition of 150	
Status:	Closed at No. 106	
Series:	Traditional Collection	
Original Issue Price:	£75.00, U.S. $230.00	

Name	U.S. $	Can. $	U.K. £
Golden Splendour	230.00	325.00	75.00

CT-1316
SUMMER POSY

Designer:	William Manson
Type:	Weight — Spherical
Edition:	1996 in a limited edition of 150
Status:	Closed at No. 118
Series:	Traditional Collection
Original Issue Price:	£75.00, U.S. $230.00

Name	U.S. $	Can. $	U.K. £
Summer Posy	230.00	325.00	75.00

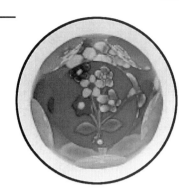

CT-1317
PINK BLOSSOM

Designer:	William Manson
Type:	Weight — Spherical
Edition:	1996 in a limited edition of 150
Status:	Closed at No. 108
Series:	Traditional Collection
Original Issue Price:	£75.00, U.S. $230.00

Name	U.S. $	Can. $	U.K. £
Pink Blossom	230.00	325.00	75.00

CT-1318
PINK BUTTERFLY — MINIATURE

Designer:	Allan Scott
Type:	Weight — Spherical
Edition:	1996 in a limited edition of 150
Status:	Closed at No. 63
Series:	Traditional Collection — Nature Study
Original Issue Price:	£99.00, U.S. $295.00

Name	U.S. $	Can. $	U.K. £
Pink Butterfly — Miniature	300.00	425.00	100.00

CT-1319
BLUE BUTTERFLY — MINIATURE

Designer:	Allan Scott
Type:	Weight — Spherical
Edition:	1996 in a limited edition of 150
Status:	Closed at No. 62
Series:	Traditional Collection — Nature Study
Original Issue Price:	£99.00, U.S. $295.00

Name	U.S. $	Can. $	U.K. £
Blue Butterfly — Miniature	300.00	425.00	100.00

CT-1320
EMERALD SPRAY

Designer:	Allan Scott
Type:	Weight — Spherical
Edition:	1996 in a limited edition of 25
Status:	Fully subscribed
Series:	Traditional Collection — Nature Study
Original Issue Price:	£495.00, U.S. $1,500.00

Name	U.S. $	Can. $	U.K. £
Emerald Spray	1,500.00	2,000.00	500.00

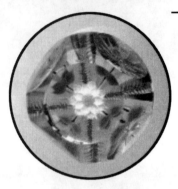

CT-1321A
SPRING

Designer:	Rosette Fleming
Type:	Weight — Spherical
Edition:	1996 in a limited edition of 25
Status:	Fully subscribed
Series:	Four Seasons Set
Original Issue Price:	£750.00/set, U.S. $2,500.00/set

Name	U.S. $	Can. $	U.K. £
Spring	625.00	900.00	200.00
Set	2,500.00	3,600.00	800.00

Note: CT-1321A, B, C and D were issued and sold as a set.

CT-1321B
SUMMER

Designer:	Rosette Fleming
Type:	Weight — Spherical
Edition:	1996 in a limited edition of 25
Status:	Fully subscribed
Series:	Four Seasons Set
Original Issue Price:	£750.00/set, U.S. $2,500.00/set

Name	U.S. $	Can. $	U.K. £
Summer	625.00	900.00	200.00

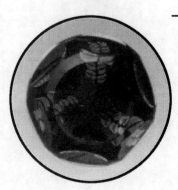

CT-1321C
AUTUMN

Designer:	Rosette Fleming
Type:	Weight — Spherical
Edition:	1996 in a limited edition of 25
Status:	Fully subscribed
Series:	Four Seasons Set
Original Issue Price:	£750.00/set, U.S. $2,500.00/set

Name	U.S. $	Can. $	U.K. £
Autumn	625.00	900.00	200.00

CT-1321D
WINTER

Designer:	Rosette Fleming
Type:	Weight — Spherical
Edition:	1996 in a limited edition of 25
Status:	Fully subscribed
Series:	Four Seasons Set
Original Issue Price:	£750.00/set, U.S. $2,500.00/set

Name	U.S. $	Can. $	U.K. £
Winter	625.00	900.00	200.00

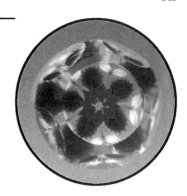

CT-1322
POPPIES

Designer:	Allan Scott
Type:	Weight — Spherical
Edition:	1996 in a limited edition of 25
Status:	Fully subscribed
Series:	Traditional Collection — Nature Study
Original Issue Price:	£595.00, U.S. $1,795.00

Name	U.S. $	Can. $	U.K. £
Poppies	1,800.00	2,800.00	600.00

CT-1323
WILD ORCHIDS

Designer:	Allan Scott
Type:	Weight — Spherical
Edition:	1996 in a limited edition of 25
Status:	Fully subscribed
Series:	Traditional Collection — Nature Study
Original Issue Price:	£550.00, U.S. $1,795.00

Name	U.S. $	Can. $	U.K. £
Wild Orchids	1,900.00	2,800.00	550.00

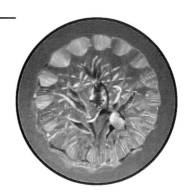

CT-1324
BLUE BUTTERFLY — GOLD FLOWER

Designer:	Allan Scott
Type:	Weight — Spherical
Edition:	1996 in a limited edition of 50
Status:	Closed at No. 39
Series:	Traditional Collection — Nature Study
Original Issue Price:	£195.00, U.S. $595.00

Name	U.S. $	Can. $	U.K. £
Blue Butterfly — Gold Flower	600.00	850.00	200.00

CT-1325
PINK BUTTERFLY — BLUE FLOWER

Designer: Allan Scott
Type: Weight — Spherical
Edition: 1996 in a limited edition of 50
Status: Closed at No. 46
Series: Traditional Collection — Nature Study
Original Issue Price: £195.00, U.S. $595.00

Name	U.S. $	Can. $	U.K. £
Pink Butterfly — Blue Flower	600.00	850.00	200.00

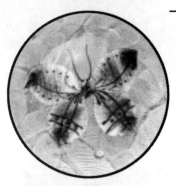

CT-1326
BLUE BUTTERFLY — LATTICINO BASE

Designer: Allan Scott
Type: Weight — Spherical
Edition: 1996 in a limited edition of 50
Status: Fully subscribed
Series: Traditional Collection — Nature Study
Original Issue Price: £175.00, U.S. $525.00

Name	U.S. $	Can. $	U.K. £
Blue Butterfly — Latticino Base	525.00	750.00	175.00

CT-1327
FLAME NASTURTIUM

Designer: Margot Thomson
Type: Weight — Spherical
Edition: 1996 in a limited edition of 50
Status: Closed at No. 36
Series: Whitefriars Collection
Original Issue Price: £215.00, U.S. $750.00

Name	U.S. $	Can. $	U.K. £
Flame Nasturtium	750.00	1,050.00	215.00

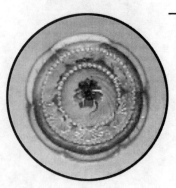

CT-1328
PANSY

Designer: Margot Thomson
Type: Weight — Spherical
Edition: 1996 in a limited edition of 50
Status: Closed at No. 25
Series: Whitefriars Collection
Original Issue Price: £295.00, U.S. $895.00

Name	U.S. $	Can. $	U.K. £
Pansy	900.00	1,250.00	300.00

CT-1329
HOSTA

Designer:	Margot Thomson
Type:	Weight — Spherical
Edition:	1996 in a limited edition of 50
Status:	Closed at No. 30
Series:	Whitefriars Collection
Original Issue Price:	£165.00, U.S. $550.00

Name	U.S. $	Can. $	U.K. £
Hosta	550.00	775.00	165.00

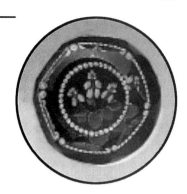

CT-1330
ROCK ROSE

Designer:	Margot Thomson
Type:	Weight — Spherical
Edition:	1996 in a limited edition of 50
Status:	Closed at No. 30
Series:	Whitefriars Collection
Original Issue Price:	£175.00, U.S. $550.00

Name	U.S. $	Can. $	U.K. £
Rock Rose	550.00	775.00	175.00

CT-1331
FUCHSIA

Designer:	Margot Thomson
Type:	Weight — Spherical
Edition:	1996 in a limited edition of 50
Status:	Fully subscribed
Series:	Whitefriars Collection
Original Issue Price:	£135.00, U.S. $450.00

Name	U.S. $	Can. $	U.K. £
Fuchsia	450.00	650.00	135.00

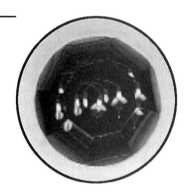

CT-1332
AURICULA

Designer:	Margot Thomson
Type:	Weight — Spherical
Edition:	1996 in a limited edition of 50
Status:	Closed at No. 29
Series:	Whitefriars Collection
Original Issue Price:	£165.00, U.S. $550.00

Name	U.S. $	Can. $	U.K. £
Auricula	550.00	775.00	165.00

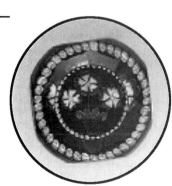

CT-1333
CAMOMILE

Designer: Margot Thomson
Type: Weight — Spherical
Edition: 1996 in a limited edition of 50
Status: Closed at No. 30
Series: Whitefriars Collection
Original Issue Price: £195.00, U.S. $595.00

Name	U.S. $	Can. $	U.K. £
Camomile	650.00	895.00	200.00

CT-1334
TITANIA

Designer: Colin Terris
Type: Weight — Spherical
Edition: 1996
Status: Active
Series: Unlimited — Modern Design
Original Issue Price: £26.00, U.S. $87.50

Name	U.S. $	Can. $	U.K. £
Titania	87.50	120.00	27.50

CT-1335
TARTAN TWIRL

Designer: Alastair MacIntosh
Type: Weight — Spherical
Edition: 1996
Status: Closed
Series: Unlimited — Modern Design
Original Issue Price: £27.00, U.S. $87.50

Name	U.S. $	Can. $	U.K. £
Tartan Twirl	90.00	120.00	27.00

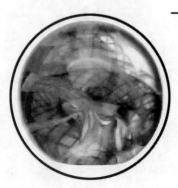

CT-1336
SORCERER'S APPRENTICE

Designer: Alastair MacIntosh
Type: Weight — Spherical
Edition: 1996
Status: Active
Series: Unlimited — Modern Design
Original Issue Price: £23.00, U.S. $72.50

Name	U.S. $	Can. $	U.K. £
Sorcerer's Apprentice	79.50	105.00	24.00

CT-1337
HARMONICS

Designer:	Alastair MacIntosh
Type:	Weight — Spherical
Colour:	Pink
Edition:	1996
Status:	Closed
Series:	Unlimited — Modern Design
Original Issue Price:	£20.00, U.S. $72.50

Name	U.S. $	Can. $	U.K. £
Harmonics	75.00	100.00	25.00

CT-1338
DEW DROPS

Designer:	Colin Terris
Type:	Weight — Spherical
Edition:	1996
Status:	Active
Series:	Unlimited — Modern Design
Original Issue Price:	£25.00, U.S. $87.50

Name	U.S. $	Can. $	U.K. £
Dew Drops	87.50	115.00	26.50

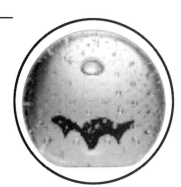

CT-1339
MOONFLOWER GREEN

Designer:	Colin Terris
Type:	Weight — Spherical
Edition:	1996
Status:	Active
Series:	Unlimited — Modern Design
Original Issue Price:	£34.50, U.S. $110.00

Name	U.S. $	Can. $	U.K. £
Moonflower Green	110.00	155.00	35.00

CT-1340
BAMBOOZLED

Designer:	Helen MacDonald
Type:	Weight — Domed
Edition:	1996 in a limited edition of 25
Status:	Fully subscribed
Series:	Limited — Modern Design
Original Issue Price:	£495.00, U.S. $1,600.00

Name	U.S. $	Can. $	U.K. £
Bamboozled	1,600.00	2,300.00	500.00

CT-1341
RING OF FIRE

Designer:	Helen MacDonald
Type:	Weight — Spherical
Edition:	1996 in a limited edition of 75
Status:	Fully subscribed
Series:	Limited — Modern Design
Original Issue Price:	£195.00, U.S. $575.00

Name	U.S. $	Can. $	U.K. £
Ring of Fire	575.00	825.00	195.00

CT-1342
NORTHERN EXPOSURE

Designer:	Helen MacDonald
Type:	Weight — Sculptural
Edition:	1996 in a limited edition of 25
Status:	Fully subscribed
Series:	Limited — Modern Design
Original Issue Price:	£650.00, U.S. $2,000.00

Name	U.S. $	Can. $	U.K. £
Northern Exposure	2,000.00	2,800.00	650.00

CT-1343
SHOWTIME

Designer:	Helen MacDonald
Type:	Weight — Domed
Edition:	1996 in a limited edition of 50
Status:	Fully subscribed
Series:	Limited — Modern Design
Original Issue Price:	£225.00, U.S. $650.00

Name	U.S. $	Can. $	U.K. £
Showtime	650.00	925.00	225.00

CT-1344
TRANQUIL POOL

Designer:	Colin Terris
Type:	Weight — Spherical
Edition:	1996 in a limited edition of 50
Status:	Fully subscribed
Series:	Limited — Modern Design
Original Issue Price:	£275.00, U.S. $795.00

Name	U.S. $	Can. $	U.K. £
Tranquil Pool	800.00	1,150.00	275.00

CT-1345
MASQUERADE

Designer:	Colin Terris	
Type:	Weight — Spherical	
Edition:	1996 in a limited edition of 75	
Status:	Fully subscribed	
Series:	Limited — Modern Design	
Original Issue Price:	£195.00, U.S. $575.00	

Name	U.S. $	Can. $	U.K. £
Masquerade	575.00	825.00	200.00

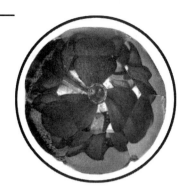

CT-1346
CONQUISTADOR

Designer:	Colin Terris	
Type:	Weight — Spherical	
Edition:	1996 in a limited edition of 50	
Status:	Fully subscribed	
Series:	Limited — Modern Design	
Original Issue Price:	£250.00, U.S. $750.00	

Name	U.S. $	Can. $	U.K. £
Conquistador	750.00	1,050.00	250.00

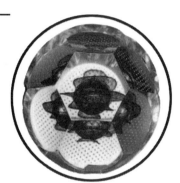

CT-1347
SERENDIPITY

Designer:	Colin Terris	
Type:	Weight — Spherical	
Edition:	1996 in a limited edition of 50	
Status:	Fully subscribed	
Series:	Limited — Modern Design	
Original Issue Price:	£295.00, U.S. $850.00	

Name	U.S. $	Can. $	U.K. £
Serendipity	850.00	1,200.00	300.00

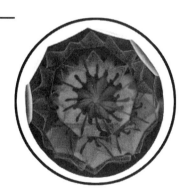

CT-1348
RAPTURE

Designer:	Alastair MacIntosh	
Type:	Weight — Spherical, magnum size	
Edition:	1996 in a limited edition of 75	
Status:	Closed at No. 53	
Series:	Limited — Modern Design	
Original Issue Price:	£350.00, U.S. $995.00	

Name	U.S. $	Can. $	U.K. £
Rapture	1,000.00	1,400.00	350.00

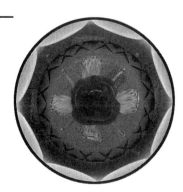

CT-1349
KINGDOM OF THE DEEP

Designer: Colin Terris
Type: Weight — Spherical, magnum size
Edition: 1996 in a limited edition of 100
Status: Closed at No. 59
Series: Limited — Modern Design
Original Issue Price: £250.00, U.S. $750.00

Name	U.S. $	Can. $	U.K. £
Kingdom of the Deep	750.00	1,050.00	250.00

CT-1350
SILKEN STRANDS

Designer: Helen MacDonald
Type: Weight — Spherical
Edition: 1996 in a limited edition of 350
Status: Fully subscribed
Series: Limited — Modern Design
Original Issue Price: £85.00, U.S. $250.00

Name	U.S. $	Can. $	U.K. £
Silken Strands	250.00	350.00	85.00

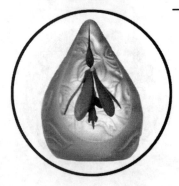

CT-1351
ALLURE

Designer: Helen MacDonald
Type: Weight — Teardrop
Edition: 1996 in a limited edition of 100
Status: Fully subscribed
Series: Limited — Modern Design
Original Issue Price: £235.00, U.S. $695.00

Name	U.S. $	Can. $	U.K. £
Allure	700.00	1,000.00	235.00

CT-1352
PHANTOM

Designer: Helen MacDonald
Type: Weight — Domed
Edition: 1996 in a limited edition of 100
Status: Fully subscribed
Series: Limited — Modern Design
Original Issue Price: £250.00, U.S. $750.00

Name	U.S. $	Can. $	U.K. £
Phantom	750.00	1,050.00	250.00

CT-1353
SPRING CROCUS

Designer:	Helen MacDonald
Type:	Weight — Domed
Edition:	1996 in a limited edition of 350
Status:	Fully subscribed
Series:	Limited — Modern Design
Original Issue Price:	£99.00, U.S. $295.00

Name	U.S. $	Can. $	U.K. £
Spring Crocus	300.00	425.00	100.00

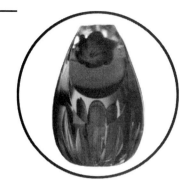

CT-1354
COSMIC COLLISION

Designer:	Colin Terris
Type:	Weight — Spherical
Edition:	1996 in a limited edition of 650
Status:	Closed at No. 397
Series:	Limited — Modern Design
Original Issue Price:	£75.00, U.S. $225.00

Name	U.S. $	Can. $	U.K. £
Cosmic Collision	225.00	325.00	75.00

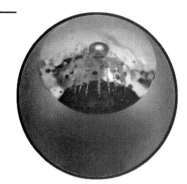

CT-1355
AVENTURINE

Designer:	Caithness Design Studio
Type:	Weight — Spherical
Edition:	1996 in a limited edition of 750
Status:	Fully subscribed
Series:	Limited — Modern Design
Original Issue Price:	£50.00, U.S. $150.00

Name	U.S. $	Can. $	U.K. £
Aventurine	150.00	200.00	50.00

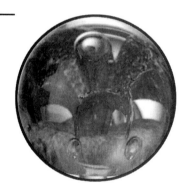

CT-1356
HIBERNATION

Designer:	Colin Terris
Type:	Weight — Ovoid
Edition:	1996 in a limited edition of 650
Status:	Closed at No. 544
Series:	Limited — Modern Design
Original Issue Price:	£75.00, U.S. $225.00

Name	U.S. $	Can. $	U.K. £
Hibernation	225.00	325.00	75.00

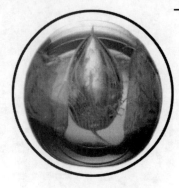

CT-1357
HYPNOSIS

Designer:	Philip Chaplain
Type:	Weight — Spherical
Edition:	1996 in a limited edition of 750
Status:	Closed at No. 473
Series:	Limited — Modern Design
Original Issue Price:	£60.00, U.S. $175.00

Name	U.S. $	Can. $	U.K. £
Hypnosis	175.00	250.00	60.00

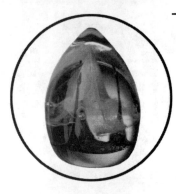

CT-1358
KATMANDU

Designer:	Philip Chaplain
Type:	Weight — Domed
Edition:	1996 in a limited edition of 750
Status:	Fully subscribed
Series:	Limited — Modern Design
Original Issue Price:	£60.00, U.S. $175.00

Name	U.S. $	Can. $	U.K. £
Katmandu	175.00	250.00	60.00

CT-1359
PASQUE FLOWER

Designer:	Margot Thomson
Type:	Weight — Spherical
Edition:	1996 in a limited edition of 50
Status:	Fully subscribed
Series:	Whitefriars Collection
Original Issue Price:	£110.00, U.S. $325.00

Name	U.S. $	Can. $	U.K. £
Pasque Flower	325.00	450.00	160.00

CT-1360
DAFFODIL SPRAY

Designer:	Allan Scott
Type:	Weight — Spherical
Edition:	1996 in a limited edition of 50
Status:	Fully subscribed
Series:	Whitefriars Collection
Original Issue Price:	£135.00, U.S. $395.00

Name	U.S. $	Can. $	U.K. £
Daffodil Spray	400.00	550.00	135.00

CT-1361
SPRING POSY

Designer:	Allan Scott	
Type:	Weight — Spherical	
Edition:	1996 in a limited edition of 25	
Status:	Closed at No. 22	
Series:	Traditional Collection — Nature Study	
Original Issue Price:	£595.00, U.S. $1,700.00	

Name	U.S. $	Can. $	U.K. £
Spring Posy	1,700.00	2,400.00	600.00

CT-1362
TERRARIUM

Designer:	Allan Scott	
Type:	Weight — Spherical	
Edition:	1996 in a limited edition of 25	
Status:	Fully subscribed	
Series:	Traditional Collection — Nature Study	
Original Issue Price:	£595.00, U.S. $1,700.00	

Name	U.S. $	Can. $	U.K. £
Terrarium	1,700.00	2,400.00	600.00

CT-1363
TROPICAL BOUQUET

Designer:	Allan Scott	
Type:	Weight — Spherical	
Edition:	1996 in a limited edition of 25	
Status:	Fully subscribed	
Series:	Traditional Collection — Nature Study	
Original Issue Price:	£295.00, U.S. $1,700.00	

Name	U.S. $	Can. $	U.K. £
Tropical Bouquet	1,700.00	2,400.00	300.00

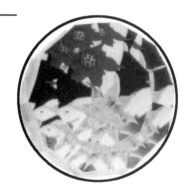

CT-1364
PURPLE BUTTERFLY — LATTICINO BASE

Designer:	Allan Scott	
Type:	Weight — Spherical	
Edition:	1996 in a limited edition of 50	
Status:	Closed at No. 39	
Series:	Traditional Collection — Nature Study	
Original Issue Price:	£175.00, U.S. $575.00	

Name	U.S. $	Can. $	U.K. £
Purple Butterfly — Latticino Base	575.00	825.00	175.00

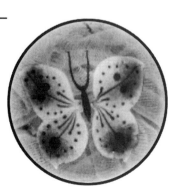

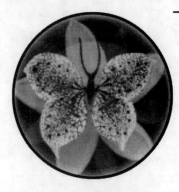

CT-1365
WHITE BUTTERFLY — YELLOW FLOWER

Designer:	Allan Scott
Type:	Weight — Spherical
Edition:	1996 in a limited edition of 50
Status:	Closed at No. 26
Series:	Traditional Collection — Nature Study
Original Issue Price:	£195.00, U.S. $575.00

Name	U.S. $	Can. $	U.K. £
White Butterfly — Yellow Flower	575.00	800.00	200.00

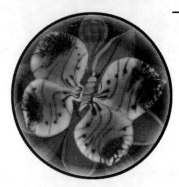

CT-1366
GOLD BUTTERFLY — PINK FLOWER

Designer:	Allan Scott
Type:	Weight — Spherical
Edition:	1996 in a limited edition of 50
Status:	Closed at No. 33
Series:	Traditional Collection — Nature Study
Original Issue Price:	£195.00, U.S. $575.00

Name	U.S. $	Can. $	U.K. £
Gold Butterfly — Pink Flower	575.00	800.00	200.00

CT-1367
BOYHOOD MEMORIES

Designer:	William Manson
Type:	Weight — Cylindrical
Edition:	1996 in a limited edition of 50
Status:	Closed at No. 36
Series:	Traditional Collection
Original Issue Price:	£395.00, U.S. $1,200.00

Name	U.S. $	Can. $	U.K. £
Boyhood Memories	1,200.00	1,700.00	400.00

CT-1368
SCARECROW

Designer:	Colin Terris and William Manson
Type:	Weight — Spherical
Edition:	1996 in a limited edition of 50
Status:	Closed at No. 41
Series:	Traditional Collection
Original Issue Price:	£275.00, U.S. $775.00

Name	U.S. $	Can. $	U.K. £
Scarecrow	775.00	1,100.00	275.00

CT-1369
MEADOW POOL

Designer:	William Manson
Type:	Weight — Spherical, magnum size
Edition:	1996 in a limited edition of 25
Status:	Closed at No. 18
Series:	Traditional Collection
Original Issue Price:	£850.00, U.S. $2,750.00

Name	U.S. $	Can. $	U.K. £
Meadow Pool	2,750.00	3,950.00	850.00

CT-1370
DEEP SEA DIVER

Designer:	William Manson
Type:	Weight — Spherical
Edition:	1996 in a limited edition of 50
Status:	Closed at No. 36
Series:	Traditional Collection
Original Issue Price:	£295.00, U.S. $995.00

Name	U.S. $	Can. $	U.K. £
Deep Sea Diver	1,000.00	1,400.00	300.00

CT-1371
WHIZZ

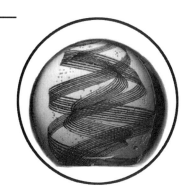

Designer:	Alastair MacIntosh
Type:	Weight — Spherical
Edition:	1996
Status:	Closed
Series:	Unlimited — Modern Design
Original Issue Price:	£26.00, U.S. $79.50

Name	U.S. $	Can. $	U.K. £
Whizz	80.00	110.00	30.00

CT-1372
CASCADE

Designer:	Helen MacDonald
Type:	Weight — Spherical
Edition:	1996
Status:	Active
Series:	Unlimited — Modern Design
Original Issue Price:	£30.00, U.S. $95.00

Name	U.S. $	Can. $	U.K. £
Cascade	99.50	135.00	31.00

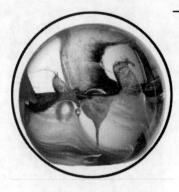

CT-1373
DEBUTANTE

Designer: Colin Terris
Type: Weight — Spherical
Colour: See below
Edition: 1996
Status: Active
Series: Unlimited — Modern Design
Original Issue Price: £25.00, U.S. $79.50

Colourways	U.S. $	Can. $	U.K. £
1. Azure	79.50	100.00	25.00
2. Emerald	79.50	100.00	25.00
3. Ruby	79.50	100.00	25.00

CT-1374
FOURSOME

Designer: Alastair MacIntosh
Type: Weight — Spherical
Edition: 1996
Status: Active
Series: Unlimited — Modern Design
Original Issue Price: £27.00, U.S. $79.50

Name	U.S. $	Can. $	U.K. £
Foursome	87.50	125.00	28.00

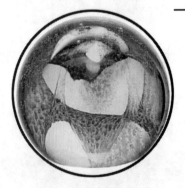

CT-1375
BIG TOP

Designer: Alastair MacIntosh
Type: Weight — Spherical
Edition: 1996
Status: Active
Series: Unlimited — Modern Design
Original Issue Price: £28.00, U.S. $87.50

Name	U.S. $	Can. $	U.K. £
Big Top	95.00	130.00	29.00

CT-1376
EXTRAVAGANZA

Designer: Colin Terris
Type: Weight — Spherical
Colour: See below
Edition: 1996
Status: Active
Series: Unlimited — Modern Design
Original Issue Price: £24.00, U.S. $72.50

Colourways	U.S. $	Can. $	U.K. £
1. Black	79.50	100.00	25.00
2. Blue	79.50	100.00	25.00
3. Green	79.50	100.00	25.00

CT-1377
HM QUEEN ELIZABETH II 70TH BIRTHDAY CROWN OVERLAY

Designer: Colin Terris
Type: Weight — Spherical
Edition: 1996 in a limited edition of 70
Status: Closed at No. 34
Original Issue Price: £200.00

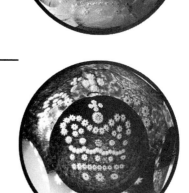

Name	U.S. $	Can. $	U.K. £
HM Queen Elizabeth II 70th Birthday Crown Overlay	350.00	525.00	200.00

Note: The 70th birthday weights and perfume bottle were not issued in the U.S.

CT-1378
HM QUEEN ELIZABETH II 70TH BIRTHDAY CROWN

Designer: Colin Terris
Type: Weight — Spherical
Edition: 1996 in a limited edition of 250
Status: Closed at No. 69
Original Issue Price: £125.00

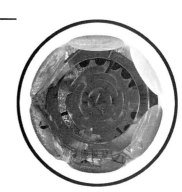

Name	U.S. $	Can. $	U.K. £
HM Queen Elizabeth II 70th Birthday Crown	250.00	350.00	125.00

CT-1379
HM QUEEN ELIZABETH II 70TH BIRTHDAY ROSE

Designer: Colin Terris
Type: Weight — Spherical
Edition: 1996 in a limited edition of 70
Status: Closed at No. 42
Original Issue Price: £195.00

Name	U.S. $	Can. $	U.K. £
HM Queen Elizabeth II 70th Birthday Rose	350.00	525.00	200.00

CT-1380
HM QUEEN ELIZABETH II 70TH BIRTHDAY ROSE PERFUME BOTTLE

Designer: Colin Terris
Type: Perfume bottle
Edition: 1996 in a limited edition of 70
Status: Closed at No. 37
Original Issue Price: £250.00

Name	U.S. $	Can. $	U.K. £
HM Queen Elizabeth II 70th Birthday Rose Perfume Bottle	450.00	650.00	250.00

CT-1381
TARANTELLA

Designer:	Philip Chaplain
Type:	Weight — Spherical
Edition:	1997 in a limited edition of 650
Status:	Active
Series:	Limited — Modern Design
Original Issue Price:	£70.00, U.S. $225.00

Name	U.S. $	Can. $	U.K. £
Tarantella	235.00	325.00	75.00

CT-1382
IT'S LIFE JIM

Designer:	Helen MacDonald
Type:	Weight — Spherical, with plinth
Edition:	1997 in a limited edition of 25
Status:	Closed at No. 23
Series:	Limited — Modern Design
Original Issue Price:	£650.00, U.S. $2,125.00

Name	U.S. $	Can. $	U.K. £
It's Life Jim	2,125.00	3,050.00	650.00

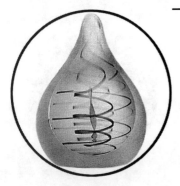

CT-1383
TWISTER

Designer:	Simon Langdon
Type:	Weight — Teardrop
Edition:	1997 in a limited edition of 650
Status:	Closed at No. 249
Series:	Limited — Modern Design
Original Issue Price:	£80.00, U.S. $265.00

Name	U.S. $	Can. $	U.K. £
Twister	265.00	375.00	85.00

CT-1384
NORSE LEGEND

Designer:	Philip Chaplain
Type:	Weight — Spherical
Edition:	1997 in a limited edition of 750
Status:	Fully subscribed
Series:	Limited — Modern Design
Original Issue Price:	£60.00, U.S. $195.00

Name	U.S. $	Can. $	U.K. £
Norse Legend	200.00	275.00	65.00

CT-1385
HOMEWARD BOUND

Designer:	Colin Terris
Type:	Weight — Spherical
Edition:	1997 in a limited edition of 750
Status:	Active
Series:	Limited — Modern Design
Original Issue Price:	£55.00, U.S. $175.00

Name	U.S. $	Can. $	U.K. £
Homeward Bound	175.00	250.00	60.00

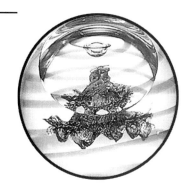

CT-1386
FRAMBOISE

Designer:	Philip Chaplain
Type:	Weight — Spherical
Edition:	1997 in a limited edition of 650
Status:	Fully subscribed
Series:	Limited — Modern Design
Original Issue Price:	£70.00, U.S. $225.00

Name	U.S. $	Can. $	U.K. £
Framboise	225.00	325.00	70.00

CT-1387
DOUBLE MAGNUM 97

Designer:	Franco Toffolo
Type:	Weight — Spherical, double magnum
Edition:	1997 in a limited edition of 150
Status:	Closed at No. 79
Series:	Limited — Modern Design
Original Issue Price:	£195.00, U.S. $595.00

Name	U.S. $	Can. $	U.K. £
Double Magnum 97	600.00	850.00	200.00

CT-1388
GOLDEN MITRE

Designer:	Alastair MacIntosh
Type:	Weight — Domed
Edition:	1997 in a limited edition of 50
Status:	Fully subscribed
Series:	Limited — Modern Design
Original Issue Price:	£275.00, U.S. $895.00

Name	U.S. $	Can. $	U.K. £
Golden Mitre	900.00	1,250.00	275.00

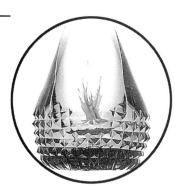

CT-1389
AZTEC RAINFLOWER

Designer:	Alastair MacIntosh
Type:	Weight — Domed
Edition:	1997 in a limited edition of 350
Status:	Fully subscribed
Series:	Limited — Modern Design
Original Issue Price:	£125.00, U.S. $395.00

Name	U.S. $	Can. $	U.K. £
Aztec Rainflower	400.00	550.00	125.00

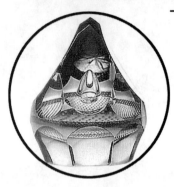

CT-1390
HERMITAGE

Designer:	Alastair MacIntosh
Type:	Weight — Sculptural
Edition:	1997 in a limited edition of 50
Status:	Fully subscribed
Series:	Limited — Modern Design
Original Issue Price:	£275.00, U.S. $895.00

Name	U.S. $	Can. $	U.K. £
Hermitage	900.00	1,300.00	275.00

CT-1391
WHITE NARCISSUS

Designer:	Helen MacDonald
Type:	Weight — Spherical
Edition:	1997 in a limited edition of 75
Status:	Fully subscribed
Series:	Limited — Modern Design
Original Issue Price:	£250.00, U.S. $825.00

Name	U.S. $	Can. $	U.K. £
White Narcissus	825.00	1,150.00	250.00

CT-1392
OUT OF THE BLUE

Designer:	Philip Chaplain
Type:	Weight — Spherical
Edition:	1997 in a limited edition of 650
Status:	Closed at No. 618
Series:	Limited — Modern Design
Original Issue Price:	£70.00, U.S. $225.00

Name	U.S. $	Can. $	U.K. £
Out of the Blue	225.00	325.00	70.00

CT-1393
HICKORY DICKORY DOCK

Designer:	Helen MacDonald
Type:	Weight — Domed
Edition:	1997 in a limited edition of 100
Status:	Closed at No. 78
Series:	Limited — Modern Design
Original Issue Price:	£300.00, U.S. $950.00

Name	U.S. $	Can. $	U.K. £
Hickory Dickory Dock	950.00	1,350.00	300.00

CT-1394
SOUTHERN EXPOSURE

Designer:	Helen MacDonald
Type:	Weight — Sculptural
Edition:	1997 in a limited edition of 25
Status:	Fully subscribed
Series:	Limited — Modern Design
Original Issue Price:	£650.00, U.S. $2,125.00

Name	U.S. $	Can. $	U.K. £
Southern Exposure	2,125.00	3,050.00	650.00

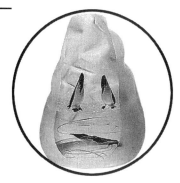

CT-1395
DREAM WEAVER

Designer:	Philip Chaplain
Type:	Weight — Domed
Edition:	1997 in a limited edition of 750
Status:	Fully subscribed
Series:	Limited — Modern Design
Original Issue Price:	£60.00, U.S. $195.00

Name	U.S. $	Can. $	U.K. £
Dream Weaver	200.00	275.00	60.00

CT-1396
INNOCENCE

Designer:	Colin Terris
Type:	Weight — Spherical
Edition:	1997 in a limited edition of 75
Status:	Fully subscribed
Series:	Limited — Modern Design
Original Issue Price:	£250.00, U.S. $825.00

Name	U.S. $	Can. $	U.K. £
Innocence	825.00	1,150.00	250.00

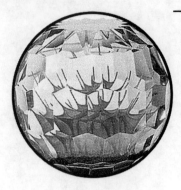

CT-1397
CACTUS CITY

Designer:	Alastair MacIntosh
Type:	Weight — Spherical
Edition:	1997 in a limited edition of 50
Status:	Fully subscribed
Series:	Limited — Modern Design

Original Issue Price: £295.00, U.S. $975.00

Name	U.S. $	Can. $	U.K. £
Cactus City	975.00	1,400.00	300.00

CT-1398
AULD LANG SYNE

Designer:	Helen MacDonald
Type:	Weight — Domed
Edition:	1997 in a limited edition of 125
Status:	Closed at No. 96
Series:	Limited — Modern Design

Original Issue Price: £250.00, U.S. $795.00

Name	U.S. $	Can. $	U.K. £
Auld Lang Syne	800.00	1,150.00	250.00

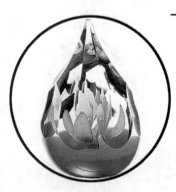

CT-1399
ADMIRATION

Designer:	Colin Terris
Type:	Weight — Teardrop, magnum size
Edition:	1997 in a limited edition of 75
Status:	Fully subscribed
Series:	Limited — Modern Design

Original Issue Price: £300.00, U.S. $975.00

Name	U.S. $	Can. $	U.K. £
Admiration	975.00	1,400.00	300.00

CT-1400
SPIRIT DANCER

Designer:	Jason Green
Type:	Weight — Teardrop
Edition:	1997 in a limited edition of 650
Status:	Fully subscribed
Series:	Limited — Modern Design

Original Issue Price: £75.00, U.S. $250.00

Name	U.S. $	Can. $	U.K. £
Spirit Dancer	250.00	350.00	75.00

CT-1401
SPRING SENTINEL

Designer: Helen MacDonald
Type: Weight — Teardrop
Edition: 1997 in a limited edition of 125
Status: Closed at No. 102
Series: Limited — Modern Design
Original Issue Price: £250.00, U.S. $795.00

Name	U.S. $	Can. $	U.K. £
Spring Sentinel	800.00	1,150.00	250.00

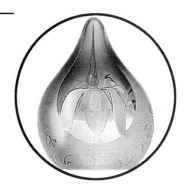

CT-1402
NORMAN CONQUEST

Designer: Colin Terris
Type: Weight — Domed
Edition: 1997 in a limited edition of 100
Status: Fully subscribed
Series: Limited — Modern Design
Original Issue Price: £275.00, U.S. $875.00

Name	U.S. $	Can. $	U.K. £
Norman Conquest	875.00	1,250.00	275.00

CT-1403
MAGIC POTION

Designer: Alastair MacIntosh
Type: Weight — Spherical
Edition: 1997 in a limited edition of 750
Status: Fully subscribed
Series: Limited — Modern Design
Original Issue Price: £45.00, U.S. $150.00

Name	U.S. $	Can. $	U.K. £
Magic Potion	150.00	200.00	45.00

CT-1404
TEMPTATION

Designer: Helen MacDonald
Type: Weight — Spherical
Edition: 1997 in a limited edition of 100
Status: Closed at No. 62
Series: Limited — Modern Design
Original Issue Price: £275.00, U.S. $875.00

Name	U.S. $	Can. $	U.K. £
Temptation	875.00	1,250.00	275.00

CT-1405
ACQUIESCENCE

Designer:	Colin Terris
Type:	Weight — Spherical
Edition:	1997 in a limited edition of 650
Status:	Fully subscribed
Series:	Limited — Modern Design
Original Issue Price:	£65.00, U.S. $210.00

Name	U.S. $	Can. $	U.K. £
Acquiescence	210.00	300.00	65.00

CT-1406
TRINCULO

Designer:	Alan Scrimgeour
Type:	Weight — Domed
Edition:	1997 in a limited edition of 150
Status:	Fully subscribed
Series:	Limited — Modern Design
Original Issue Price:	£195.00, U.S. $625.00

Name	U.S. $	Can. $	U.K. £
Trinculo	625.00	900.00	200.00

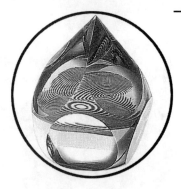

CT-1407
IMPRINT

Designer:	Alastair MacIntosh
Type:	Weight — Pyramid facets
Edition:	1997 in a limited edition of 200
Status:	Active
Series:	Limited — Modern Design
Original Issue Price:	£160.00, U.S. $525.00

Name	U.S. $	Can. $	U.K. £
Imprint	525.00	715.00	165.00

CT-1408
CRITICAL MASS

Designer:	Philip Chaplain
Type:	Weight — Spherical
Edition:	1997 in a limited edition of 750
Status:	Active
Series:	Limited — Modern Design
Original Issue Price:	£55.00, U.S. $175.00

Name	U.S. $	Can. $	U.K. £
Critical Mass	185.00	260.00	60.00

CT-1409
LIFE'S A BEACH

Designer:	Allan Scott
Type:	Weight — Spherical
Edition:	1997 in a limited edition of 75
Status:	Fully subscribed
Series:	Limited — Modern Design
Original Issue Price:	£295.00, U.S. $975.00

Name	U.S. $	Can. $	U.K. £
Life's a Beach	975.00	1,400.00	300.00

CT-1410
AMMADORA

Designer:	Caithness Design Studio
Type:	Weight — Hexagonal column
Edition:	1997 in a limited edition of 50
Status:	Fully subscribed
Series:	Limited — Modern Design
Original Issue Price:	£275.00, U.S. $895.00

Name	U.S. $	Can. $	U.K. £
Ammadora	900.00	1,250.00	275.00

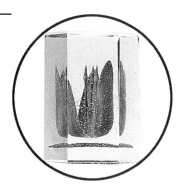

CT-1411
LOS TRES AMIGOS

Designer:	Neil Allan and Jason Green
Type:	Weight — Domed
Edition:	1997 in a limited edition of 350
Status:	Closed at No. 304
Series:	Limited — Modern Design
Original Issue Price:	£115.00, U.S. $375.00

Name	U.S. $	Can. $	U.K. £
Los Tres Amigos	375.00	525.00	120.00

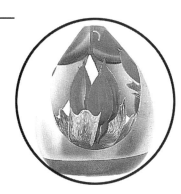

CT-1412
SACRED SPIRIT

Designer:	Helen MacDonald
Type:	Weight — Sculptural
Edition:	1997 in a limited edition of 250
Status:	Closed at No. 237
Series:	Limited — Modern Design
Original Issue Price:	£150.00, U.S. $475.00

Name	U.S. $	Can. $	U.K. £
Sacred Spirit	475.00	675.00	150.00

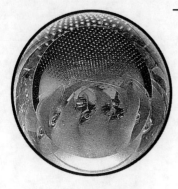

CT-1413
INCOGNITO

Designer:	Alastair MacIntosh
Type:	Weight — Spherical
Edition:	1997 in a limited edition of 650
Status:	Active
Series:	Limited — Modern Design
Original Issue Price:	£70.00, U.S. $225.00

Name	U.S. $	Can. $	U.K. £
Incognito	225.00	325.00	75.00

CT-1414
METAMORPHOSIS

Designer:	Philip Chaplain
Type:	Weight — Spherical
Edition:	1997 in a limited edition of 650
Status:	Active
Series:	Limited — Modern Design
Original Issue Price:	£70.00, U.S. $225.00

Name	U.S. $	Can. $	U.K. £
Metamorphosis	240.00	325.00	75.00

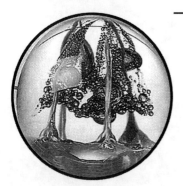

CT-1415
NEMESIS

Designer:	Philip Chaplain
Type:	Weight — Spherical
Edition:	1997 in a limited edition of 750
Status:	Active
Series:	Limited — Modern Design
Original Issue Price:	£60.00, U.S. $195.00

Name	U.S. $	Can. $	U.K. £
Nemesis	210.00	285.00	65.00

CT-1416
PENTECOST

Designer:	Helen MacDonald
Type:	Weight — Domed
Edition:	1997 in a limited edition of 75
Status:	Fully subscribed
Series:	Limited — Modern Design
Original Issue Price:	£250.00, U.S. $825.00

Name	U.S. $	Can. $	U.K. £
Pentecost	825.00	1,150.00	250.00

CT-1417
GLADIATORS

Designer: Garry Kean
Type: Weight — Domed
Edition: 1997 in a limited edition of 150
Status: Closed at No. 130
Series: Limited — Modern Design
Original Issue Price: £175.00, U.S. $575.00

Name	U.S. $	Can. $	U.K. £
Gladiators	575.00	825.00	175.00

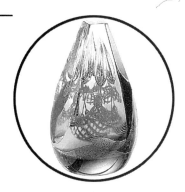

CT-1418
SALADIN

Designer: Colin Terris
Type: Weight — Domed
Edition: 1997 in a limited edition of 1,995
Status: Closed at No. 1,995
Original Issue Price: £75.00, U.S. $215.00

Name	U.S. $	Can. $	U.K. £
Saladin	215.00	300.00	85.00

Note: This is the 1997 Collectors' Weight.

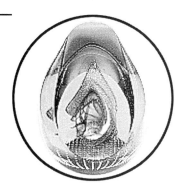

CT-1419
VISITATION

Designer: Colin Terris
Type: Weight — Spherical, magnum size
Edition: 1997 in a limited edition of 100
Status: Closed at No. 61
Series: Limited — Modern Design
Original Issue Price: £225.00, U.S. $875.00

Name	U.S. $	Can. $	U.K. £
Visitation	875.00	1,250.00	225.00

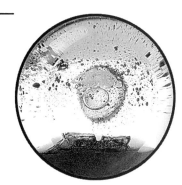

CT-1420
BIOSPHERE

Designer: Alastair MacIntosh
Type: Weight — Spherical
Edition: 1997 in a limited edition of 500
Status: Fully subscribed
Series: Limited — Modern Design
Original Issue Price: £90.00, U.S. $295.00

Name	U.S. $	Can. $	U.K. £
Biosphere	300.00	425.00	90.00

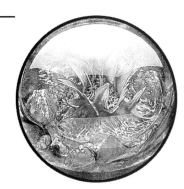

CT-1421
DOWN ON THE FARM

Designer: Colin Terris
Type: Weight — Spherical
Edition: 1997 in a limited edition of 50
Status: Closed at No. 30
Series: Traditional Collection
Original Issue Price: £325.00, U.S. $1,050.00

Name	U.S. $	Can. $	U.K. £
Down on the Farm	1,050.00	1,500.00	325.00

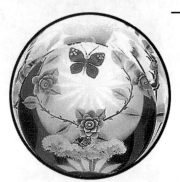

CT-1422
RED ADMIRAL

Designer: William Manson
Type: Weight — Spherical
Edition: 1997 in a limited edition of 50
Status: Closed at No. 28
Series: Traditional Collection
Original Issue Price: £395.00, U.S. $1,295.00

Name	U.S. $	Can. $	U.K. £
Red Admiral	1,300.00	1,875.00	400.00

CT-1423
WALKABOUT

Designer: William Manson
Type: Weight — Spherical
Edition: 1997 in a limited edition of 50
Status: Closed at No. 34
Series: Traditional Collection
Original Issue Price: £325.00, U.S. $1,050.00

Name	U.S. $	Can. $	U.K. £
Walkabout	1,050.00	1,500.00	325.00

Note: This paperweight features surface lampwork.

CT-1424
FLAMINGO

Designer: William Manson
Type: Weight — Spherical, medium-sized
Edition: 1997 in a limited edition of 150
Status: Closed at No. 112
Series: Traditional Collection — Medium Sized
Original Issue Price: £85.00, U.S. $265.00

Name	U.S. $	Can. $	U.K. £
Flamingo	265.00	375.00	85.00

CT-1425
KINGFISHER

Designer:	William Manson
Type:	Weight — Spherical, medium-sized
Edition:	1997 in a limited edition of 150
Status:	Closed at No. 90
Series:	Traditional Collection — Medium Sized

Original Issue Price: £85.00, U.S. $265.00

Name	U.S. $	Can. $	U.K. £
Kingfisher	265.00	375.00	85.00

CT-1426
HERON

Designer:	William Manson
Type:	Weight — Spherical, medium-sized
Edition:	1997 in a limited edition of 150
Status:	Closed at No. 112
Series:	Traditional Collection — Medium Sized

Original Issue Price: £85.00, U.S. $265.00

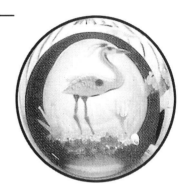

Name	U.S. $	Can. $	U.K. £
Heron	265.00	375.00	85.00

CT-1427
SWAN

Designer:	William Manson
Type:	Weight — Spherical, medium-sized
Edition:	1997 in a limited edition of 150
Status:	Fully subscribed
Series:	Traditional Collection — Medium Sized

Original Issue Price: £85.00, U.S. $265.00

Name	U.S. $	Can. $	U.K. £
Swan	265.00	375.00	85.00

CT-1428
SNAKE BASKET

Designer:	Colin Terris and William Manson
Type:	Weight — Spherical
Edition:	1997 in a limited edition of 50
Status:	Closed at No. 29
Series:	Traditional Collection

Original Issue Price: £350.00, U.S. $1,150.00

Name	U.S. $	Can. $	U.K. £
Snake Basket	1,150.00	1,650.00	350.00

CT-1429
ROCK POOL

Designer:	William Manson
Type:	Weight — Spherical
Edition:	1997 in a limited edition of 50
Status:	Closed at No. 40
Series:	Traditional Collection
Original Issue Price:	£360.00, U.S. $1,175.00

Name	U.S. $	Can. $	U.K. £
Rock Pool	1,175.00	1,700.00	550.00

CT-1430
DESTINATION MARS

Designer:	Colin Terris
Type:	Weight — Spherical
Edition:	1997 in a limited edition of 500
Status:	Closed
Original Issue Price:	£70.00, U.S. $225.00

Name	U.S. $	Can. $	U.K. £
Destination Mars	225.00	325.00	70.00

CT-1431
DRIFTING BY

Designer:	William Manson
Type:	Weight — Spherical
Edition:	1997 in a limited edition of 50
Status:	Closed at No. 36
Series:	Traditional Collection
Original Issue Price:	£315.00, U.S. $975.00

Name	U.S. $	Can. $	U.K. £
Drifting By	975.00	1,400.00	315.00

CT-1432
TREASURE TROVE

Designer:	William Manson
Type:	Weight — Spherical
Edition:	1997 in a limited edition of 50
Status:	Closed at No. 31
Series:	Traditional Collection
Original Issue Price:	£395.00, U.S. $1,295.00

Name	U.S. $	Can. $	U.K. £
Treasure Trove	1,300.00	1,875.00	400.00

CT-1433
CRAB APPLE

Designer: Allan Scott
Type: Weight — Spherical
Edition: 1997 in a limited edition of 50
Status: Closed at No. 31
Series: Traditional Collection — Nature Study
Original Issue Price: £350.00, U.S. $1,125.00

Name	U.S. $	Can. $	U.K. £
Crab Apple	1,125.00	1,600.00	350.00

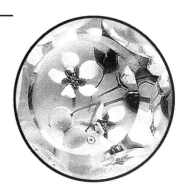

CT-1434
SUNSET DUET

Designer: Allan Scott
Type: Weight — Spherical
Edition: 1997 in a limited edition of 25
Status: Closed at No. 20
Series: Traditional Collection — Nature Study
Original Issue Price: £595.00, U.S. $1,925.00

Name	U.S. $	Can. $	U.K. £
Sunset Duet	1,925.00	2,750.00	600.00

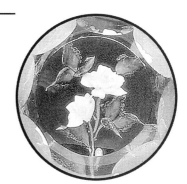

CT-1435
FLEUR ROUGE

Designer: Allan Scott
Type: Weight — Spherical
Edition: 1997 in a limited edition of 25
Status: Closed at No. 23
Series: Traditional Collection — Nature Study
Original Issue Price: £595.00, U.S. $1,925.00

Name	U.S. $	Can. $	U.K. £
Fleur Rouge	1,925.00	2,750.00	600.00

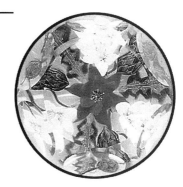

CT-1436
TOKEN OF LOVE

Designer: Allan Scott
Type: Weight — Spherical
Edition: 1997 in a limited edition of 25
Status: Fully subscribed
Series: Traditional Collection — Nature Study
Original Issue Price: £595.00, U.S. $1,925.00

Name	U.S. $	Can. $	U.K. £
Token of Love	1,925.00	2,750.00	600.00

CT-1437
CASTLE GARDEN

Designer: Harry McKay
Type: Weight — Pyramid facets
Edition: 1997 in a limited edition of 50
Status: Closed at No. 47
Series: Traditional Collection — Nature Study
Original Issue Price: £400.00, U.S. $1,300.00

Name	U.S. $	Can. $	U.K. £
Castle Garden	1,300.00	1,850.00	400.00

CT-1438A
FRUIT

Designer: Margot Thomson
Type: Weight — Spherical
Edition: 1997 in a limited edition of 25
Status: Fully subscribed
Series: Traditional Collection — Nature Study
Original Issue Price: £850.00/set, U.S. $2,775.00/set

Name	U.S. $	Can. $	U.K. £
Fruit	1,400.00	2,000.00	425.00
Set	2,800.00	4,000.00	850.00

Note: CT-1438A and B were issued and sold as a set.

CT-1438B
VEG

Designer: Margot Thomson
Type: Weight — Spherical
Edition: 1997 in a limited edition of 25
Status: Fully subscribed
Series: Traditional Collection — Nature Study
Original Issue Price: £850.00/set, U.S. $2,775.00/set

Name	U.S. $	Can. $	U.K. £
Veg	1,400.00	2,000.00	425.00

CT-1439
SPRING BOTANICAL

Designer: Rosette Fleming
Type: Weight — Spherical
Edition: 1997 in a limited edition of 50
Status: Fully subscribed
Series: Whitefriars Collection
Original Issue Price: £175.00, U.S. $575.00

Name	U.S. $	Can. $	U.K. £
Spring Botanical	575.00	825.00	175.00

CT-1440
AUTUMN GOLD

Designer: Rosette Fleming
Type: Weight — Spherical
Edition: 1997 in a limited edition of 50
Status: Fully subscribed
Series: Whitefriars Collection
Original Issue Price: £150.00, U.S. $495.00

Name	U.S. $	Can. $	U.K. £
Autumn Gold	500.00	700.00	150.00

CT-1441
DIAMOND BOUQUET

Designer: Rosette Fleming
Type: Weight — Spherical
Edition: 1997 in a limited edition of 50
Status: Closed at No. 41
Series: Whitefriars Collection
Original Issue Price: £195.00, U.S. $650.00

Name	U.S. $	Can. $	U.K. £
Diamond Bouquet	650.00	925.00	200.00

CT-1442
FESTIVE DELIGHT

Designer: Rosette Fleming
Type: Weight — Spherical
Edition: 1997 in a limited edition of 50
Status: Closed at No. 40
Series: Whitefriars Collection
Original Issue Price: £175.00, U.S. $575.00

Name	U.S. $	Can. $	U.K. £
Festive Delight	575.00	825.00	150.00

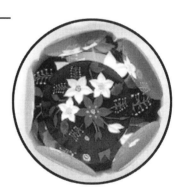

CT-1443
TRILLIUM

Designer: Rosette Fleming
Type: Weight — Spherical
Edition: 1997 in a limited edition of 50
Status: Closed at No. 30
Series: Whitefriars Collection
Original Issue Price: £150.00, U.S. $495.00

Name	U.S. $	Can. $	U.K. £
Trillium	500.00	700.00	150.00

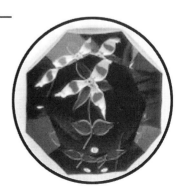

CT-1444
BRIGHT NEW DAY

Designer: Rosette Fleming
Type: Weight — Spherical
Edition: 1997 in a limited edition of 50
Status: Fully subscribed
Series: Whitefriars Collection
Original Issue Price: £135.00, U.S. $475.00

Name	U.S. $	Can. $	U.K. £
Bright New Day	475.00	675.00	135.00

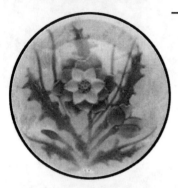

CT-1445
TRADITIONAL TRIBUTE

Designer: Allan Scott
Type: Weight — Spherical
Edition: 1997 in a limited edition of 50
Status: Fully subscribed
Series: Whitefriars Collection
Original Issue Price: £110.00, U.S. $375.00

Name	U.S. $	Can. $	U.K. £
Traditional Tribute	375.00	525.00	110.00

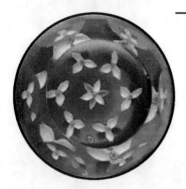

CT-1446
EMERALD DANCERS

Designer: Rosette Fleming
Type: Weight — Spherical
Edition: 1997 in a limited edition of 50
Status: Fully subscribed
Series: Whitefriars Collection
Original Issue Price: £175.00, U.S. $575.00

Name	U.S. $	Can. $	U.K. £
Emerald Dancers	575.00	825.00	175.00

CT-1447
VICTORIAN MEMORIES

Designer: Allan Scott
Type: Weight — Spherical
Edition: 1997 in a limited edition of 50
Status: Fully subscribed
Series: Whitefriars Collection
Original Issue Price: £110.00, U.S. $395.00

Name	U.S. $	Can. $	U.K. £
Victorian Memories	400.00	550.00	110.00

CT-1448
BURGUNDY BLOOM

Designer:	Rosette Fleming		
Type:	Weight — Spherical		
Edition:	1997 in a limited edition of 50		
Status:	Closed at No. 40		
Series:	Whitefriars Collection		
Original Issue Price: £135.00, U.S. $450.00			

Name	U.S. $	Can. $	U.K. £
Burgundy Bloom	450.00	650.00	135.00

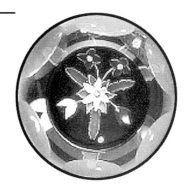

CT-1449
SWEET SENSATION KINGFISHER

Designer:	Rosette Fleming		
Type:	Weight — Spherical, medium-sized		
Edition:	1997 in a limited edition of 150		
Status:	Closed at No. 55		
Series:	Whitefriars Collection — Medium Sized		
Original Issue Price: £80.00, U.S. $250.00			

Name	U.S. $	Can. $	U.K. £
Sweet Sensation Kingfisher	250.00	350.00	80.00

CT-1450
SWEET SENSATION COBALT

Designer:	Rosette Fleming		
Type:	Weight — Spherical, medium-sized		
Edition:	1997 in a limited edition of 150		
Status:	Closed at No. 60		
Series:	Whitefriars Collection — Medium Sized		
Original Issue Price: £80.00, U.S. $250.00			

Name	U.S. $	Can. $	U.K. £
Sweet Sensation Cobalt	250.00	350.00	80.00

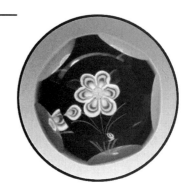

CT-1451
CHERRY PIE

Designer:	Stuart Cumming		
Type:	Weight — Spherical		
Edition:	1997		
Status:	Active		
Series:	Unlimited — Modern Design		
Original Issue Price: £28.50, U.S. $95.00			

Name	U.S. $	Can. $	U.K. £
Cherry Pie	95.00	130.00	29.00

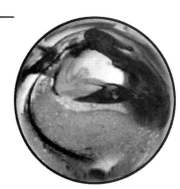

CT-1452
RHYTHM 'N BLUES

Designer:	Helen MacDonald
Type:	Weight — Spherical
Edition:	1997
Status:	Active
Series:	Unlimited — Modern Design
Original Issue Price:	£30.00, U.S. $95.00

Name	U.S. $	Can. $	U.K. £
Rhythm 'n Blues	95.00	125.00	30.00

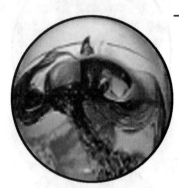

CT-1453
MOONCRYSTAL

Designer:	Colin Terris
Type:	Weight — Spherical, medium-sized
Colour:	See below
Edition:	1997
Status:	Active
Series:	Medium and Miniature Size
Original Issue Price:	£15.00, U.S. $49.50

Colourways	U.S. $	Can. $	U.K. £
1. Black	49.50	60.00	15.00
2. Blue	49.50	60.00	15.00
3. Green	49.50	60.00	15.00
4. Hyacinth	49.50	60.00	15.00
5. Pink	49.50	60.00	15.00
6. Yellow	49.50	60.00	15.00

CT-1454
OPTIX

Designer:	Philip Chaplain
Type:	Weight — Spherical
Colour:	See below
Edition:	1997
Status:	Active
Series:	Unlimited — Modern Design
Original Issue Price:	£20.00, U.S. $65.00

Colourways	U.S. $	Can. $	U.K. £
1. Gold and aqua	65.00	90.00	20.00
2. Green and blue	65.00	90.00	20.00
3. Purple and violet	65.00	90.00	20.00

Note: This paperweight has a ribbed finish.

CT-1455
HARMONICS

Designer: Alastair MacIntosh
Type: Weight — Spherical
Colour: See below
Edition: 1997
Status: Active
Series: Unlimited — Modern Design
Original Issue Price: £24.00, U.S. $79.50

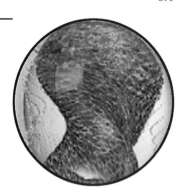

Colourways	U.S. $	Can. $	U.K. £
1. Blue	79.50	110.00	24.50
2. Emerald	79.50	110.00	24.50
3. Purple	79.50	110.00	24.50

CT-1456
SUGAR FRUITS

Designer: Philip Chaplain and Stuart Cumming
Type: Weight — Spherical
Colour: See below
Edition: 1997
Status: Active
Series: Unlimited — Modern Design
Original Issue Price: £29.00, U.S. $95.00

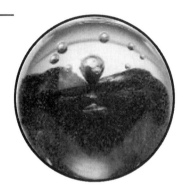

Colourways	U.S. $	Can. $	U.K. £
1. Blackberry (fuchsia)	95.00	130.00	29.50
2. Blueberry (blue)	95.00	130.00	29.50
3. Gooseberry (green)	95.00	130.00	29.50
4. Raspberry (red)	95.00	130.00	29.50

CT-1457
STRANGE BREW

Designer: Franco Toffolo
Type: Weight — Spherical, magnum size
Edition:·   1997
Status: Closed
Series: Unlimited — Modern Design
Original Issue Price: £60.00, U.S. $195.00

Name	U.S. $	Can. $	U.K. £
Strange Brew	300.00	450.00	195.00

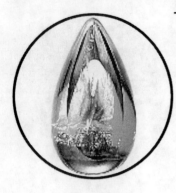

CT-1458
APPARITION

Designer:	Alastair MacIntosh
Type:	Weight — Domed
Edition:	1997 in a limited edition of 500
Status:	Active
Series:	Premier Stockist Paperweight Collection
Original Issue Price:	£104.00

Name	U.S. $	Can. $	U.K. £
Apparition	—	—	104.00

Note: Weights CT-1458 through 1463 were offered only through U.K. Premier Stockists.

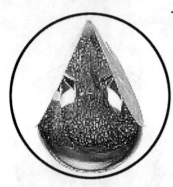

CT-1459
GOLDEN SANCTUARY

Designer:	Alastair MacIntosh
Type:	Weight — Pyramid facets
Edition:	1997 in a limited edition of 200
Status:	Active
Series:	Premier Stockist Paperweight Collection
Original Issue Price:	£165.00

Name	U.S. $	Can. $	U.K. £
Golden Sanctuary	—	—	165.00

CT-1460
KNOSSOS

Designer:	Alastair MacIntosh
Type:	Weight — Domed
Edition:	1997 in a limited edition of 100
Status:	Active
Series:	Premier Stockist Paperweight Collection
Original Issue Price:	£258.00

Name	U.S. $	Can. $	U.K. £
Knossos	—	—	258.00

CT-1461
STELLA MARIS

Designer:	Colin Terris
Type:	Weight — Spherical
Edition:	1997 in a limited edition of 75
Status:	Closed at No. 57
Series:	Premier Stockist Paperweight Collection
Original Issue Price:	£250.00

Name	U.S. $	Can. $	U.K. £
Stella Maris	425.00	600.00	250.00

CT-1462
REINCARNATION

Designer:	Alastair MacIntosh
Type:	Weight — Domed, multifaceted
Edition:	1997 in a limited edition of 50
Status:	Closed at No. 42
Series:	Premier Stockist Paperweight Collection
Original Issue Price:	£275.00

Name	U.S. $	Can. $	U.K. £
Reincarnation	450.00	675.00	275.00

CT-1463
FRIVOLITY

Designer:	Philip Chaplain
Type:	Weight — Spherical
Edition:	1997 in a limited edition of 350
Status:	Active
Series:	Premier Stockist Paperweight Collection
Original Issue Price:	£105.00

Name	U.S. $	Can. $	U.K. £
Frivolity	—	—	105.00

CT-1464
CARNIVAL CASCADE

Designer:	Colin Terris
Type:	Weight — Domed
Edition:	1997 in a limited edition of 650
Status:	Fully subscribed
Series:	Colin Terris Designer Collection
Original Issue Price:	£60.00, U.S. $195.00

Name	U.S. $	Can. $	U.K. £
Carnival Cascade	195.00	275.00	60.00

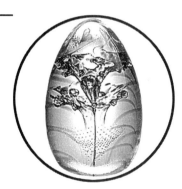

CT-1465
CACTUS REFLECTION

Designer:	Colin Terris
Type:	Weight — Domed
Edition:	1997 in a limited edition of 350
Status:	Fully subscribed
Series:	Colin Terris Designer Collection
Original Issue Price:	£125.00, U.S. $395.00

Name	U.S. $	Can. $	U.K. £
Cactus Reflection	400.00	575.00	130.00

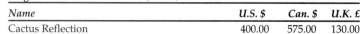

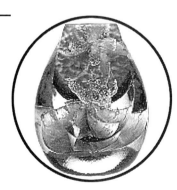

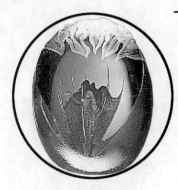

CT-1466
BLUE LAGOON

Designer:	Colin Terris
Type:	Weight — Domed
Edition:	1997 in a limited edition of 100
Status:	Fully subscribed
Series:	Colin Terris Designer Collection
Original Issue Price:	£225.00, U.S. $695.00

Name	U.S. $	Can. $	U.K. £
Blue Lagoon	700.00	1,000.00	225.00

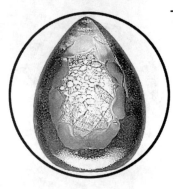

CT-1467
EMERALD GROTTO

Designer:	Colin Terris
Type:	Weight — Domed
Edition:	1997 in a limited edition of 100
Status:	Fully subscribed
Series:	Colin Terris Designer Collection
Original Issue Price:	£250.00, U.S. $795.00

Name	U.S. $	Can. $	U.K. £
Emerald Grotto	800.00	1,150.00	250.00

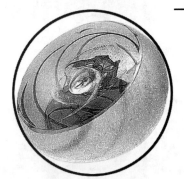

CT-1468
CHUCKIE STANE

Designer:	Colin Terris
Type:	Weight — Ovoid
Edition:	1997 in a limited edition of 150
Status:	Active
Series:	Colin Terris Designer Collection
Original Issue Price:	£175.00, U.S. $550.00

Name	U.S. $	Can. $	U.K. £
Chuckie Stane	550.00	785.00	180.00

Note: "Chuckie stane" is a Scottish expression for a pebble or stone found at the edge of the ocean.

CT-1469
CORAL GARDEN

Designer:	Colin Terris
Type:	Weight — Spherical
Edition:	1997 in a limited edition of 500
Status:	Fully subscribed
Series:	Colin Terris Designer Collection
Original Issue Price:	£80.00, U.S. $250.00

Name	U.S. $	Can. $	U.K. £
Coral Garden	250.00	350.00	80.00

CT-1470
PINK BEAUTY

Designer: Colin Terris
Type: Weight — Spherical
Edition: 1997 in a limited edition of 650
Status: Fully subscribed
Series: Colin Terris Designer Collection
Original Issue Price: £60.00, U.S. $195.00

Name	U.S. $	Can. $	U.K. £
Pink Beauty	200.00	275.00	65.00

CT-1471
CAMELOT II

Designer: Colin Terris
Type: Weight — Domed
Edition: 1997 in a limited edition of 250
Status: Closed at No. 228
Series: Colin Terris Designer Collection
Original Issue Price: £150.00, U.S. $475.00

Name	U.S. $	Can. $	U.K. £
Camelot II	475.00	675.00	150.00

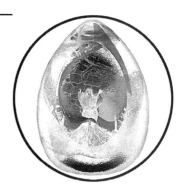

CT-1472
ROYAL GOLDEN WEDDING

Designer: Colin Terris
Type: Weight — Spherical, engraved
Edition: 1997
Status: Closed
Series: HM The Queen's 50th Wedding Anniversary Collection
Original Issue Price: £40.00

Name	U.S. $	Can. $	U.K. £
Royal Golden Wedding	70.00	95.00	40.00

Note: Weights CT-1472, 1473 and 1475 were not issued in the U.S.

CT-1473
ROYAL GOLDEN WEDDING CROWN

Designer: Colin Terris
Type: Weight — Spherical
Edition: 1997 in a limited edition of 50
Status: Fully subscribed
Series: HM The Queen's 50th Wedding Anniversary Collection
Original Issue Price: £350.00

Name	U.S. $	Can. $	U.K. £
Royal Golden Wedding Crown	600.00	900.00	350.00

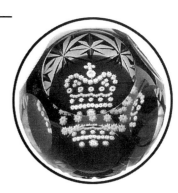

CT-1474
ROYAL GOLDEN WEDDING PERFUME BOTTLE

Designer: Colin Terris
Type: Perfume bottle
Edition: 1997 in a limited edition of 50
Status: Fully subscribed
Series: HM The Queen's 50th Wedding Anniversary Collection
Original Issue Price: £350.00

Name	U.S. $	Can. $	U.K. £
Royal Golden Wedding Perfume Bottle	600.00	900.00	350.00

Note: This perfume bottle was not issued in the U.S.

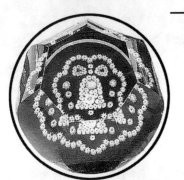

CT-1475
ROYAL GOLDEN WEDDING BELL

Designer: Colin Terris
Type: Weight — Spherical
Edition: 1997 in a limited edition of 50
Status: Fully subscribed
Series: HM The Queen's 50th Wedding Anniversary Collection
Original Issue Price: £275.00

Name	U.S. $	Can. $	U.K. £
Royal Golden Wedding Bell	450.00	600.00	275.00

CT-1476
SEA NYMPHS

Designer: Helen MacDonald
Type: Weight — Pyramid facets
Edition: 1997 in a limited edition of 350
Status: Fully subscribed
Series: Limited — Modern Design
Original Issue Price: £125.00, U.S. $395.00

Name	U.S. $	Can. $	U.K. £
Sea Nymphs	400.00	550.00	125.00

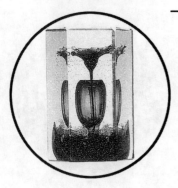

CT-1477
AMAZONIA

Designer: Colin Terris
Type: Weight — Hexagonal column
Edition: 1997 in a limited edition of 50
Status: Fully subscribed
Series: Limited — Modern Design
Original Issue Price: £325.00, U.S. $1,050.00

Name	U.S. $	Can. $	U.K. £
Amazonia	1,050.00	1,500.00	325.00

CT-1478
SHE

Designer: Helen MacDonald
Type: Weight — Domed
Edition: 1997 in a limited edition of 75
Status: Fully subscribed
Series: Limited — Modern Design
Original Issue Price: £295.00, U.S. $950.00

Name	U.S. $	Can. $	U.K. £
She	950.00	1,350.00	300.00

CT-1479
FUJIYAMA

Designer: Alastair MacIntosh
Type: Weight — Domed
Edition: 1997 in a limited edition of 650
Status: Active
Series: Limited — Modern Design
Original Issue Price: £80.00, U.S. $250.00

Name	U.S. $	Can. $	U.K. £
Fujiyama	275.00	370.00	85.00

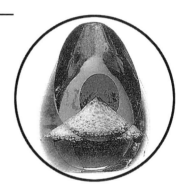

CT-1480
IONIAN VOYAGER

Designer: Colin Terris
Type: Weight — Spherical
Edition: 1997 in a limited edition of 750
Status: Active
Series: Limited — Modern Design
Original Issue Price: £65.00, U.S. $210.00

Name	U.S. $	Can. $	U.K. £
Ionian Voyager	225.00	305.00	70.00

CT-1481
SWEET DREAMS

Designer:	Colin Terris
Type:	Weight — Spherical
Edition:	1997 in a limited edition of 750
Status:	Active
Series:	Limited — Modern Design
Original Issue Price:	£80.00, U.S. $250.00

Name	U.S. $	Can. $	U.K. £
Sweet Dreams	250.00	370.00	85.00

CT-1482
MAGIC ROUNDABOUT

Designer:	Colin Terris
Type:	Weight — Spherical
Edition:	1997 in a limited edition of 750
Status:	Active
Series:	Limited — Modern Design
Original Issue Price:	£65.00, U.S. $210.00

Name	U.S. $	Can. $	U.K. £
Magic Roundabout	225.00	305.00	70.00

CT-1483
THE RED SEA

Designer:	Helen MacDonald
Type:	Weight — Spherical
Edition:	1997 in a limited edition of 75
Status:	Fully subscribed
Series:	Limited — Modern Design
Original Issue Price:	£295.00, U.S. $950.00

Name	U.S. $	Can. $	U.K. £
The Red Sea	950.00	1,350.00	300.00

CT-1484
ABRACADABRA

Designer: Helen MacDonald
Type: Weight — Sculptural
Edition: 1997 in a limited edition of 25
Status: Fully subscribed
Series: Limited — Modern Design
Original Issue Price: £650.00, U.S. $2,125.00

Name	U.S. $	Can. $	U.K. £
Abracadabra	2,125.00	3,000.00	650.00

CT-1485
HALLUCINATION

Designer: Philip Chaplain
Type: Weight — Spherical
Edition: 1997 in a limited edition of 350
Status: Active
Series: Limited — Modern Design
Original Issue Price: £99.00, U.S. $310.00

Name	U.S. $	Can. $	U.K. £
Hallucination	330.00	460.00	105.00

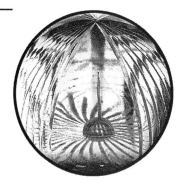

CT-1486
FIREWORK FIESTA

Designer: Colin Terris
Type: Weight — Spherical
Edition: 1997 in a limited edition of 50
Status: Fully subscribed
Series: Limited — Modern Design
Original Issue Price: £325.00, U.S. $1,050.00

Name	U.S. $	Can. $	U.K. £
Firework Fiesta	1,050.00	1,500.00	325.00

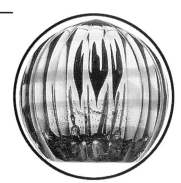

CT-1487
GOLDEN CITADEL

Designer: Colin Terris
Type: Weight — Domed
Edition: 1997 in a limited edition of 650
Status: Active
Series: Limited — Modern Design
Original Issue Price: £80.00, U.S. $250.00

Name	U.S. $	Can. $	U.K. £
Golden Citadel	275.00	370.00	85.00

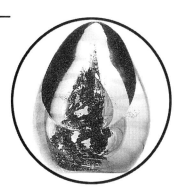

CT-1488
FINALE

Designer: Helen MacDonald
Type: Weight — Teardrop
Edition: 1997 in a limited edition of 50
Status: Fully subscribed
Series: Limited — Modern Design
Original Issue Price: £325.00, U.S. $1,050.00

Name	U.S. $	Can. $	U.K. £
Finale	1,050.00	1,500.00	325.00

CT-1489
ORATION

Designer: Colin Terris
Type: Weight — Spherical
Edition: 1997 in a limited edition of 750
Status: Closed at No. 264
Series: Limited — Modern Design
Original Issue Price: £70.00, U.S. $225.00

Name	U.S. $	Can. $	U.K. £
Oration	225.00	325.00	75.00

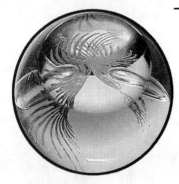

CT-1490
FIRE BIRDS

Designer: Helen MacDonald
Type: Weight — Spherical
Edition: 1997 in a limited edition of 500
Status: Active
Series: Limited — Modern Design
Original Issue Price: £90.00, U.S. $275.00

Name	U.S. $	Can. $	U.K. £
Fire Birds	295.00	415.00	95.00

CT-1491
ROUND THE TWIST

Designer: Alastair MacIntosh
Type: Weight — Spherical
Edition: 1997 in a limited edition of 750
Status: Active
Series: Limited — Modern Design
Original Issue Price: £55.00, U.S. $175.00

Name	U.S. $	Can. $	U.K. £
Round the Twist	185.00	265.00	60.00

CT-1492
ICE FOREST

Designer:	Colin Terris
Type:	Weight — Spherical
Edition:	1997 in a limited edition of 750
Status:	Fully subscribed
Series:	Limited — Modern Design
Original Issue Price:	£60.00, U.S. $195.00

Name	U.S. $	Can. $	U.K. £
Ice Forest	195.00	275.00	65.00

CT-1493
EMERALD CITY

Designer:	Colin Terris
Type:	Weight — Sculptural
Edition:	1997 in a limited edition of 50
Status:	Fully subscribed
Series:	Limited — Modern Design
Original Issue Price:	£350.00, U.S. $1,100.00

Name	U.S. $	Can. $	U.K. £
Emerald City	1,100.00	1,550.00	350.00

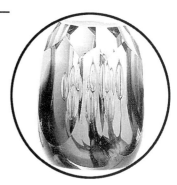

CT-1494
PURITY

Designer:	Alastair MacIntosh and Stuart Cumming
Type:	Weight — Domed
Edition:	1997 in a limited edition of 350
Status:	Fully subscribed
Series:	Limited — Modern Design
Original Issue Price:	£115.00, U.S. $350.00

Name	U.S. $	Can. $	U.K. £
Purity	350.00	500.00	115.00

CT-1495
ANOUSHKA

Designer:	Philip Chaplain
Type:	Weight — Spherical
Edition:	1997 in a limited edition of 650
Status:	Active
Series:	Limited — Modern Design
Original Issue Price:	£75.00, U.S. $250.00

Name	U.S. $	Can. $	U.K. £
Anoushka	250.00	350.00	80.00

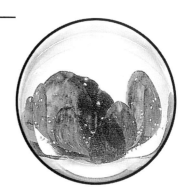

CT-1496
PASSION FLOWER

Designer: Helen MacDonald
Type: Weight — Spherical
Edition: 1997 in a limited edition of 125
Status: Closed at No. 55
Series: Limited — Modern Design
Original Issue Price: £275.00, U.S. $875.00

Name	U.S. $	Can. $	U.K. £
Passion Flower	875.00	1,250.00	300.00

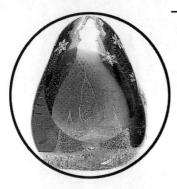

CT-1497
WINTER PALACE

Designer: Helen MacDonald
Type: Weight — Domed
Edition: 1997 in a limited edition of 125
Status: Closed at No. 106
Series: Limited — Modern Design
Original Issue Price: £275.00, U.S. $875.00

Name	U.S. $	Can. $	U.K. £
Winter Palace	875.00	1,250.00	300.00

CT-1498
THE AGE OF CHIVALRY

Designer: Helen MacDonald
Type: Weight — Sculptural
Edition: 1997 in a limited edition of 25
Status: Closed at No. 21
Series: Limited — Modern Design
Original Issue Price: £650.00, U.S. $2,125.00

Name	U.S. $	Can. $	U.K. £
The Age of Chivalry	2,125.00	3,050.00	650.00

CT-1499
TEMPUS FUGIT

Designer: Helen MacDonald
Type: Weight — Spherical
Edition: 1997 in a limited edition of 125
Status: Closed at No. 91
Series: Limited — Modern Design
Original Issue Price: £275.00, U.S. $875.00

Name	U.S. $	Can. $	U.K. £
Tempus Fugit	875.00	1,250.00	275.00

CT-1500
ASTRAL NAVIGATOR

Designer: Colin Terris
Type: Weight — Sculptural/ovoid
Edition: 1997 in a limited edition of 75
Status: Closed at No. 70
Series: Limited — Modern Design
Original Issue Price: £295.00, U.S. $950.00

Name	U.S. $	Can. $	U.K. £
Astral Navigator	950.00	1,350.00	300.00

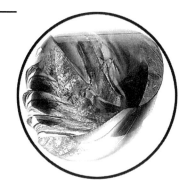

CT-1501
KALEIDOSCOPE '97

Designer: Colin Terris
Type: Weight — Spherical
Edition: 1997 in a limited edition of 200
Status: Closed at No. 111
Series: Limited — Modern Design
Original Issue Price: £150.00, U.S. $475.00

Name	U.S. $	Can. $	U.K. £
Kaleidoscope '97	475.00	675.00	150.00

Note: This paperweight is supplied with a stand.

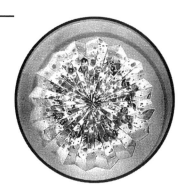

CT-1502
DIVINITY

Designer: Colin Terris
Type: Weight — Spherical
Edition: 1997 in a limited edition of 75
Status: Closed at No. 62
Series: Limited — Modern Design
Original Issue Price: £295.00, U.S. $950.00

Name	U.S. $	Can. $	U.K. £
Divinity	950.00	1,350.00	300.00

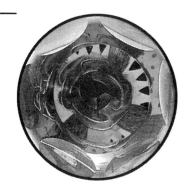

CT-1503
MOONLIGHT BLOSSOM

Designer: Philip Chaplain
Type: Weight — Spherical
Edition: 1997 in a limited edition of 250
Status: Closed at No. 68
Series: Limited — Modern Design
Original Issue Price: £125.00, U.S. $395.00

Name	U.S. $	Can. $	U.K. £
Moonlight Blossom	400.00	550.00	125.00

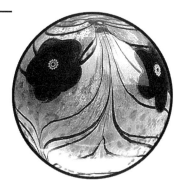

CT-1504
COMPASSION

Designer:	Rosette Fleming
Type:	Weight — Spherical
Edition:	1997 in a limited edition of 50
Status:	Closed at No. 27
Series:	Traditional Collection — Nature Study
Original Issue Price:	£350.00, U.S. $1,100.00

Name	U.S. $	Can. $	U.K. £
Compassion	1,100.00	1,600.00	350.00

CT-1505
WOOD VIOLET

Designer:	Allan Scott
Type:	Weight — Spherical
Edition:	1997 in a limited edition of 50
Status:	Closed at No. 34
Series:	Traditional Collection — Nature Study
Original Issue Price:	£395.00, U.S. $1,250.00

Name	U.S. $	Can. $	U.K. £
Wood Violet	1,250.00	1,800.00	400.00

CT-1506
OCEAN SERENADE

Designer:	Helen MacDonald
Type:	Weight — Domed
Edition:	1997 in a limited edition of 25
Status:	Fully subscribed
Series:	Traditional Collection — Nature Study
Original Issue Price:	£595.00, U.S. $1,850.00

Name	U.S. $	Can. $	U.K. £
Ocean Serenade	1,850.00	2,650.00	600.00

CT-1507
SUMMER LILIES

Designer:	Rosette Fleming
Type:	Weight — Domed
Edition:	1997 in a limited edition of 75
Status:	Closed at No. 40
Series:	Traditional Collection — Nature Study
Original Issue Price:	£350.00, U.S. $1,100.00

Name	U.S. $	Can. $	U.K. £
Summer Lilies	1,100.00	1,550.00	350.00

CT-1508
BRANCHING OUT

Designer:	Allan Scott
Type:	Weight — Spherical
Edition:	1997 in a limited edition of 25
Status:	Closed at No. 22
Series:	Traditional Collection — Nature Study
Original Issue Price:	£595.00, U.S. $1,850.00

Name	U.S. $	Can. $	U.K. £
Branching Out	1,900.00	2,800.00	600.00

CT-1509
SWISH

Designer:	Philip Chaplain
Type:	Weight — Domed
Colour:	See below
Edition:	1997
Status:	Active
Series:	Unlimited — Modern Design
Original Issue Price:	£25.00, U.S. $79.50

Colourways	U.S. $	Can. $	U.K. £
1. Cerise	79.50	100.00	25.00
2. Cobalt	79.50	100.00	25.00
3. Emerald	79.50	100.00	25.00

CT-1510
WHIRLPOOL

Designer:	Alastair MacIntosh
Type:	Weight — Domed
Edition:	1997
Status:	Active
Series:	Unlimited — Modern Design
Original Issue Price:	£29.50, U.S. $95.00

Name	U.S. $	Can. $	U.K. £
Whirlpool	95.00	125.00	30.00

CT-1511
MOONFLOWER CARNIVAL

Designer:	Colin Terris
Type:	Weight — Spherical
Colour:	Yellow, orange, red, pink and blue
Edition:	1997
Status:	Closed
Series:	Unlimited — Modern Design
Original Issue Price:	£34.50, U.S. $110.00

Name	U.S. $	Can. $	U.K. £
Moonflower Carnival	110.00	150.00	35.00

CT-1512
JUMPING FOR JOY

Designer:	Helen MacDonald
Type:	Weight — Spherical
Edition:	1997
Status:	Active
Series:	Unlimited — Modern Design

Original Issue Price: £30.00, U.S. $79.50

Name	U.S. $	Can. $	U.K. £
Jumping for Joy	95.00	125.00	31.00

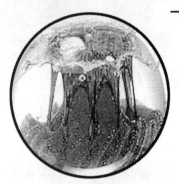

CT-1513
MARQUEE

Designer:	Philip Chaplain
Type:	Weight — Spherical
Colour:	See below
Edition:	1997
Status:	Active
Series:	Unlimited — Modern Design

Original Issue Price: £28.00, U.S. $87.50

Colourways	U.S. $	Can. $	U.K. £
1. Amethyst	95.00	125.00	28.50
2. Cobalt	95.00	125.00	28.50
3. Kingfisher	95.00	125.00	28.50

CT-1514
DOLPHINARIUM

Designer:	Helen MacDonald
Type:	Weight — Spherical, magnum size
Edition:	1997
Status:	Active
Series:	Unlimited — Modern Design

Original Issue Price: £60.00, U.S. $195.00

Name	U.S. $	Can. $	U.K. £
Dolphinarium	195.00	260.00	60.00

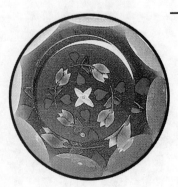

CT-1515
ETERNAL LOVE

Designer:	Rosette Fleming
Type:	Weight — Spherical
Edition:	1997 in a limited edition of 50
Status:	Closed at No. 44
Series:	Whitefriars Collection

Original Issue Price: £135.00, U.S. $450.00

Name	U.S. $	Can. $	U.K. £
Eternal Love	450.00	650.00	135.00

CT-1516
CLASSICAL MOMENT

Designer: Rosette Fleming
Type: Weight — Spherical
Edition: 1997 in a limited edition of 50
Status: Closed at No. 31
Series: Whitefriars Collection
Original Issue Price: £175.00, U.S. $550.00

Name	U.S. $	Can. $	U.K. £
Classical Moment	550.00	775.00	175.00

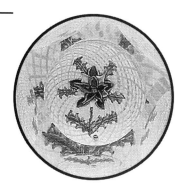

CT-1517
SPOILT FOR CHOICE

Designer: Rosette Fleming
Type: Weight — Spherical
Edition: 1997 in a limited edition of 50
Status: Closed at No. 31
Series: Whitefriars Collection
Original Issue Price: £195.00, U.S. $595.00

Name	U.S. $	Can. $	U.K. £
Spoilt for Choice	600.00	850.00	200.00

CT-1518
FRENCH FANCY

Designer: Rosette Fleming
Type: Weight — Spherical
Edition: 1997 in a limited edition of 50
Status: Closed at No. 39
Series: Whitefriars Collection
Original Issue Price: £150.00, U.S. $475.00

Name	U.S. $	Can. $	U.K. £
French Fancy	475.00	675.00	150.00

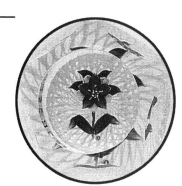

CT-1519
PRETTY IN PINK

Designer: Rosette Fleming
Type: Weight — Spherical
Edition: 1997 in a limited edition of 50
Status: Closed at No. 35
Series: Whitefriars Collection
Original Issue Price: £250.00, U.S. $795.00

Name	U.S. $	Can. $	U.K. £
Pretty in Pink	800.00	1,150.00	250.00

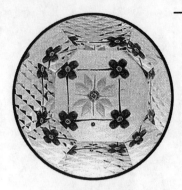

CT-1520
ALPINE GLORY

Designer: Rosette Fleming
Type: Weight — Spherical
Edition: 1997 in a limited edition of 50
Status: Closed at No. 44
Series: Whitefriars Collection
Original Issue Price: £175.00, U.S. $550.00

Name	U.S. $	Can. $	U.K. £
Alpine Glory	550.00	775.00	175.00

CT-1521
MOONWALK

Designer: William Manson
Type: Weight — Spherical
Edition: 1997 in a limited edition of 50
Status: Closed at No. 28
Series: William Manson Traditionals
Original Issue Price: £295.00, U.S. $895.00

Name	U.S. $	Can. $	U.K. £
Moonwalk	900.00	1,250.00	300.00

CT-1522
THE LOST CITY

Designer: William Manson
Type: Weight — Spherical
Edition: 1997 in a limited edition of 50
Status: Closed at No. 24
Series: William Manson Traditionals
Original Issue Price: £295.00, U.S. $895.00

Name	U.S. $	Can. $	U.K. £
The Lost City	900.00	1,250.00	300.00

CT-1523
AQUARIUM

Designer: William Manson
Type: Weight — Spherical
Edition: 1997 in a limited edition of 50
Status: Closed at No. 29
Series: William Manson Traditionals
Original Issue Price: £295.00, U.S. $895.00

Name	U.S. $	Can. $	U.K. £
Aquarium	900.00	1,250.00	300.00

CT-1524
FESTIVE WINDOW

Designer:	William Manson
Type:	Weight — Spherical
Edition:	1997 in a limited edition of 50
Status:	Fully subscribed
Series:	William Manson Traditionals
Original Issue Price:	£350.00, U.S. $1,100.00

Name	U.S. $	Can. $	U.K. £
Festive Window	1,100.00	1,550.00	350.00

CT-1525
DOUBLE MAGNUM 98

Designer:	Franco Toffolo
Type:	Weight — Spherical, double magnum
Edition:	1998 in a limited edition of 100
Status:	Closed at No. 51
Series:	Limited — Modern Design
Original Issue Price:	£350.00, U.S. $1,125.00

Name	U.S. $	Can. $	U.K. £
Double Magnum 98	1,125.00	1,600.00	350.00

CT-1526
REGAL IRIS

Designer:	Helen MacDonald
Type:	Weight — Domed
Edition:	1998 in a limited edition of 100
Status:	Fully subscribed
Series:	Limited — Modern Design
Original Issue Price:	£295.00, U.S. $925.00

Name	U.S. $	Can. $	U.K. £
Regal Iris	925.00	1,300.00	300.00

CT-1527
SIR PERCIVAL'S QUEST

Designer:	Colin Terris
Type:	Weight — Domed
Edition:	1998 in a limited edition of 650
Status:	Active
Series:	Limited — Modern Design
Original Issue Price:	£80.00, U.S. $250.00

Name	U.S. $	Can. $	U.K. £
Sir Percival's Quest	250.00	350.00	80.00

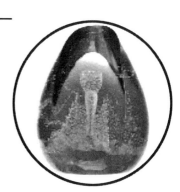

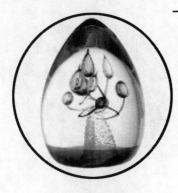

CT-1528
ONCE UPON A TIME

Designer: Colin Terris
Type: Weight — Domed
Edition: 1998 in a limited edition of 650
Status: Fully subscribed
Series: Limited — Modern Design
Original Issue Price: £75.00, U.S. $250.00

Name	U.S. $	Can. $	U.K. £
Once upon a Time	250.00	325.00	75.00

CT-1529
CASTLES IN THE AIR

Designer: Colin Terris
Type: Weight — Spherical
Edition: 1998 in a limited edition of 750
Status: Active
Series: Limited — Modern Design
Original Issue Price: £65.00, U.S. $210.00

Name	U.S. $	Can. $	U.K. £
Castles in the Air	210.00	285.00	65.00

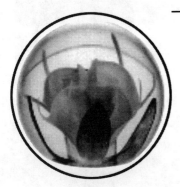

CT-1530
SNOW ORCHID

Designer: Colin Terris
Type: Weight — Spherical
Edition: 1998 in a limited edition of 750
Status: Active
Series: Limited — Modern Design
Original Issue Price: £65.00, U.S. $210.00

Name	U.S. $	Can. $	U.K. £
Snow Orchid	210.00	285.00	65.00

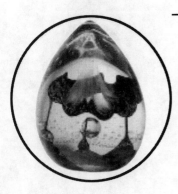

CT-1531
CINNABAR

Designer: Philip Chaplain
Type: Weight — Domed
Edition: 1998 in a limited edition of 750
Status: Fully subscribed
Series: Limited — Modern Design
Original Issue Price: £60.00, U.S. $195.00

Name	U.S. $	Can. $	U.K. £
Cinnabar	195.00	260.00	60.00

CT-1532
CHASM

Designer:	Philip Chaplain
Type:	Weight — Domed
Edition:	1998 in a limited edition of 125
Status:	Closed at No. 94
Series:	Limited — Modern Design
Original Issue Price:	£250.00, U.S. $795.00

Name	U.S. $	Can. $	U.K. £
Chasm	800.00	1,100.00	250.00

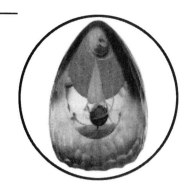

CT-1533
LATE SUMMER SPLENDOUR

Designer:	Helen MacDonald
Type:	Weight — Sculptural
Edition:	1998 in a limited edition of 25
Status:	Fully subscribed
Series:	Limited — Modern Design
Original Issue Price:	£595.00, U.S. $1,925.00

Name	U.S. $	Can. $	U.K. £
Late Summer Splendour	1,925.00	2,750.00	600.00

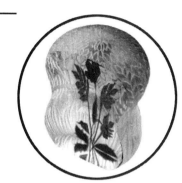

CT-1534
VIRIDIAN

Designer:	Philip Chaplain
Type:	Weight — Domed
Edition:	1998 in a limited edition of 75
Status:	Fully subscribed
Series:	Limited — Modern Design
Original Issue Price:	£295.00, U.S. $950.00

Name	U.S. $	Can. $	U.K. £
Viridian	950.00	1,350.00	300.00

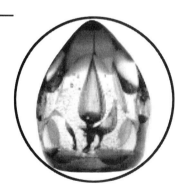

CT-1535
THE RAJ

Designer:	Helen MacDonald
Type:	Weight — Teardrop
Edition:	1998 in a limited edition of 50
Status:	Fully subscribed
Series:	Limited — Modern Design
Original Issue Price:	£425.00, U.S. $1,375.00

Name	U.S. $	Can. $	U.K. £
The Raj	1,375.00	1,950.00	425.00

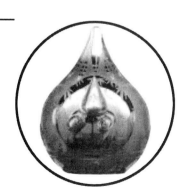

CT-1536
SCOTIA

Designer: Philip Chaplain
Type: Weight — Domed
Edition: 1998 in a limited edition of 650
Status: Fully subscribed
Series: Limited — Modern Design
Original Issue Price: £80.00, U.S. $250.00

Name	U.S. $	Can. $	U.K. £
Scotia	250.00	350.00	80.00

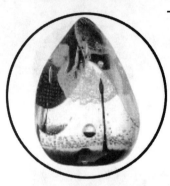

CT-1537
BANSHEE

Designer: Philip Chaplain
Type: Weight — Domed
Edition: 1998 in a limited edition of 350
Status: Fully subscribed
Series: Limited — Modern Design
Original Issue Price: £99.00, U.S. $325.00

Name	U.S. $	Can. $	U.K. £
Banshee	325.00	450.00	100.00

CT-1538
FLAMBOYANCE

Designer: Helen MacDonald
Type: Weight — Sculptural
Edition: 1998 in a limited edition of 125
Status: Active
Series: Limited — Modern Design
Original Issue Price: £250.00, U.S. $795.00

Name	U.S. $	Can. $	U.K. £
Flamboyance	795.00	1,085.00	250.00

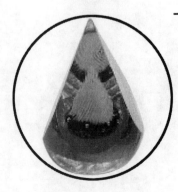

CT-1539
JALAL

Designer: Alastair MacIntosh
Type: Weight — Pyramid facets
Edition: 1998 in a limited edition of 350
Status: Fully subscribed
Series: Limited — Modern Design
Original Issue Price: £99.00, U.S. $325.00

Name	U.S. $	Can. $	U.K. £
Jalal	325.00	450.00	100.00

CT-1540
TIME TUNNEL

Designer:	Helen MacDonald
Type:	Weight — Spherical
Edition:	1998 in a limited edition of 750
Status:	Fully subscribed
Series:	Limited — Modern Design
Original Issue Price:	£55.00, U.S. $175.00

Name	U.S. $	Can. $	U.K. £
Time Tunnel	175.00	240.00	55.00

CT-1541
TECHNO-TRIP

Designer:	Alastair MacIntosh
Type:	Weight — Spherical
Edition:	1998 in a limited edition of 750
Status:	Active
Series:	Limited — Modern Design
Original Issue Price:	£70.00, U.S. $225.00

Name	U.S. $	Can. $	U.K. £
Techno-Trip	225.00	310.00	70.00

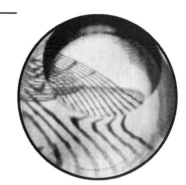

CT-1542
LIVE WIRE

Designer:	Alastair MacIntosh
Type:	Weight — Domed
Edition:	1998 in a limited edition of 150
Status:	Active
Series:	Limited — Modern Design
Original Issue Price:	£195.00, U.S. $625.00

Name	U.S. $	Can. $	U.K. £
Live Wire	625.00	850.00	200.00

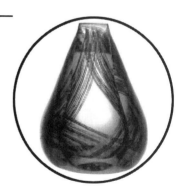

CT-1543
ABERRATION

Designer:	Helen MacDonald
Type:	Weight — Pyramid facets
Edition:	1998 in a limited edition of 150
Status:	Active
Series:	Limited — Modern Design
Original Issue Price:	£175.00, U.S. $550.00

Name	U.S. $	Can. $	U.K. £
Aberration	550.00	760.00	175.00

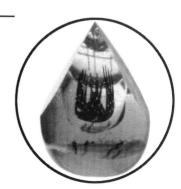

CT-1544
COBALT SPLENDOUR

Designer:	Alastair MacIntosh
Type:	Weight — Domed
Edition:	1998 in a limited edition of 50
Status:	Fully subscribed
Series:	Limited — Modern Design
Original Issue Price:	£325.00, U.S. $1,050.00

Name	U.S. $	Can. $	U.K. £
Cobalt Splendour	1,050.00	1,400.00	325.00

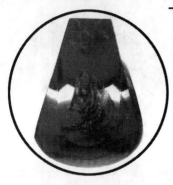

CT-1545
PARADISE LOST

Designer:	Alastair MacIntosh
Type:	Weight — Domed
Edition:	1998 in a limited edition of 350
Status:	Fully subscribed
Series:	Limited — Modern Design
Original Issue Price:	£99.00, U.S. $325.00

Name	U.S. $	Can. $	U.K. £
Paradise Lost	325.00	450.00	100.00

CT-1546
THE LOST WORLD

Designer:	Alastair MacIntosh
Type:	Weight — Domed
Edition:	1998 in a limited edition of 350
Status:	Fully subscribed
Series:	Limited — Modern Design
Original Issue Price:	£99.00, U.S. $325.00

Name	U.S. $	Can. $	U.K. £
The Lost World	325.00	450.00	100.00

CT-1547
INCANDESCENCE

Designer:	Philip Chaplain
Type:	Weight — Domed
Edition:	1998 in a limited edition of 500
Status:	Closed at No. 486
Series:	Limited — Modern Design
Original Issue Price:	£90.00, U.S. $295.00

Name	U.S. $	Can. $	U.K. £
Incandescence	300.00	390.00	90.00

CT-1548
BUSY BEES

Designer:	Helen MacDonald	
Type:	Weight — Spherical	
Edition:	1998 in a limited edition of 350	
Status:	Active	
Series:	Limited — Modern Design	
Original Issue Price:	£99.00, U.S. $350.00	

Name	U.S. $	Can. $	U.K. £
Busy Bees	350.00	430.00	99.00

CT-1549
CHARTREUSE

Designer:	Helen MacDonald	
Type:	Weight — Spherical	
Edition:	1998 in a limited edition of 500	
Status:	Active	
Series:	Limited — Modern Design	
Original Issue Price:	£90.00, U.S. $295.00	

Name	U.S. $	Can. $	U.K. £
Chartreuse	295.00	400.00	90.00

CT-1550
COTTAGE GARDEN

Designer:	Helen MacDonald	
Type:	Weight — Spherical	
Edition:	1998 in a limited edition of 150	
Status:	Active	
Series:	Limited — Modern Design	
Original Issue Price:	£195.00, U.S. $675.00	

Name	U.S. $	Can. $	U.K. £
Cottage Garden	675.00	850.00	195.00

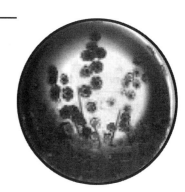

CT-1551
EYE OF THE STORM

Designer:	Alastair MacIntosh	
Type:	Weight — Spherical	
Edition:	1998 in a limited edition of 750	
Status:	Active	
Series:	Limited — Modern Design	
Original Issue Price:	£70.00, U.S. $225.00	

Name	U.S. $	Can. $	U.K. £
Eye of the Storm	225.00	310.00	70.00

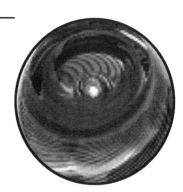

CT-1552
CELTIC KNOT

Designer:	Helen MacDonald	
Type:	Weight — Spherical	
Edition:	1998 in a limited edition of 750	
Status:	Active	
Series:	Limited — Modern Design	
Original Issue Price:	£50.00, U.S. $165.00	

Name	U.S. $	Can. $	U.K. £
Celtic Knot	165.00	220.00	50.00

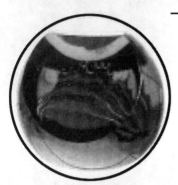

CT-1553
SHOCKWAVE

Designer:	Alastair MacIntosh	
Type:	Weight — Spherical	
Edition:	1998 in a limited edition of 500	
Status:	Active	
Series:	Limited — Modern Design	
Original Issue Price:	£90.00, U.S. $295.00	

Name	U.S. $	Can. $	U.K. £
Shockwave	295.00	400.00	90.00

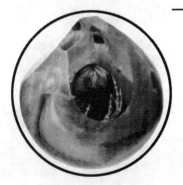

CT-1554
DEEP ENDEAVOUR

Designer:	Philip Chaplain	
Type:	Weight — Sculptural	
Edition:	1998 in a limited edition of 250	
Status:	Active	
Series:	Limited — Modern Design	
Original Issue Price:	£125.00, U.S. $395.00	

Name	U.S. $	Can. $	U.K. £
Deep Endeavour	395.00	550.00	125.00

CT-1555
ARCTIC CRYSTAL

Designer:	Colin Terris	
Type:	Weight — Domed	
Edition:	1998 in a limited edition of 50	
Status:	Fully subscribed	
Series:	Limited — Modern Design	
Original Issue Price:	£295.00, U.S. $950.00	

Name	U.S. $	Can. $	U.K. £
Arctic Crystal	950.00	1,280.00	295.00

CT-1556
CRYSTAL VOYAGER

Designer: Helen MacDonald
Type: Weight — Ovoid
Edition: 1998 in a limited edition of 125
Status: Active
Series: Limited — Modern Design
Original Issue Price: £250.00, U.S. $795.00

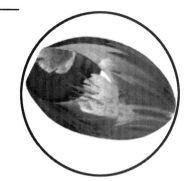

Name	*U.S. $*	*Can. $*	*U.K. £*
Crystal Voyager	795.00	1,085.00	250.00

CT-1557
DEVOTION

Designer: Helen MacDonald
Type: Weight — Teardrop
Edition: 1998 in a limited edition of 250
Status: Fully subscribed
Series: Limited — Modern Design
Original Issue Price: £125.00, U.S. $395.00

Name	*U.S. $*	*Can. $*	*U.K. £*
Devotion	395.00	550.00	125.00

CT-1558
STAR CRYSTAL

Designer: Helen MacDonald
Type: Weight — Sculptural
Edition: 1998 in a limited edition of 50
Status: Fully subscribed
Series: Limited — Modern Design
Original Issue Price: £325.00, U.S. $1,050.00

Name	*U.S. $*	*Can. $*	*U.K. £*
Star Crystal	1,050.00	1,425.00	325.00

CT-1559
ETERNAL FLAME

Designer: Helen MacDonald
Type: Weight — Sculptural
Edition: 1998 in a limited edition of 100
Status: Active
Series: Limited — Modern Design
Original Issue Price: £275.00, U.S. $875.00

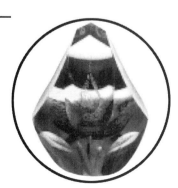

Name	*U.S. $*	*Can. $*	*U.K. £*
Eternal Flame	875.00	1,200.00	275.00

CT-1560
STARSTRUCK

Designer:	Helen MacDonald
Type:	Weight — Diamond
Edition:	1998 in a limited edition of 50
Status:	Fully subscribed
Series:	Limited — Modern Design
Original Issue Price:	£325.00, U.S. $1,050.00

Name	U.S. $	Can. $	U.K. £
Starstruck	1,050.00	1,425.00	325.00

CT-1561
MARINE FANTASY

Designer:	Colin Terris
Type:	Weight — Spherical
Edition:	1998 in a limited edition of 75
Status:	Active
Series:	Limited — Modern Design
Original Issue Price:	£250.00, U.S. $795.00

Name	U.S. $	Can. $	U.K. £
Marine Fantasy	795.00	1,100.00	250.00

CT-1562
BOUNTEOUS

Designer:	Philip Chaplain
Type:	Weight — Cylindrical
Edition:	1998 in a limited edition of 50
Status:	Active
Series:	Limited — Modern Design
Original Issue Price:	£350.00, U.S. $1,125.00

Name	U.S. $	Can. $	U.K. £
Bounteous	1,125.00	1,500.00	350.00

CT-1563
WALLS OF JERICHO

Designer:	Helen MacDonald
Type:	Weight — Spherical
Edition:	1998 in a limited edition of 75
Status:	Closed at No. 38
Series:	Limited — Modern Design
Original Issue Price:	£250.00, U.S. $795.00

Name	U.S. $	Can. $	U.K. £
Walls of Jericho	800.00	1,100.00	250.00

CT-1564
EMERALD POPPY

Designer:	Helen MacDonald
Type:	Weight — Spherical
Edition:	1998 in a limited edition of 150
Status:	Active
Series:	Limited — Modern Design
Original Issue Price:	£195.00, U.S. $625.00

Name	U.S. $	Can. $	U.K. £
Emerald Poppy	625.00	850.00	195.00

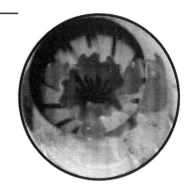

CT-1565
AFRICAN ADVENTURE

Designer:	Helen MacDonald
Type:	Weight — Sculptural
Edition:	1998 in a limited edition of 25
Status:	Fully subscribed
Series:	Limited — Modern Design
Original Issue Price:	£650.00, U.S. $2,100.00

Name	U.S. $	Can. $	U.K. £
African Adventure	2,100.00	3,000.00	650.00

CT-1566
AQUAMARINA

Designer:	Philip Chaplain
Type:	Weight — Spherical
Edition:	1998 in a limited edition of 2,092
Status:	Closed at No. 2,092
Original Issue Price:	£85.00, U.S. $225.00

Name	U.S. $	Can. $	U.K. £
Aquamarina	225.00	325.00	100.00

Note: This is the 1998 Collectors' Paperweight.

CT-1567A
NATIONAL QUARTET — ONE

Designer:	Rosette Fleming
Type:	Weight — Spherical
Edition:	1998 in a limited edition of 25
Status:	Closed at No. 18
Series:	National Quartet Set
Original Issue Price:	£695.00/set, U.S. $2,250.00/set

Name	U.S. $	Can. $	U.K. £
National Quartet - One	575.00	800.00	175.00
Set	2,300.00	3,200.00	700.00

Note: CT-1567A, B, C and D were issued and sold as a set.

CT-1567B
NATIONAL QUARTET — TWO

Designer:	Rosette Fleming	
Type:	Weight — Spherical	
Edition:	1998 in a limited edition of 25	
Status:	Closed at No. 18	
Series:	National Quartet Set	
Original Issue Price:	£695.00/set, U.S. $2,250.00/set	

Name	U.S. $	Can. $	U.K. £
National Quartet - Two	575.00	800.00	175.00

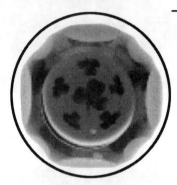

CT-1567C
NATIONAL QUARTET — THREE

Designer:	Rosette Fleming	
Type:	Weight — Spherical	
Edition:	1998 in a limited edition of 25	
Status:	Closed at No. 18	
Series:	National Quartet Set	
Original Issue Price:	£695.00/set, U.S. $2,250.00/set	

Name	U.S. $	Can. $	U.K. £
National Quartet - Three	575.00	800.00	175.00

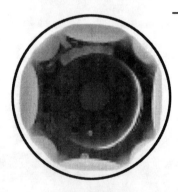

CT-1567D
NATIONAL QUARTET — FOUR

Designer:	Rosette Fleming	
Type:	Weight — Spherical	
Edition:	1998 in a limited edition of 25	
Status:	Closed at No. 18	
Series:	National Quartet Set	
Original Issue Price:	£695.00/set, U.S. $2,250.00/set	

Name	U.S. $	Can. $	U.K. £
National Quartet - Four	575.00	800.00	175.00

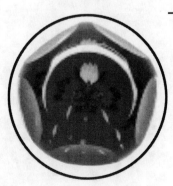

CT-1568
ALPINE SUMMER

Designer:	Rosette Fleming	
Type:	Weight — Spherical	
Edition:	1998 in a limited edition of 50	
Status:	Closed at No. 28	
Series:	Whitefriars Collection	
Original Issue Price:	£135.00, U.S. $425.00	

Name	U.S. $	Can. $	U.K. £
Alpine Summer	425.00	600.00	135.00

CT-1569
RED ROSE BOUQUET

Designer:	Allan Scott
Type:	Weight — Spherical
Edition:	1998 in a limited edition of 50
Status:	Closed at No. 26
Series:	Whitefriars Collection
Original Issue Price:	£175.00, U.S. $575.00

Name	U.S. $	Can. $	U.K. £
Red Rose Bouquet	575.00	825.00	175.00

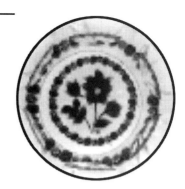

CT-1570
SYMPHONY IN BLUE

Designer:	Rosette Fleming
Type:	Weight — Spherical
Edition:	1998 in a limited edition of 50
Status:	Closed at No. 23
Series:	Whitefriars Collection
Original Issue Price:	£150.00, U.S. $485.00

Name	U.S. $	Can. $	U.K. £
Symphony in Blue	485.00	700.00	150.00

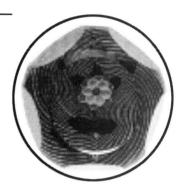

CT-1571
FRAGRANT ORCHID

Designer:	Allan Scott
Type:	Weight — Spherical
Edition:	1998 in a limited edition of 50
Status:	Closed at No. 35
Series:	Whitefriars Collection
Original Issue Price:	£135.00, U.S. $425.00

Name	U.S. $	Can. $	U.K. £
Fragrant Orchid	425.00	600.00	135.00

CT-1572
SUNNY DAYS PERFUME BOTTLE

Designer:	Allan Scott
Type:	Perfume bottle
Edition:	1998 in a limited edition of 50
Status:	Closed at No. 36
Series:	Whitefriars Collection
Original Issue Price:	£250.00, U.S. $875.00

Name	U.S. $	Can. $	U.K. £
Sunny Days Perfume Bottle	875.00	1,250.00	250.00

CT-1573
DAISY BOUQUET

Designer:	Allan Scott
Type:	Weight — Spherical
Edition:	1998 in a limited edition of 75
Status:	Closed at No. 39
Series:	Whitefriars Collection
Original Issue Price:	£120.00, U.S. $385.00

Name	U.S. $	Can. $	U.K. £
Daisy Bouquet	385.00	550.00	120.00

CT-1574
PANSY LATTICINO

Designer:	Allan Scott
Type:	Weight — Spherical
Edition:	1998 in a limited edition of 75
Status:	Closed at No. 34
Series:	Whitefriars Collection
Original Issue Price:	£120.00, U.S. $425.00

Name	U.S. $	Can. $	U.K. £
Pansy Latticino	425.00	600.00	120.00

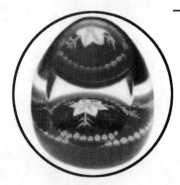

CT-1575
SPRING FLORETTE COBALT

Designer:	Rosette Fleming
Type:	Weight — Domed
Edition:	1998 in a limited edition of 150
Status:	Closed at No. 80
Series:	Whitefriars Collection
Original Issue Price:	£70.00, U.S. $250.00

Name	U.S. $	Can. $	U.K. £
Spring Florette Cobalt	250.00	350.00	70.00

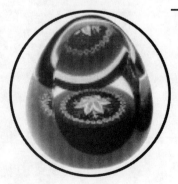

CT-1576
SPRING FLORETTE KINGFISHER

Designer:	Rosette Fleming
Type:	Weight — Domed
Edition:	1998 in a limited edition of 150
Status:	Closed at No. 64
Series:	Whitefriars Collection
Original Issue Price:	£70.00, U.S. $250.00

Name	U.S. $	Can. $	U.K. £
Spring Florette Kingfisher	250.00	350.00	70.00

CT-1577
AMETHYST GARLAND

Designer: Rosette Fleming
Type: Weight — Spherical
Edition: 1998 in a limited edition of 50
Status: Closed at No. 29
Series: Whitefriars Collection
Original Issue Price: £150.00, U.S. $485.00

Name	U.S. $	Can. $	U.K. £
Amethyst Garland	485.00	700.00	150.00

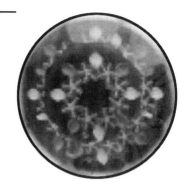

CT-1578
DAISY and FORGET-ME-NOT

Designer: Rosette Fleming
Type: Weight — Spherical
Edition: 1998 in a limited edition of 50
Status: Closed at No. 27
Series: Whitefriars Collection
Original Issue Price: £195.00, U.S. $625.00

Name	U.S. $	Can. $	U.K. £
Daisy and Forget-me-not	625.00	850.00	200.00

CT-1579
BUTTERCUPS and BUTTERFLY

Designer: Rosette Fleming
Type: Weight — Spherical
Edition: 1998 in a limited edition of 50
Status: Closed at No. 22
Series: Whitefriars Collection
Original Issue Price: £225.00, U.S. $725.00

Name	U.S. $	Can. $	U.K. £
Buttercups and Butterfly	725.00	1,000.00	225.00

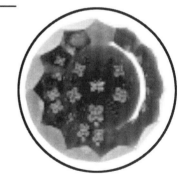

CT-1580
HYACINTH BOUQUET

Designer: Allan Scott
Type: Weight — Spherical
Edition: 1998 in a limited edition of 50
Status: Closed at No. 35
Series: Whitefriars Collection
Original Issue Price: £250.00, U.S. $795.00

Name	U.S. $	Can. $	U.K. £
Hyacinth Bouquet	800.00	1,150.00	250.00

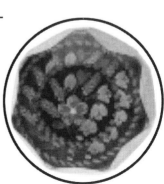

CT-1581
MORNING REFLECTIONS

Designer:	Rosette Fleming
Type:	Weight — Domed
Edition:	1998 in a limited edition of 75
Status:	Active
Series:	Traditional Collection — Nature Study
Original Issue Price:	£295.00, U.S. $950.00

Name	U.S. $	Can. $	U.K. £
Morning Reflections	950.00	1,300.00	300.00

CT-1582
AUTUMN HEDGEROW

Designer:	Allan Scott
Type:	Weight — Sculptural
Edition:	1998 in a limited edition of 25
Status:	Closed at No. 17
Series:	Traditional Collection — Nature Study
Original Issue Price:	£595.00, U.S. $1,925.00

Name	U.S. $	Can. $	U.K. £
Autumn Hedgerow	1,925.00	2,600.00	600.00

CT-1583A
FLOWERPOT PEOPLE — ONE

Designer:	Rosette Fleming
Type:	Weight — Cylindrical
Edition:	1998 in a limited edition of 25
Status:	Closed at No. 15
Series:	Traditional Collection — Nature Study
Original Issue Price:	£795.00/set, U.S. $2,550.00/set

Name	U.S. $	Can. $	U.K. £
Flowerpot People - One	1,275.00	1,800.00	400.00
Set	2,550.00	3,600.00	800.00

Note: CT-1583A and B were issued and sold as a set.

CT-1583B
FLOWERPOT PEOPLE — TWO

Designer:	Rosette Fleming
Type:	Weight — Cylindrical
Edition:	1998 in a limited edition of 25
Status:	Closed at No. 15
Series:	Traditional Collection — Nature Study
Original Issue Price:	£795.00/set, U.S. $2,550.00/set

Name	U.S. $	Can. $	U.K. £
Flowerpot People - Two	1,275.00	1,800.00	400.00

CT-1584
BUNNIES

Designer:	Allan Scott
Type:	Weight — Spherical
Edition:	1998 in a limited edition of 25
Status:	Closed at No. 23
Series:	Traditional Collection — Nature Study
Original Issue Price:	£595.00, U.S. $1,925.00

Name	U.S. $	Can. $	U.K. £
Bunnies	1,925.00	2,750.00	600.00

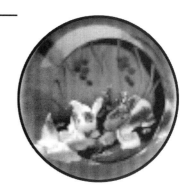

CT-1585
CLEMATIS and TRELLIS

Designer:	Rosette Fleming
Type:	Weight — Spherical
Edition:	1998 in a limited edition of 50
Status:	Active
Series:	Traditional Collection — Nature Study
Original Issue Price:	£350.00, U.S. $1,125.00

Name	U.S. $	Can. $	U.K. £
Clematis and Trellis	1,125.00	1,525.00	350.00

CT-1586
SUNFLOWERS

Designer:	Rosette Fleming
Type:	Weight — Spherical
Edition:	1998 in a limited edition of 50
Status:	Active
Series:	Traditional Collection — Nature Study
Original Issue Price:	£350.00, U.S. $1,125.00

Name	U.S. $	Can. $	U.K. £
Sunflowers	1,125.00	1,525.00	350.00

CT-1587
COUNTRY POSY

Designer:	Allan Scott
Type:	Weight — Domed
Edition:	1998 in a limited edition of 150
Status:	Closed at No. 74
Series:	Traditional Collection — Nature Study
Original Issue Price:	£125.00, U.S. $395.00

Name	U.S. $	Can. $	U.K. £
Country Posy	400.00	550.00	125.00

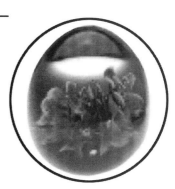

CT-1588
GARDEN POSY

Designer:	Allan Scott
Type:	Weight — Domed
Edition:	1998 in a limited edition of 150
Status:	Closed at No. 97
Series:	Traditional Collection — Nature Study
Original Issue Price:	£125.00, U.S. $395.00

Name	U.S. $	Can. $	U.K. £
Garden Posy	400.00	550.00	125.00

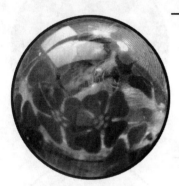

CT-1589
PERIWINKLES

Designer:	Helen MacDonald
Type:	Weight — Spherical, magnum size
Edition:	1998
Status:	Active
Series:	Unlimited — Modern Design
Original Issue Price:	£65.00, U.S. $210.00

Name	U.S. $	Can. $	U.K. £
Periwinkles	210.00	285.00	65.00

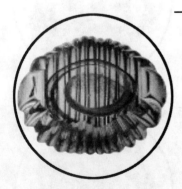

CT-1590
SEA PEARLS

Designer:	Alastair MacIntosh
Type:	Weight — Sculptural
Colour:	See below
Edition:	1998
Status:	Active
Series:	Unlimited — Modern Design
Original Issue Price:	£30.00, U.S. $95.00

Colourways	U.S. $	Can. $	U.K. £
1. Gold	95.00	125.00	30.00
2. Heather	95.00	125.00	30.00
3. Kingfisher	95.00	125.00	30.00

CT-1591
GOLDRUSH

Designer: Philip Chaplain
Type: Weight — Spherical
Colour: See below
Edition: 1998
Status: Active
Series: Unlimited — Modern Design
Original Issue Price: £25.00, U.S. $79.50

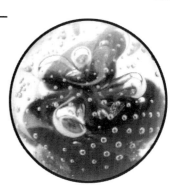

Colourways	U.S. $	Can. $	U.K. £
1. Cobalt	79.50	100.00	25.00
2. Emerald	79.50	100.00	25.00
3. Heather	79.50	100.00	25.00
4. Kingfisher	79.50	100.00	25.00

CT-1592
SPRING FESTIVAL

Designer: Helen MacDonald
Type: Weight — Spherical
Edition: 1998
Status: Active
Series: Unlimited — Modern Design
Original Issue Price: £33.50, U.S. $115.00

Name	U.S. $	Can. $	U.K. £
Spring Festival	115.00	145.00	33.50

CT-1593
SUMMER FAIR

Designer: Helen MacDonald
Type: Weight — Domed
Edition: 1998
Status: Active
Series: Unlimited — Modern Design
Original Issue Price: £33.50, U.S. $115.00

Name	U.S. $	Can. $	U.K. £
Summer Fair	115.00	150.00	33.50

CT-1594
PETUNIAS

Designer: Colin Terris
Type: Weight — Spherical
Colour: See below
Edition: 1998
Status: Active
Series: Medium and Miniature Size
Original Issue Price: £18.50, U.S. $58.50

Colourways	U.S. $	Can. $	U.K. £
1. Pink	58.50	75.00	18.50
2. Purple	58.50	75.00	18.50
3. Red	58.50	75.00	18.50
4. Sky	58.50	75.00	18.50
5. White	58.50	75.00	18.50

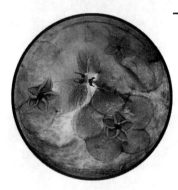

CT-1595
TRADITIONAL POOL

Designer: Colin Terris
Type: Weight — Spherical
Edition: 1998 in a limited edition of 350
Status: Fully subscribed
Series: Colin Terris Water Lily Collection
Original Issue Price: £99.00, U.S. $325.00

Name	U.S. $	Can. $	U.K. £
Traditional Pool	325.00	450.00	100.00

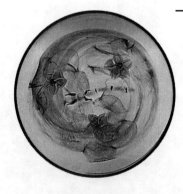

CT-1596
LILY POOL

Designer: Colin Terris
Type: Weight — Plaque
Edition: 1998 in a limited edition of 350
Status: Active
Series: Colin Terris Water Lily Collection
Original Issue Price: £150.00, U.S. $485.00

Name	U.S. $	Can. $	U.K. £
Lily Pool	485.00	650.00	150.00

CT-1597
MORNING FLIGHT

Designer:	Colin Terris
Type:	Weight — Spherical, medium-sized
Edition:	1998 in a limited edition of 500
Status:	Fully subscribed
Series:	Colin Terris Water Lily Collection
Original Issue Price:	£70.00, U.S. $225.00

Name	U.S. $	Can. $	U.K. £
Morning Flight	225.00	325.00	70.00

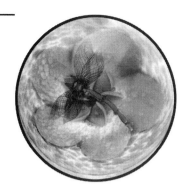

CT-1598
ORNAMENTAL POOL

Designer:	Colin Terris
Type:	Weight — Spherical
Edition:	1998 in a limited edition of 150
Status:	Active
Series:	Colin Terris Water Lily Collection
Original Issue Price:	£225.00, U.S. $725.00

Name	U.S. $	Can. $	U.K. £
Ornamental Pool	725.00	975.00	225.00

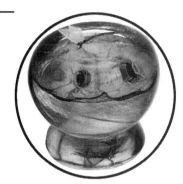

CT-1599
WATER GARDEN

Designer:	Colin Terris
Type:	Weight — Domed
Edition:	1998 in a limited edition of 250
Status:	Fully subscribed
Series:	Colin Terris Water Lily Collection
Original Issue Price:	£125.00, U.S. $395.00

Name	U.S. $	Can. $	U.K. £
Water Garden	400.00	550.00	125.00

CT-1600
TRANQUIL POND

Designer:	Colin Terris
Type:	Weight — Sculptural
Edition:	1998 in a limited edition of 100
Status:	Active
Series:	Colin Terris Water Lily Collection
Original Issue Price:	£250.00, U.S. $795.00

Name	U.S. $	Can. $	U.K. £
Tranquil Pond	800.00	1,085.00	250.00

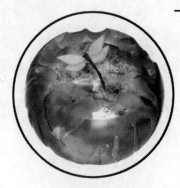

CT-1601
SCULPTURED POOL

Designer:	Colin Terris
Type:	Weight — Sculptural
Edition:	1998 in a limited edition of 75
Status:	Fully subscribed
Series:	Colin Terris Water Lily Collection
Original Issue Price:	£350.00, U.S. $1,125.00

Name	U.S. $	Can. $	U.K. £
Sculptured Pool	1,125.00	1,600.00	350.00

CT-1602
ORIENTAL POOL

Designer:	Colin Terris
Type:	Weight — Domed
Edition:	1998 in a limited edition of 100
Status:	Fully subscribed
Series:	Colin Terris Water Lily Collection
Original Issue Price:	£225.00, U.S. $950.00

Name	U.S. $	Can. $	U.K. £
Oriental Pool	950.00	1,350.00	225.00

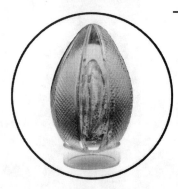

CT-1603
ARCTIC CROCUS

Designer:	Colin Terris
Type:	Weight — Domed
Edition:	1998 in a limited edition of 100
Status:	Fully subscribed
Series:	Collectable Eggs — Limited
Original Issue Price:	£120.00, U.S. $385.00

Name	U.S. $	Can. $	U.K. £
Arctic Crocus	385.00	550.00	120.00

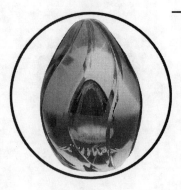

CT-1604
TURQUOISE DELIGHT

Designer:	Philip Chaplain
Type:	Weight — Domed
Edition:	1998 in a limited edition of 100
Status:	Fully subscribed
Series:	Collectable Eggs — Limited
Original Issue Price:	£99.00, U.S. $325.00

Name	U.S. $	Can. $	U.K. £
Turquoise Delight	325.00	450.00	100.00

CT-1605
CONFETTI CASCADE

Designer:	Helen MacDonald
Type:	Weight — Domed
Edition:	1998 in a limited edition of 100
Status:	Fully subscribed
Series:	Collectable Eggs — Limited
Original Issue Price:	£65.00, U.S. $225.00

Name	U.S. $	Can. $	U.K. £
Confetti Cascade	225.00	325.00	65.00

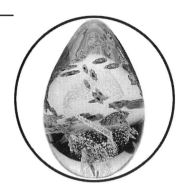

CT-1606
FROM THE FLAMES

Designer:	Colin Terris
Type:	Weight — Domed
Edition:	1998 in a limited edition of 100
Status:	Active
Series:	Collectable Eggs — Limited
Original Issue Price:	£150.00, U.S. $485.00

Name	U.S. $	Can. $	U.K. £
From the Flames	485.00	660.00	150.00

CT-1607
AMOROSO

Designer:	Colin Terris
Type:	Weight —Domed
Edition:	1998 in a limited edition of 100
Status:	Fully subscribed
Series:	Collectable Eggs — Limited
Original Issue Price:	£70.00, U.S. $225.00

Name	U.S. $	Can. $	U.K. £
Amoroso	225.00	325.00	70.00

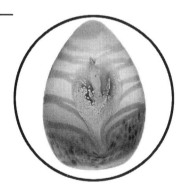

CT-1608
KHAMSIN

Designer:	Philip Chaplain
Type:	Weight — Domed
Edition:	1998 in a limited edition of 100
Status:	Fully subscribed
Series:	Collectable Eggs — Limited
Original Issue Price:	£70.00, U.S. $225.00

Name	U.S. $	Can. $	U.K. £
Khamsin	225.00	325.00	70.00

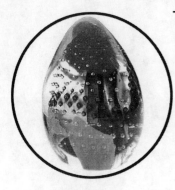

CT-1609
EFFERVESCENCE

Designer:	Philip Chaplain
Type:	Weight — Domed
Colour:	See below
Edition:	1998
Status:	Active
Series:	Collectable Eggs — Unlimited
Original Issue Price:	£37.50, U.S. $125.00

Colourways	U.S. $	Can. $	U.K. £
1. Aqua	125.00	165.00	40.00
2. Emerald	125.00	165.00	40.00
3. Sable	125.00	165.00	40.00

CT-1610
COLOUR POOL

Designer:	Philip Chaplain
Type:	Weight — Domed
Colour:	See below
Edition:	1998
Status:	Active
Series:	Collectable Eggs — Unlimited
Original Issue Price:	£37.50, U.S. $125.00

Colourways	U.S. $	Can. $	U.K. £
1. Blue	125.00	165.00	40.00
2. Green	125.00	165.00	40.00
3. Magenta	125.00	165.00	40.00

CT-1611
BLUE MOON

Designer:	Colin Terris
Type:	Weight — Spherical, dichroic
Edition:	1998 in a limited edition of 650
Status:	Active
Series:	Colin Terris Designer Collection II
Original Issue Price:	£85.00, U.S. $265.00

Name	U.S. $	Can. $	U.K. £
Blue Moon	265.00	375.00	85.00

CT-1612
CAVATINA

Designer:	Colin Terris
Type:	Weight — Spherical, dichroic
Edition:	1998 in a limited edition of 75
Status:	Active
Series:	Colin Terris Designer Collection II
Original Issue Price:	£250.00, U.S. $775.00

Name	U.S. $	Can. $	U.K. £
Cavatina	775.00	1,100.00	250.00

CT-1613
OPULENCE

Designer:	Colin Terris
Type:	Weight — Spherical, dichroic
Edition:	1998 in a limited edition of 500
Status:	Active
Series:	Colin Terris Designer Collection II

Original Issue Price: £95.00, U.S. $295.00

Name	U.S. $	Can. $	U.K. £
Opulence	295.00	420.00	95.00

CT-1614
TO BOLDLY GO...

Designer:	Colin Terris
Type:	Weight — Domed
Edition:	1998 in a limited edition of 750
Status:	Active
Series:	Colin Terris Designer Collection II

Original Issue Price: £70.00, U.S. $225.00

Name	U.S. $	Can. $	U.K. £
To Boldly Go...	225.00	310.00	70.00

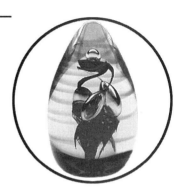

CT-1615
PATRIOT

Designer:	Colin Terris
Type:	Weight — Spherical
Edition:	1998 in a limited edition of 750
Status:	Active
Series:	Colin Terris Designer Collection II

Original Issue Price: £75.00, U.S. $240.00

Name	U.S. $	Can. $	U.K. £
Patriot	240.00	330.00	75.00

CT-1616
SECRET GARDEN '98

Designer:	Colin Terris
Type:	Weight — Domed
Edition:	1998 in a limited edition of 100
Status:	Fully subscribed
Series:	Colin Terris Designer Collection II

Original Issue Price: £295.00, U.S. $925.00

Name	U.S. $	Can. $	U.K. £
Secret Garden '98	925.00	1,300.00	300.00

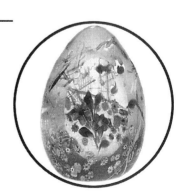

CT-1617
FAERIE DANCE

Designer: Colin Terris
Type: Weight — Domed
Edition: 1998 in a limited edition of 200
Status: Active
Series: Colin Terris Designer Collection II
Original Issue Price: £165.00, U.S. $525.00

Name	U.S. $	Can. $	U.K. £
Faerie Dance	525.00	725.00	165.00

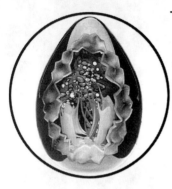

CT-1618
PAGAN RITUAL

Designer: Colin Terris
Type: Weight — Domed
Edition: 1998 in a limited edition of 150
Status: Active
Series: Colin Terris Designer Collection II
Original Issue Price: £195.00, U.S. $595.00

Name	U.S. $	Can. $	U.K. £
Pagan Ritual	595.00	855.00	195.00

CT-1619
COSMIC VISION

Designer: Colin Terris
Type: Weight — Spherical, magnum size
Edition: 1998 in a limited edition of 250
Status: Active
Series: Colin Terris Designer Collection II
Original Issue Price: £150.00, U.S. $475.00

Name	U.S. $	Can. $	U.K. £
Cosmic Vision	475.00	660.00	150.00

CT-1620
INVINCIBLE

Designer: Philip Chaplain
Type: Weight — Spherical
Edition: 1998 in a limited edition of 75
Status: Closed at No. 41
Series: Premier Stockist Paperweight Collection
Original Issue Price: £250.00

Name	U.S. $	Can. $	U.K. £
Invincible	450.00	650.00	250.00

Note: Weights CT-1620 through 1623 were offered only through U.K. Premier Stockists.

CT-1621
ELSINORE

Designer:	Philip Chaplain
Type:	Weight — Domed
Edition:	1998 in a limited edition of 75
Status:	Closed at No. 52
Series:	Premier Stockist Paperweight Collection
Original Issue Price:	£250.00

Name	U.S. $	Can. $	U.K. £
Elsinore	450.00	650.00	250.00

CT-1622
PARADOX

Designer:	Colin Terris
Type:	Weight — Domed
Edition:	1998 in a limited edition of 250
Status:	Active
Series:	Premier Stockist Paperweight Collection
Original Issue Price:	£150.00

Name	U.S. $	Can. $	U.K. £
Paradox	—	—	150.00

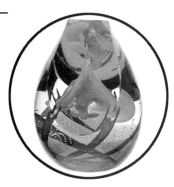

CT-1623
AEGEAN PEARL

Designer:	Colin Terris
Type:	Weight — Spherical
Edition:	1998 in a limited edition of 50
Status:	Closed at No. 38
Series:	Premier Stockist Paperweight Collection
Original Issue Price:	£275.00

Name	U.S. $	Can. $	U.K. £
Aegean Pearl	600.00	850.00	375.00

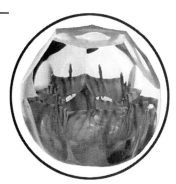

CT-1624
SOLITUDE

Designer:	Alastair MacIntosh
Type:	Weight — Sculptural
Edition:	1998 in a limited edition of 50
Status:	Fully subscribed
Series:	Limited — Modern Design
Original Issue Price:	£295.00, U.S. $895.00

Name	U.S. $	Can. $	U.K. £
Solitude	900.00	1,250.00	300.00

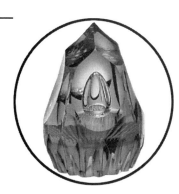

CT-1625
DESTINATION DEIMOS

Designer:	Philip Chaplain	
Type:	Weight — Domed	
Edition:	1998 in a limited edition of 75	
Status:	Fully subscribed	
Series:	Limited — Modern Design	
Original Issue Price:	£250.00, U.S. $775.00	

Name	U.S. $	Can. $	U.K. £
Destination Deimos	775.00	1,100.00	250.00

CT-1626
ETERNAL PASSION

Designer:	Helen MacDonald	
Type:	Weight — Domed	
Edition:	1998 in a limited edition of 500	
Status:	Active	
Series:	Limited — Modern Design	
Original Issue Price:	£90.00, U.S. $275.00	

Name	U.S. $	Can. $	U.K. £
Eternal Passion	275.00	395.00	90.00

CT-1627
ORIENTAL LILY

Designer:	Helen MacDonald	
Type:	Weight — Domed	
Edition:	1998 in a limited edition of 150	
Status:	Active	
Series:	Limited — Modern Design	
Original Issue Price:	£225.00, U.S. $695.00	

Name	U.S. $	Can. $	U.K. £
Oriental Lily	700.00	1,000.00	225.00

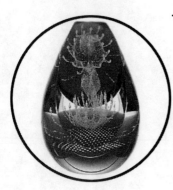

CT-1628
MYSTIC SHRINE

Designer:	Colin Terris	
Type:	Weight — Domed	
Edition:	1998 in a limited edition of 650	
Status:	Active	
Series:	Limited — Modern Design	
Original Issue Price:	£85.00, U.S. $260.00	

Name	U.S. $	Can. $	U.K. £
Mystic Shrine	260.00	375.00	85.00

CT-1629
AQUAFLORA

Designer: Helen MacDonald
Type: Weight — Spherical, magnum size
Edition: 1998 in a limited edition of 75
Status: Fully subscribed
Series: Limited — Modern Design
Original Issue Price: £275.00, U.S. $850.00

Name	U.S. $	Can. $	U.K. £
Aquaflora	850.00	1,200.00	275.00

CT-1630
MALAYSIAN MELODY

Designer: Helen MacDonald
Type: Weight — Spherical, magnum size
Edition: 1998 in a limited edition of 25
Status: Fully subscribed
Series: Limited — Modern Design
Original Issue Price: £650.00, U.S. $1,995.00

Name	U.S. $	Can. $	U.K. £
Malaysian Melody	2,000.00	2,850.00	650.00

CT-1631
REFRACTOR

Designer: Philip Chaplain
Type: Weight — Spherical
Edition: 1998 in a limited edition of 50
Status: Active
Series: Limited — Modern Design
Original Issue Price: £295.00, U.S. $895.00

Name	U.S. $	Can. $	U.K. £
Refractor	895.00	1,300.00	295.00

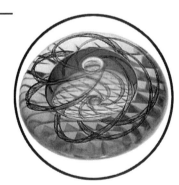

CT-1632
VIOLETTA

Designer: Helen MacDonald
Type: Weight — Spherical
Edition: 1998 in a limited edition of 500
Status: Active
Series: Limited — Modern Design
Original Issue Price: £90.00, U.S. $275.00

Name	U.S. $	Can. $	U.K. £
Violetta	275.00	395.00	90.00

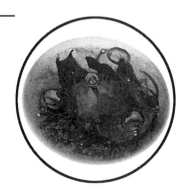

CT-1633
FIRST LOVE

Designer: Colin Terris
Type: Weight — Spherical
Edition: 1998 in a limited edition of 650
Status: Active
Series: Limited — Modern Design
Original Issue Price: £85.00, U.S. $260.00

Name	U.S. $	Can. $	U.K. £
First Love	260.00	375.00	85.00

CT-1634
TEARS OF JOY

Designer: Helen MacDonald
Type: Weight — Teardrop
Edition: 1998 in a limited edition of 750
Status: Active
Series: Limited — Modern Design
Original Issue Price: £60.00, U.S. $185.00

Name	U.S. $	Can. $	U.K. £
Tears of Joy	185.00	265.00	60.00

CT-1635
INNER SANCTUM

Designer: Philip Chaplain
Type: Weight — Domed
Edition: 1998 in a limited edition of 150
Status: Active
Series: Limited — Modern Design
Original Issue Price: £225.00, U.S. $695.00

Name	U.S. $	Can. $	U.K. £
Inner Sanctum	700.00	1,000.00	225.00

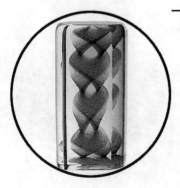

CT-1636
DOUBLE HELIX

Designer: Alastair MacIntosh
Type: Weight — Cylindrical
Edition: 1998 in a limited edition of 250
Status: Active
Series: Limited — Modern Design
Original Issue Price: £150.00, U.S. $450.00

Name	U.S. $	Can. $	U.K. £
Double Helix	450.00	660.00	150.00

CT-1637
ALCHEMIST

Designer:	Alastair MacIntosh
Type:	Weight — Domed
Edition:	1998 in a limited edition of 750
Status:	Active
Series:	Limited — Modern Design
Original Issue Price:	£75.00, U.S. $225.00

Name	U.S. $	Can. $	U.K. £
Alchemist	225.00	330.00	75.00

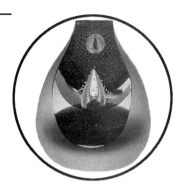

CT-1638
40 FATHOMS

Designer:	Alastair MacIntosh
Type:	Weight — Spherical
Edition:	1998 in a limited edition of 750
Status:	Active
Series:	Limited — Modern Design
Original Issue Price:	£50.00, U.S. $150.00

Name	U.S. $	Can. $	U.K. £
40 Fathoms	150.00	220.00	50.00

CT-1639
DEITY

Designer:	Alastair MacIntosh
Type:	Weight — Spherical
Edition:	1998 in a limited edition of 50
Status:	Fully subscribed
Series:	Limited — Modern Design
Original Issue Price:	£295.00, U.S. $895.00

Name	U.S. $	Can. $	U.K. £
Deity	900.00	1,250.00	300.00

CT-1640
BURNING BUSH

Designer:	Helen MacDonald
Type:	Weight — Spherical
Edition:	1998 in a limited edition of 75
Status:	Fully subscribed
Series:	Limited — Modern Design
Original Issue Price:	£250.00, U.S. $775.00

Name	U.S. $	Can. $	U.K. £
Burning Bush	775.00	1,100.00	250.00

CT-1641
SWAN VISTA

Designer:	Helen MacDonald
Type:	Weight — Domed, engraved
Edition:	1998 in a limited edition of 125
Status:	Active
Series:	Limited — Modern Design
Original Issue Price:	£285.00, U.S. $875.00

Name	U.S. $	Can. $	U.K. £
Swan Vista	875.00	1,250.00	285.00

CT-1642
SPACE HIBISCUS

Designer:	Helen MacDonald
Type:	Weight — Domed
Edition:	1998 in a limited edition of 350
Status:	Fully subscribed
Series:	Limited — Modern Design
Original Issue Price:	£99.00, U.S. $310.00

Name	U.S. $	Can. $	U.K. £
Space Hibiscus	310.00	425.00	100.00

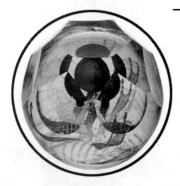

CT-1643
ULTRAMARINE

Designer:	Philip Chaplain
Type:	Weight — Spherical
Edition:	1998 in a limited edition of 75
Status:	Active
Series:	Limited — Modern Design
Original Issue Price:	£275.00, U.S. $850.00

Name	U.S. $	Can. $	U.K. £
Ultramarine	850.00	1,200.00	275.00

CT-1644
APERTURE

Designer:	Alastair MacIntosh
Type:	Weight — Spherical
Edition:	1998 in a limited edition of 50
Status:	Fully subscribed
Series:	Limited — Modern Design
Original Issue Price:	£295.00, U.S. $895.00

Name	U.S. $	Can. $	U.K. £
Aperture	900.00	1,300.00	300.00

CT-1645
TIJUANA

Designer: Alastair MacIntosh
Type: Weight — Domed
Edition: 1998 in a limited edition of 750
Status: Active
Series: Limited — Modern Design
Original Issue Price: £75.00, U.S. $235.00

Name	U.S. $	Can. $	U.K. £
Tijuana	235.00	330.00	75.00

CT-1646
PHAEDRA

Designer: Philip Chaplain
Type: Weight — Domed
Edition: 1998 in a limited edition of 750
Status: Active
Series: Limited — Modern Design
Original Issue Price: £55.00, U.S. $175.00

Name	U.S. $	Can. $	U.K. £
Phaedra	175.00	250.00	55.00

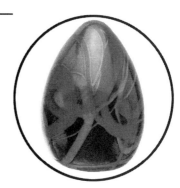

CT-1647
ARIA

Designer: Alastair MacIntosh
Type: Weight — Spherical
Edition: 1998 in a limited edition of 500
Status: Active
Series: Limited — Modern Design
Original Issue Price: £90.00, U.S. $295.00

Name	U.S. $	Can. $	U.K. £
Aria	295.00	400.00	90.00

CT-1648
ENCORE

Designer: Helen MacDonald
Type: Weight — Domed
Edition: 1998 in a limited edition of 50
Status: Active
Series: Limited — Modern Design
Original Issue Price: £325.00, U.S. $995.00

Name	U.S. $	Can. $	U.K. £
Encore	995.00	1,450.00	325.00

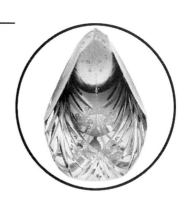

CT-1649
RITES OF SPRING

Designer:	Helen MacDonald
Type:	Weight — Domed
Edition:	1998 in a limited edition of 250
Status:	Active
Series:	Limited — Modern Design
Original Issue Price:	£175.00, U.S. $550.00

Name	U.S. $	Can. $	U.K. £
Rites of Spring	550.00	800.00	175.00

CT-1650
HIDDEN IN TIME

Designer:	Helen MacDonald
Type:	Weight — Domed, engraved
Edition:	1998 in a limited edition of 100
Status:	Fully subscribed
Series:	Limited — Modern Design
Original Issue Price:	£295.00, U.S. $895.00

Name	U.S. $	Can. $	U.K. £
Hidden in Time	895.00	1,300.00	295.00

CT-1651
SHAMBALAH

Designer:	Philip Chaplain
Type:	Weight — Domed
Edition:	1998 in a limited edition of 250
Status:	Active
Series:	Collectable Eggs — Limited
Original Issue Price:	£99.00, U.S. $310.00

Name	U.S. $	Can. $	U.K. £
Shambalah	310.00	435.00	99.00

CT-1652
ANASTASIA

Designer:	Colin Terris
Type:	Weight — Domed
Edition:	1998 in a limited edition of 100
Status:	Fully subscribed
Series:	Collectable Eggs — Limited
Original Issue Price:	£150.00, U.S. $465.00

Name	U.S. $	Can. $	U.K. £
Anastasia	465.00	660.00	150.00

CT-1653
AZURINA

Designer:	Philip Chaplain
Type:	Weight — Domed
Edition:	1998 in a limited edition of 150
Status:	Active
Series:	Collectable Eggs — Limited
Original Issue Price:	£125.00, U.S. $385.00

Name	U.S. $	Can. $	U.K. £
Azurina	385.00	550.00	125.00

CT-1654
EGGSTRAVAGANZA

Designer:	Helen MacDonald
Type:	Weight — Domed
Colour:	See below
Edition:	1998
Status:	Active
Series:	Collectable Eggs — Unlimited
Original Issue Price:	£40.00, U.S. $125.00

Colourways	U.S. $	Can. $	U.K. £
1. Blue, green and pink	125.00	180.00	40.00
2. Yellow, orange and red	125.00	180.00	40.00
3. Blue, purple and lime	125.00	180.00	40.00

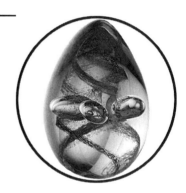

CT-1655
WAVEDANCERS

Designer:	Helen MacDonald and Stuart Cumming
Type:	Weight — Domed
Edition:	1998
Status:	Active
Series:	Collectable Eggs — Unlimited
Original Issue Price:	£40.00, U.S. $125.00

Name	U.S. $	Can. $	U.K. £
Wavedancers	125.00	180.00	40.00

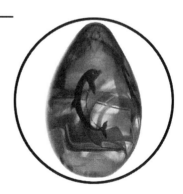

CT-1656
DINOSAURS

Designer:	Colin Terris
Type:	Weight — Spherical, medium-sized
Colour:	See below
Edition:	1998
Status:	Active
Series:	Medium and Miniature Size

Original Issue Price: £20.00, U.S. $62.50

Colourways	*U.S. $*	*Can. $*	*U.K. £*
1. Blue	62.50	90.00	20.00
2. Green	62.50	90.00	20.00
3. Pink	62.50	90.00	20.00
4. Tabac	62.50	90.00	20.00
5. Violet	62.50	90.00	20.00

Note: Each weight displays a different Dinosaur

CT-1657
CONCENTRIX

Designer:	Philip Chaplain
Type:	Weight — Domed
Colour:	See below
Edition:	1998
Status:	Active
Series:	Unlimited — Modern Design

Original Issue Price: £35.00, U.S. $110.00

Colourways	*U.S. $*	*Can. $*	*U.K. £*
1. Cobalt	110.00	155.00	35.00
2. Gold	110.00	155.00	35.00
3. Kingfisher	110.00	155.00	35.00

CT-1658
VORTICE

Designer:	Helen MacDonald
Type:	Weight — Spherical
Colour:	See below
Edition:	1998
Status:	Active
Series:	Unlimited — Modern Design

Original Issue Price: £33.50, U.S. $99.50

Colourways	*U.S. $*	*Can. $*	*U.K. £*
1. Green	99.50	145.00	33.50
2. Purple	99.50	145.00	33.50
3. Red	99.50	145.00	33.50

CT-1659
RETICELLO ROSE

Designer: Rosette Fleming
Type: Weight — Spherical
Edition: 1998 in a limited edition of 50
Status: Active
Series: Whitefriars Collection
Original Issue Price: £150.00, U.S. $495.00

Name	U.S. $	Can. $	U.K. £
Reticello Rose	495.00	660.00	150.00

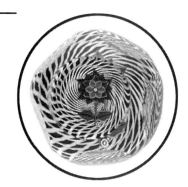

CT-1660
GOLDEN AWAKENING

Designer: Allan Scott
Type: Weight — Spherical
Edition: 1998 in a limited edition of 50
Status: Active
Series: Whitefriars Collection
Original Issue Price: £135.00, U.S. $425.00

Name	U.S. $	Can. $	U.K. £
Golden Awakening	425.00	595.00	135.00

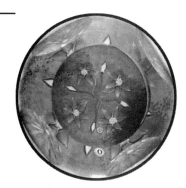

CT-1661
VALENTINO

Designer: Rosette Fleming
Type: Weight — Spherical
Edition: 1998 in a limited edition of 50
Status: Active
Series: Whitefriars Collection
Original Issue Price: £200.00, U.S. $595.00

Name	U.S. $	Can. $	U.K. £
Valentino	595.00	880.00	200.00

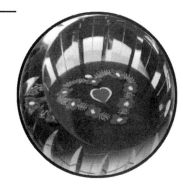

CT-1662
FLORAL DIAMOND

Designer: Rosette Fleming
Type: Weight — Spherical
Edition: 1998 in a limited edition of 50
Status: Active
Series: Whitefriars Collection
Original Issue Price: £125.00, U.S. $385.00, $550.00

Name	U.S. $	Can. $	U.K. £
Floral Diamond	385.00	550.00	125.00

CT-1663
DIAMOND LILY

Designer:	Allan Scott
Type:	Weight — Spherical
Edition:	1998 in a limited edition of 25
Status:	Fully subscribed
Series:	Traditional Collection — Nature Study
Original Issue Price:	£595.00, U.S. $1,825.00

Name	U.S. $	Can. $	U.K. £
Diamond Lily	1,825.00	2,700.00	600.00

CT-1664
TWILIGHT MYSTERY

Designer:	Allan Scott
Type:	Weight — Spherical
Edition:	1998 in a limited edition of 25
Status:	Fully subscribed
Series:	Traditional Collection — Nature Study
Original Issue Price:	£595.00, U.S. $1,825.00

Name	U.S. $	Can. $	U.K. £
Twilight Mystery	1,825.00	2,700.00	600.00

CT-1665
HEATHER CORSAGE

Designer:	Rosette Fleming
Type:	Weight — Spherical
Edition:	1998 in a limited edition of 25
Status:	Fully subscribed
Series:	Traditional Collection — Nature Study
Original Issue Price:	£595.00, U.S. $1,825.00

Name	U.S. $	Can. $	U.K. £
Heather Corsage	1,825.00	2,700.00	600.00

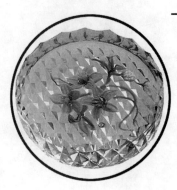

CT-1666
VICTORIANA

Designer:	Allan Scott
Type:	Weight — Disk, faceted
Edition:	1998 in a limited edition of 50
Status:	Closed at No. 43
Series:	Traditional Collection — Nature Study
Original Issue Price:	£350.00, U.S. $1,100.00

Name	U.S. $	Can. $	U.K. £
Victoriana	1,100.00	1,500.00	350.00

CT-1667
STRAWBERRY SURPRISE

Designer: Alastair MacIntosh
Type: Weight — Spherical
Edition: 1999 in a limited edition of 750
Status: Active
Series: Limited — Modern Design
Original Issue Price: £65.00, U.S. $195.00, Can. $285.00

Name	U.S. $	Can. $	U.K. £
Strawberry Surprise	195.00	285.00	65.00

CT-1668
GREENMANTLE

Designer: Helen MacDonald
Type: Weight — Domed
Edition: 1999 in a limited edition of 350
Status: Active
Series: Limited — Modern Design
Original Issue Price: £99.00, U.S. $295.00, Can. $435.00

Name	U.S. $	Can. $	U.K. £
Greenmantle	295.00	435.00	99.00

CT-1669
ORIENTAL DREAM

Designer: Helen MacDonald
Type: Weight — Teardrop
Edition: 1999 in a limited edition of 125
Status: Active
Series: Limited — Modern Design
Original Issue Price: £285.00, U.S. $875.00, Can. $1,245.00

Name	U.S. $	Can. $	U.K. £
Oriental Dream	875.00	1,245.00	285.00

CT-1670
BRILLIANCE

Designer: Colin Terris
Type: Weight — Spherical
Edition: 1999 in a limited edition of 750
Status: Active
Series: Limited — Modern Design
Original Issue Price: £75.00, U.S. $225.00, Can. $325.00

Name	U.S. $	Can. $	U.K. £
Brilliance	225.00	325.00	75.00

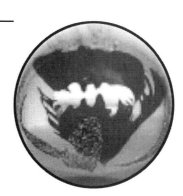

CT-1671
TOURNAMENT

Designer:	Colin Terris
Type:	Weight — Domed
Edition:	1999 in a limited edition of 125
Status:	Active
Series:	Limited — Modern Design
Original Issue Price:	£250.00, U.S. $775.00, Can. $1,095.00

Name	U.S. $	Can. $	U.K. £
Tournament	775.00	1,095.00	250.00

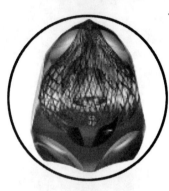

CT-1672
INTERNET

Designer:	Alastair MacIntosh
Type:	Weight — Domed
Edition:	1999 in a limited edition of 50
Status:	Active
Series:	Limited — Modern Design
Original Issue Price:	£295.00, U.S. $895.00, Can. $1,295.00

Name	U.S. $	Can. $	U.K. £
Internet	900.00	1,295.00	295.00

CT-1673
SNOWFIRE ORCHID '99

Designer:	Helen MacDonald
Type:	Weight — Spherical
Edition:	1999 in a limited edition of 500
Status:	Fully subscribed
Series:	Limited — Modern Design
Original Issue Price:	£95.00, U.S. $295.00, Can. $415.00

Name	U.S. $	Can. $	U.K. £
Snowfire Orchid '99	300.00	415.00	95.00

Note: This paperweight was introduced in the U.S. in 1996.

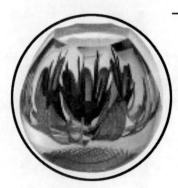

CT-1674
TROPICAL DELIGHT '99

Designer:	Colin Terris
Type:	Weight — Spherical
Edition:	1999 in a limited edition of 75
Status:	Fully subscribed
Series:	Limited — Modern Design
Original Issue Price:	£250.00, U.S. $795.00, Can. $1,095.00

Name	U.S. $	Can. $	U.K. £
Tropical Delight '99	800.00	1,100.00	250.00

Note: This paperweight was introduced in the U.S. in 1996.

CT-1675
KALEIDOSCOPE '99

Designer: Colin Terris
Type: Weight — Spherical
Edition: 1999 in a limited edition of 650
Status: Active
Series: Limited — Modern Design
Original Issue Price: £85.00, U.S. $265.00, Can. $375.00

Name	U.S. $	Can. $	U.K. £
Kaleidoscope '99	265.00	375.00	85.00

CT-1676
SHEER INDULGENCE '99

Designer: Colin Terris
Type: Weight — Spherical
Edition: 1999 in a limited edition of 75
Status: Active
Series: Limited — Modern Design
Original Issue Price: £250.00, U.S. $795.00, Can. $1,095.00

Name	U.S. $	Can. $	U.K. £
Sheer Indulgence '99	795.00	1,095.00	250.00

Note: This paperweight was introduced in the U.S. in 1996.

CT-1677
DOUBLE MAGNUM '99

Designer: Franco Toffolo
Type: Weight — Spherical, double magnum
Edition: 1999 in a limited edition of 100
Status: Active
Series: Limited — Modern Design
Original Issue Price: £350.00, U.S. $1,075.00, Can. $1,550.00

Name	U.S. $	Can. $	U.K. £
Double Magnum '99	1,075.00	1,550.00	350.00

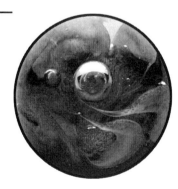

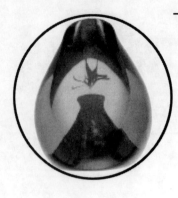

CT-1678
CASCADIA

Designer: Helen MacDonald
Type: Weight — Domed
Edition: 1999 in a limited edition of 650
Status: Active
Series: Limited — Modern Design
Original Issue Price: £85.00, U.S. $265.00, Can. $375.00

Name	U.S. $	Can. $	U.K. £
Cascadia	265.00	375.00	85.00

CT-1679
IMPULSE

Designer: Alastair MacIntosh
Type: Weight — Spherical
Edition: 1999 in a limited edition of 750
Status: Active
Series: Limited — Modern Design
Original Issue Price: £49.00, U.S. $150.00, Can. $215.00

Name	U.S. $	Can. $	U.K. £
Impulse	150.00	215.00	49.00

CT-1680
BEDOUIN

Designer: Alastair MacIntosh
Type: Weight — Domed
Edition: 1999 in a limited edition of 350
Status: Active
Series: Limited — Modern Design
Original Issue Price: £99.00, U.S. $295.00, Can. $435.00

Name	U.S. $	Can. $	U.K. £
Bedouin	295.00	435.00	99.00

CT-1681
SHAMAN

Designer:	Colin Terris
Type:	Weight — Spherical
Edition:	1999 in a limited edition of 650
Status:	Active
Series:	Limited — Modern Design
Original Issue Price:	£85.00, U.S. $265.00, Can. $375.00

Name	U.S. $	Can. $	U.K. £
Shaman	265.00	375.00	85.00

CT-1682
TURKISH DELIGHT

Designer:	Colin Terris
Type:	Weight — Domed
Edition:	1999 in a limited edition of 50
Status:	Fully subscribed
Series:	Limited — Modern Design
Original Issue Price:	£350.00, U.S. $895.00, Can. $1,535.00

Name	U.S. $	Can. $	U.K. £
Turkish Delight	895.00	1,535.00	350.00

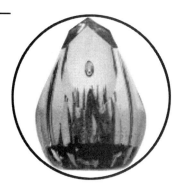

CT-1683
BLAST OFF

Designer:	Philip Chaplain
Type:	Weight — Domed
Edition:	1999 in a limited edition of 750
Status:	Active
Series:	Limited — Modern Design
Original Issue Price:	£75.00, U.S. $225.00, Can. $325.00

Name	U.S. $	Can. $	U.K. £
Blast Off	225.00	325.00	75.00

CT-1684
FAR FRONTIERS

Designer:	Colin Terris
Type:	Weight — Domed
Edition:	1999 in a limited edition of 500
Status:	Active
Series:	Limited — Modern Design
Original Issue Price:	£90.00, U.S. $295.00, Can. $395.00

Name	U.S. $	Can. $	U.K. £
Far Frontiers	295.00	395.00	90.00

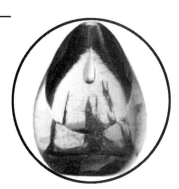

440

CT-1685
SPINDRIFT '99

Designer:	Colin Terris and Stuart Cumming		
Type:	Weight — Spherical		
Edition:	1999 in a limited edition of 1,000		
Status:	Active		
Series:	Limited — Modern Design		
Original Issue Price:	£40.00, U.S. $140.00, Can. $175.00		

Name	U.S. $	Can. $	U.K. £
Spindrift '99	140.00	175.00	40.00

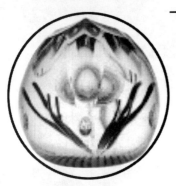

CT-1686
SILVER ORB '99

Designer:	Philip Chaplain
Type:	Weight — Spherical
Edition:	1999 in a limited edition of 75
Status:	Active
Series:	Limited — Modern Design
Original Issue Price:	£250.00, U.S. $795.00, Can. $1.095.00

Name	U.S. $	Can. $	U.K. £
Silver Orb '99	795.00	1,095.00	250.00

Note: This paperweight was introduced in the U.S. in 1996.

CT-1687
ZANZIBAR

Designer:	Alan Scrimgeour
Type:	Weight — Domed
Edition:	1999 in a limited edition of 350
Status:	Active
Series:	Limited — Modern Design
Original Issue Price:	£99.00, U.S. $295.00, Can. $435.00

Name	U.S. $	Can. $	U.K. £
Zanzibar	295.00	435.00	99.00

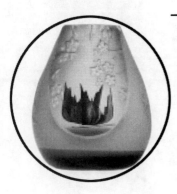

CT-1688
ONE FINE DAY

Designer:	Philip Chaplain
Type:	Weight — Domed
Edition:	1999 in a limited edition of 100
Status:	Active
Series:	Limited — Modern Design
Original Issue Price:	£325.00, U.S. $875.00, Can. $1,425.00

Name	U.S. $	Can. $	U.K. £
One Fine Day	875.00	1,425.00	325.00

CT-1689
ELECTRIC SOUP

Designer: Colin Terris
Type: Weight — Spherical
Edition: 1999 in a limited edition of 650
Status: Active
Series: Limited — Modern Design
Original Issue Price: £80.00, U.S. $250.00, Can. $350.00

Name	U.S. $	Can. $	U.K. £
Electric Soup	250.00	350.00	80.00

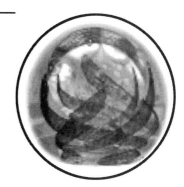

CT-1690
TOUCH OF FROST

Designer: Philip Chaplain
Type: Weight — Spherical
Edition: 1999 in a limited edition of 750
Status: Active
Series: Limited — Modern Design
Original Issue Price: £75.00, U.S. $210.00, Can. $330.00

Name	U.S. $	Can. $	U.K. £
Touch of Frost	210.00	330.00	75.00

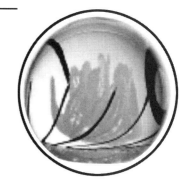

CT-1691
FAIRY LIGHTS '99

Designer: Colin Terris
Type: Weight — Spherical
Edition: 1999 in a limited edition of 250
Status: Active
Series: Limited — Modern Design
Original Issue Price: £75.00, U.S. $225.00, Can. $330.00

Name	U.S. $	Can. $	U.K. £
Fairy Lights '99	225.00	330.00	75.00

Note: This paperweight was introduced in the U.S. in 1997.

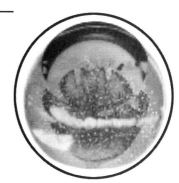

CT-1692
TIME MACHINE

Designer: Helen MacDonald
Type: Weight — Sculptural/ovoid
Edition: 1999 in a limited edition of 150
Status: Active
Series: Limited — Modern Design
Original Issue Price: £225.00, U.S. $695.00, Can. $985.00

Name	U.S. $	Can. $	U.K. £
Time Machine	695.00	985.00	225.00

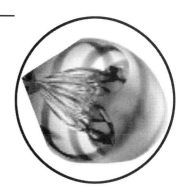

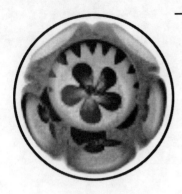

CT-1693
EVENING FLIGHT

Designer:	Colin Terris
Type:	Weight — Spherical
Edition:	1999 in a limited edition of 30
Status:	Fully subscribed
Series:	Limited — Modern Design

Original Issue Price: £450.00, U.S. $1,375.00, Can. $1,975.00

Name	U.S. $	Can. $	U.K. £
Evening Flight	1,375.00	1,975.00	450.00

CT-1694
LANDING ZONE

Designer:	Colin Terris
Type:	Weight — Spherical
Edition:	1999 in a limited edition of 650
Status:	Active
Series:	Limited — Modern Design

Original Issue Price: £75.00, U.S. $250.00, Can. $325.00

Name	U.S. $	Can. $	U.K. £
Landing Zone	250.00	325.00	75.00

CT-1695
NEMO'S KINGDOM

Designer:	Philip Chaplain
Type:	Weight — Domed
Edition:	1999 in a limited edition of 500
Status:	Active
Series:	Limited — Modern Design

Original Issue Price: £90.00, U.S. $295.00, Can. $395.00

Name	U.S. $	Can. $	U.K. £
Nemo's Kingdom	295.00	395.00	90.00

CT-1696
CROWN JEWEL

Designer:	Colin Terris
Type:	Weight — Spherical
Edition:	1999 in a limited edition of 50
Status:	Active
Series:	Limited — Modern Design

Original Issue Price: £350.00, U.S. $995.00, Can. $1,550.00

Name	U.S. $	Can. $	U.K. £
Crown Jewel	995.00	1,550.00	350.00

CT-1697
MAGIC MOMENT

Designer:	Colin Terris
Type:	Weight — Spherical
Edition:	1999 in a limited edition of 50
Status:	Active
Series:	Limited — Modern Design

Original Issue Price: £350.00, U.S. $995.00, Can. $1,535.00

Name	U.S. $	Can. $	U.K. £
Magic Moment	995.00	1,535.00	350.00

CT-1698
AMBER GAMBLER

Designer:	Philip Chaplain
Type:	Weight — Domed
Edition:	1999 in a limited edition of 750
Status:	Active
Series:	Limited — Modern Design

Original Issue Price: £75.00, U.S. $250.00, Can. $330.00

Name	U.S. $	Can. $	U.K. £
Amber Gambler	250.00	330.00	75.00

CT-1699
METROPOLIS '99

Designer:	Philip Chaplain
Type:	Weight — Domed
Edition:	1999 in a limited edition of 250
Status:	Active
Series:	Limited — Modern Design

Original Issue Price: £80.00, U.S. $275.00, Can. $350.00

Name	U.S. $	Can. $	U.K. £
Metropolis '99	275.00	350.00	80.00

Note: This paperweight was introduced in the U.S. in 1997.

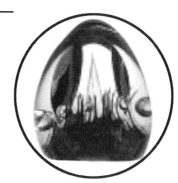

CT-1700
DUSKY MAIDEN

Designer:	Philip Chaplain
Type:	Weight — Spherical
Edition:	1999 in a limited edition of 750
Status:	Active
Series:	Limited — Modern Design

Original Issue Price: £75.00, U.S. $225.00, Can. $330.00

Name	U.S. $	Can. $	U.K. £
Dusky Maiden	225.00	330.00	75.00

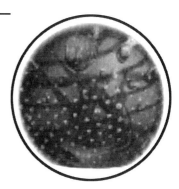

CT-1701
TRIBAL DANCE

Designer:	Colin Terris
Type:	Weight — Spherical
Edition:	1999 in a limited edition of 750
Status:	Active
Series:	Limited — Modern Design

Original Issue Price: £70.00, U.S. $225.00, Can. $300.00

Name	U.S. $	Can. $	U.K. £
Tribal Dance	225.00	300.00	70.00

CT-1702
POLYNESIAN PARADISE

Designer:	Helen MacDonald
Type:	Weight — Spherical, magnum size
Edition:	1999 in a limited edition of 30
Status:	Fully subscribed
Series:	Limited — Modern Design

Original Issue Price: £650.00, U.S. $1,995.00, Can. $2,860.00

Name	U.S. $	Can. $	U.K. £
Polynesian Paradise	1,995.00	2,860.00	650.00

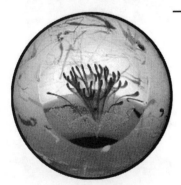

CT-1703
CORAL FANTASY '99

Designer:	Colin Terris
Type:	Weight — Spherical, magnum size
Edition:	1999 in a limited edition of 75
Status:	Active
Series:	Limited — Modern Design

Original Issue Price: £275.00, U.S. $975.00, Can. $1,205.00

Name	U.S. $	Can. $	U.K. £
Coral Fantasy '99	975.00	1,205.00	275.00

Note: This paperweight was introduced in the U.S. in 1996.

CT-1704
CORAL CITY

Designer:	Colin Terris
Type:	Weight — Domed, magnum size, engraved
Edition:	1999 in a limited edition of 250
Status:	Active
Series:	Limited — Modern Design

Original Issue Price: £150.00, U.S. $475.00, Can. $660.00

Name	U.S. $	Can. $	U.K. £
Coral City	475.00	660.00	150.00

CT-1705
SPRING MELODY

Designer: Helen MacDonald
Type: Weight — Drawn teardrop
Edition: 1999 in a limited edition of 250
Status: Active
Series: Limited — Modern Design
Original Issue Price: £150.00, U.S. $425.00, Can. $660.00

Name	U.S. $	Can. $	U.K. £
Spring Melody	425.00	660.00	150.00

CT-1706
CORAL FRONDS

Designer: Philip Chaplain
Type: Weight — Domed
Edition: 1999 in a limited edition of 750
Status: Active
Series: Limited — Modern Design
Original Issue Price: £70.00, U.S. $225.00, Can. $305.00

Name	U.S. $	Can. $	U.K. £
Coral Fronds	225.00	305.00	70.00

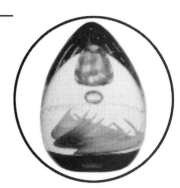

CT-1707
CITY LIMITS

Designer: Alastair MacIntosh
Type: Weight — Domed
Edition: 1999 in a limited edition of 125
Status: Active
Series: Limited — Modern Design
Original Issue Price: £250.00, U.S. $775.00, Can. $1,095.00

Name	U.S. $	Can. $	U.K. £
City Limits	775.00	1,095.00	250.00

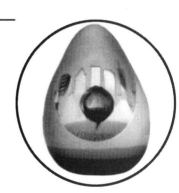

CT-1708
DESPERADO '99

Designer: Philip Chaplain
Type: Weight — Domed
Edition: 1999 in a limited edition of 250
Status: Active
Series: Limited — Modern Design
Original Issue Price: £86.00, U.S. $275.00, Can. $375.00

Name	U.S. $	Can. $	U.K. £
Desperado '99	275.00	375.00	86.00

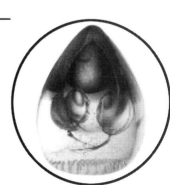

Note: This paperweight was introduced in the U.S. in 1997.

CT-1709
WISDOM

Designer: Philip Chaplain
Type: Weight — Spherical
Edition: 1999 in a limited edition of 750
Status: Active
Series: Limited — Modern Design
Original Issue Price: £75.00, U.S. $225.00, Can. $330.00

Name	U.S. $	Can. $	U.K. £
Wisdom	225.00	330.00	75.00

CT-1710
FOUNTAIN OF DESIRE

Designer: Colin Terris
Type: Weight — Spherical
Edition: 1999 in a limited edition of 75
Status: Active
Series: Limited — Modern Design
Original Issue Price: £250.00, U.S. $775.00, Can. $1,095.00

Name	U.S. $	Can. $	U.K. £
Fountain of Desire	775.00	1,095.00	250.00

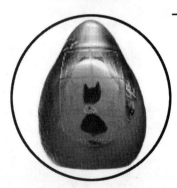

CT-1711
PEEPING TOM

Designer: Helen MacDonald
Type: Weight — Domed
Edition: 1999 in a limited edition of 100
Status: Active
Series: Limited — Modern Design
Original Issue Price: £325.00, U.S. $895.00, Can. $1,425.00

Name	U.S. $	Can. $	U.K. £
Peeping Tom	895.00	1,425.00	325.00

CT-1712
FLAMBÉ

Designer: Alastair MacIntosh
Type: Weight — Domed
Edition: 1999 in a limited edition of 350
Status: Active
Series: Limited — Modern Design
Original Issue Price: £99.00, U.S. $295.00, Can. $435.00

Name	U.S. $	Can. $	U.K. £
Flambé	295.00	435.00	99.00

CT-1713
EVANGELINE '99

Designer: Colin Terris
Type: Weight — Domed
Edition: 1999 in a limited edition of 250
Status: Fully subscribed
Series: Limited — Modern Design
Original Issue Price: £75.00, U.S. $250.00, Can. $330.00

Name	U.S. $	Can. $	U.K. £
Evangeline '99	250.00	330.00	75.00

Note: This paperweight was introduced in the U.S. in 1997.

CT-1714
ART DECO

Designer: Alastair MacIntosh
Type: Weight — Sculptural
Edition: 1999 in a limited edition of 250
Status: Active
Series: Limited — Modern Design
Original Issue Price: £150.00, U.S. $475.00, Can. $650.00

Name	U.S. $	Can. $	U.K. £
Art Deco	475.00	650.00	150.00

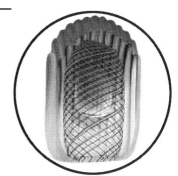

CT-1715
NORDIC CASTLE

Designer: Colin Terris
Type: Weight — Sculptural
Edition: 1999 in a limited edition of 350
Status: Active
Series: Limited — Modern Design
Original Issue Price: £99.00, U.S. $295.00, Can. $435.00

Name	U.S. $	Can. $	U.K. £
Nordic Castle	295.00	435.00	99.00

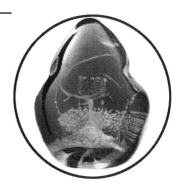

CT-1716
BREAKOUT

Designer: Alastair MacIntosh
Type: Weight — Domed, multifaceted/pyramidal
Edition: 1999 in a limited edition of 150
Status: Active
Series: Limited — Modern Design
Original Issue Price: £225.00, U.S. $695.00, Can. $985.00

Name	U.S. $	Can. $	U.K. £
Breakout	695.00	985.00	225.00

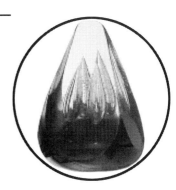

CT-1717
SWEET SURRENDER

Designer: Helen MacDonald
Type: Weight — Pyramid facets
Edition: 1999 in a limited edition of 150
Status: Active
Series: Limited — Modern Design
Original Issue Price: £195.00, U.S. $595.00, Can. $855.00

Name	U.S. $	Can. $	U.K. £
Sweet Surrender	595.00	855.00	195.00

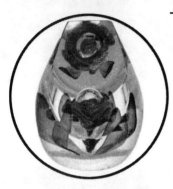

CT-1718
JACOBEAN ROSE

Designer: Colin Terris
Type: Weight — Domed
Edition: 1999 in a limited edition of 350
Status: Active
Series: Colin Terris Rose Collection
Original Issue Price: £99.00, U.S. $325.00, Can. $435.00

Name	U.S. $	Can. $	U.K. £
Jacobean Rose	325.00	435.00	99.00

CT-1719
LUNAR ROSE

Designer: Colin Terris
Type: Weight — Spherical, medium-sized
Edition: 1999 in a limited edition of 750
Status: Active
Series: Colin Terris Rose Collection
Original Issue Price: £55.00, U.S. $175.00, Can. $240.00

Name	U.S. $	Can. $	U.K. £
Lunar Rose	175.00	240.00	55.00

CT-1720
FRAGRANT ROSE

Designer: Colin Terris
Type: Weight — Spherical
Edition: 1999 in a limited edition of 650
Status: Active
Series: Colin Terris Rose Collection
Original Issue Price: £80.00, U.S. $250.00, Can. $350.00

Name	U.S. $	Can. $	U.K. £
Fragrant Rose	250.00	350.00	80.00

CT-1721
RADIANT ROSE

Designer: Colin Terris
Type: Weight — Spherical
Edition: 1999 in a limited edition of 75
Status: Active
Series: Colin Terris Rose Collection
Original Issue Price: £250.00, U.S. $775.00, Can. $1,095.00

Name	U.S. $	Can. $	U.K. £
Radiant Rose	775.00	1,095.00	250.00

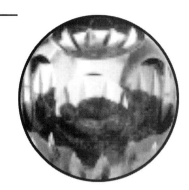

CT-1722
TWILIGHT ROSE

Designer: Colin Terris
Type: Weight — Spherical
Edition: 1999 in a limited edition of 75
Status: Active
Series: Colin Terris Rose Collection
Original Issue Price: £250.00, U.S. $775.00, Can. $1,095.00

Name	U.S. $	Can. $	U.K. £
Twilight Rose	775.00	1,095.00	250.00

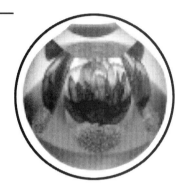

CT-1723
GOLDEN ROSE

Designer: Colin Terris
Type: Weight — Spherical
Edition: 1999 in a limited edition of 75
Status: Active
Series: Colin Terris Rose Collection
Original Issue Price: £275.00, U.S. $825.00, Can. $1,205.00

Name	U.S. $	Can. $	U.K. £
Golden Rose	825.00	1,205.00	275.00

CT-1724
DELILAH

Designer: Alastair MacIntosh
Type: Weight — Spherical
Edition: 1999 in a limited edition of 500
Status: Active
Series: Alastair MacIntosh Collection
Original Issue Price: £90.00, U.S. $285.00, Can. $395.00

Name	U.S. $	Can. $	U.K. £
Delilah	285.00	395.00	90.00

CT-1725
DIZZY LIZZY

Designer: Alastair MacIntosh
Type: Weight — Spherical
Edition: 1999 in a limited edition of 750
Status: Active
Series: Alastair MacIntosh Collection
Original Issue Price: £55.00, U.S. $175.00, Can. $240.00

Name	U.S. $	Can. $	U.K. £
Dizzy Lizzy	175.00	240.00	55.00

CT-1726
MAGIC CASTLE

Designer: Alastair MacIntosh
Type: Weight — Pyramidal, multifaceted
Edition: 1999 in a limited edition of 200
Status: Active
Series: Alastair MacIntosh Collection
Original Issue Price: £195.00, U.S. $595.00, Can. $855.00

Name	U.S. $	Can. $	U.K. £
Magic Castle	595.00	855.00	195.00

CT-1727
PROPULSION

Designer: Alastair MacIntosh
Type: Weight — Triple faceted
Edition: 1999 in a limited edition of 350
Status: Active
Series: Alastair MacIntosh Collection
Original Issue Price: £99.00, U.S. $310.00, Can. $435.00

Name	U.S. $	Can. $	U.K. £
Propulsion	310.00	435.00	99.00

CT-1728
SOLEMNITY

Designer: Alastair MacIntosh
Type: Weight — Domed
Edition: 1999 in a limited edition of 75
Status: Active
Series: Alastair MacIntosh Collection
Original Issue Price: £250.00, U.S. $785.00, Can. $1,095.00

Name	U.S. $	Can. $	U.K. £
Solemnity	785.00	1,095.00	250.00

CT-1729
PERPLEXITY

Designer: Alastair MacIntosh
Type: Weight — Domed
Edition: 1999 in a limited edition of 50
Status: Active
Series: Alastair MacIntosh Collection
Original Issue Price: £275.00, U.S. $865.00, Can. $1,205.00

Name	U.S. $	Can. $	U.K. £
Perplexity	865.00	1,205.00	275.00

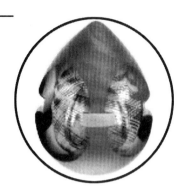

CT-1730
OVER THE HILLS

Designer: Alastair MacIntosh
Type: Weight — Spherical, magnum size
Edition: 1999 in a limited edition of 250
Status: Active
Series: Alastair MacIntosh Collection
Original Issue Price: £175.00, U.S. $550.00, Can. $770.00

Name	U.S. $	Can. $	U.K. £
Over the Hills	550.00	770.00	175.00

CT-1731
DAFFODIL

Designer: Colin Terris
Type: Weight — Domed
Edition: 1999
Status: Active
Series: Collectable Eggs — Unlimited
Original Issue Price: £49.00, U.S. $165.00, Can. $215.00

Name	U.S. $	Can. $	U.K. £
Daffodil	165.00	215.00	49.00

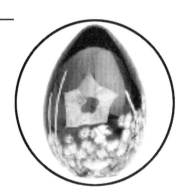

CT-1732
ORCHID

Designer: Colin Terris
Type: Weight — Domed
Edition: 1999
Status: Active
Series: Collectable Eggs — Unlimited
Original Issue Price: £49.00, U.S. $165.00, Can. $215.00

Name	U.S. $	Can. $	U.K. £
Orchid	165.00	215.00	49.00

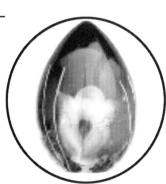

CT-1733
VIOLET

Designer:	Colin Terris
Type:	Weight — Domed
Edition:	1999
Status:	Active
Series:	Collectable Eggs — Unlimited

Original Issue Price: £49.00, U.S. $165.00, Can. $215.00

Name	U.S. $	Can. $	U.K. £
Violet	165.00	215.00	49.00

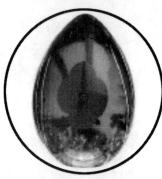

CT-1734
POPPY

Designer:	Colin Terris
Type:	Weight — Domed
Edition:	1999
Status:	Active
Series:	Collectable Eggs — Unlimited

Original Issue Price: £49.00, U.S. $165.00, Can. $215.00

Name	U.S. $	Can. $	U.K. £
Poppy	165.00	215.00	49.00

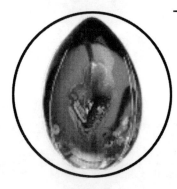

CT-1735
CROCUS

Designer:	Colin Terris
Type:	Weight — Domed
Edition:	1999
Status:	Active
Series:	Collectable Eggs — Unlimited

Original Issue Price: £49.00, U.S. $165.00, Can. $215.00

Name	U.S. $	Can. $	U.K. £
Crocus	165.00	215.00	49.00

CT-1736
KATARINA

Designer:	Colin Terris
Type:	Weight — Domed
Edition:	1999 in a limited edition of 100
Status:	Active
Series:	Collectable Eggs — Limited

Original Issue Price: £175.00, U.S. $550.00, Can. $770.00

Name	U.S. $	Can. $	U.K. £
Katarina	550.00	770.00	175.00

CT-1737
CITRON

Designer: Philip Chaplain
Type: Weight — Domed
Edition: 1999 in a limited edition of 150
Status: Active
Series: Collectable Eggs — Limited
Original Issue Price: £125.00, U.S. $385.00, Can. $550.00

Name	U.S. $	Can. $	U.K. £
Citron	385.00	550.00	125.00

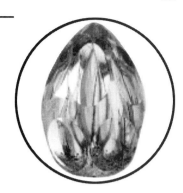

CT-1738
SUMATRA

Designer: Philip Chaplain
Type: Weight — Domed
Edition: 1999 in a limited edition of 250
Status: Active
Series: Collectable Eggs — Limited
Original Issue Price: £99.00, U.S. $310.00, Can. $435.00

Name	U.S. $	Can. $	U.K. £
Sumatra	310.00	435.00	99.00

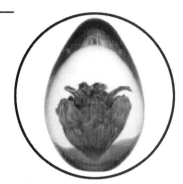

CT-1739
DAISIES and TRELLIS

Designer: Allan Scott
Type: Weight — Spherical
Edition: 1999 in a limited edition of 50
Status: Active
Series: Whitefriars Collection
Original Issue Price: £120.00, U.S. $375.00, Can. $525.00

Name	U.S. $	Can. $	U.K. £
Daisies and Trellis	375.00	525.00	120.00

CT-1740
DIAMOND REFLECTIONS

Designer: Rosette Fleming
Type: Weight — Spherical
Edition: 1999 in a limited edition of 50
Status: Active
Series: Whitefriars Collection
Original Issue Price: £120.00, U.S. $395.00, Can. $525.00

Name	U.S. $	Can. $	U.K. £
Diamond Reflections	395.00	525.00	120.00

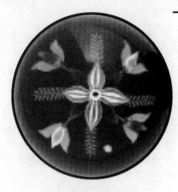

CT-1741
BURGUNDY QUARTET

Designer: Rosette Fleming
Type: Weight — Spherical
Edition: 1999 in a limited edition of 50
Status: Active
Series: Whitefriars Collection
Original Issue Price: £99.00, U.S. $325.00, Can. $435.00

Name	U.S. $	Can. $	U.K. £
Burgundy Quartet	325.00	435.00	99.00

CT-1742
VICTORIAN BLOSSOM

Designer: Rosette Fleming
Type: Weight — Spherical
Edition: 1999 in a limited edition of 50
Status: Active
Series: Whitefriars Collection
Original Issue Price: £99.00, U.S. $325.00, Can. $435.00

Name	U.S. $	Can. $	U.K. £
Victorian Blossom	325.00	435.00	99.00

CT-1743
FLORAL SPLENDOUR

Designer: Melanie Stuart
Type: Weight — Spherical
Edition: 1999 in a limited edition of 50
Status: Fully subscribed
Series: Whitefriars Collection
Original Issue Price: £120.00, U.S. $350.00, Can. $525.00

Name	U.S. $	Can. $	U.K. £
Floral Splendour	350.00	525.00	120.00

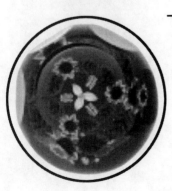

CT-1744
SUNFLOWER CELEBRATION

Designer: Rosette Fleming
Type: Weight — Spherical
Edition: 1999 in a limited edition of 50
Status: Active
Series: Whitefriars Collection
Original Issue Price: £145.00, U.S. $450.00, Can. $635.00

Name	U.S. $	Can. $	U.K. £
Sunflower Celebration	450.00	635.00	145.00

CT-1745
DAWN BOUQUET

Designer: Melanie Stuart
Type: Weight — Spherical
Edition: 1999 in a limited edition of 50
Status: Active
Series: Whitefriars Collection
Original Issue Price: £125.00, U.S. $385.00, Can. $550.00

Name	U.S. $	Can. $	U.K. £
Dawn Bouquet	385.00	550.00	125.00

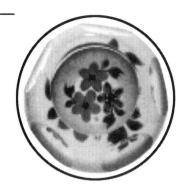

CT-1746
BLUE RHAPSODY

Designer: Rosette Fleming
Type: Weight — Spherical
Edition: 1999 in a limited edition of 50
Status: Active
Series: Whitefriars Collection
Original Issue Price: £145.00, U.S. $450.00, Can. $635.00

Name	U.S. $	Can. $	U.K. £
Blue Rhapsody	450.00	635.00	145.00

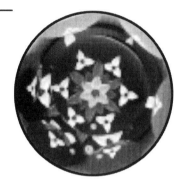

CT-1747
TWO OF A KIND

Designer: Rosette Fleming
Type: Weight — Spherical
Edition: 1999 in a limited edition of 50
Status: Active
Series: Whitefriars Collection
Original Issue Price: £155.00, U.S. $475.00, Can. $675.00

Name	U.S. $	Can. $	U.K. £
Two of a Kind	475.00	675.00	155.00

CT-1748
LATTICINO POSY

Designer: Allan Scott
Type: Weight — Spherical
Edition: 1999 in a limited edition of 50
Status: Active
Series: Whitefriars Collection
Original Issue Price: £120.00, U.S. $395.00, Can. $525.00

Name	U.S. $	Can. $	U.K. £
Latticino Posy	395.00	525.00	120.00

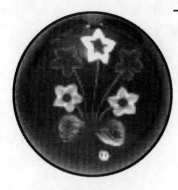

CT-1749
GOLDEN GLORY

Designer:	Rosette Fleming
Type:	Weight — Spherical
Edition:	1999 in a limited edition of 50
Status:	Active
Series:	Whitefriars Collection
Original Issue Price:	£99.00, U.S. $325.00, Can. $435.00

Name	U.S. $	Can. $	U.K. £
Golden Glory	325.00	435.00	99.00

CT-1750
ISLAND DREAM

Designer:	Rosette Fleming
Type:	Weight — Spherical
Edition:	1999 in a limited edition of 75
Status:	Active
Series:	Traditional Collection — Nature Study
Original Issue Price:	£275.00, U.S. $825.00, Can. $1,200.00

Name	U.S. $	Can. $	U.K. £
Island Dream	825.00	1,200.00	275.00

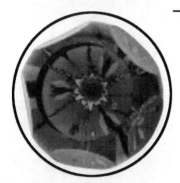

CT-1751
HARVEST FESTIVAL

Designer:	Rosette Fleming
Type:	Weight — Spherical
Edition:	1999 in a limited edition of 50
Status:	Active
Series:	Traditional Collection — Nature Study
Original Issue Price:	£295.00, U.S. $895.00, Can. $1,295.00

Name	U.S. $	Can. $	U.K. £
Harvest Festival	895.00	1,295.00	295.00

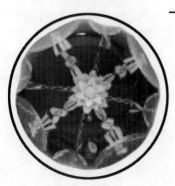

CT-1752
CELTIC CELEBRATION

Designer:	Rosette Fleming
Type:	Weight — Spherical
Edition:	1999 in a limited edition of 50
Status:	Active
Series:	Traditional Collection — Nature Study
Original Issue Price:	£295.00, U.S. $895.00, Can. $1,295.00

Name	U.S. $	Can. $	U.K. £
Celtic Celebration	895.00	1,295.00	295.00

CT-1753
LOVE TOKEN

Designer: Rosette Fleming
Type: Weight — Spherical
Edition: 1999 in a limited edition of 75
Status: Active
Series: Traditional Collection — Nature Study
Original Issue Price: £275.00, U.S. $825.00, Can. $1,200.00

Name	U.S. $	Can. $	U.K. £
Love Token	825.00	1,200.00	275.00

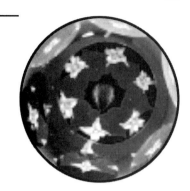

CT-1754
TRUE ROMANCE

Designer: Allan Scott
Type: Weight — Spherical, faceted
Edition: 1999 in a limited edition of 50
Status: Active
Series: Traditional Collection — Nature Study
Original Issue Price: £295.00, U.S. $895.00, Can. $1,295.00

Name	U.S. $	Can. $	U.K. £
True Romance	895.00	1,295.00	295.00

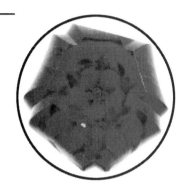

CT-1755
BURGUNDY TREFOIL

Designer: Rosette Fleming
Type: Weight — Spherical
Edition: 1999 in a limited edition of 50
Status: Active
Series: Traditional Collection — Nature Study
Original Issue Price: £295.00, U.S. $895.00, Can. $1,295.00

Name	U.S. $	Can. $	U.K. £
Burgundy Trefoil	895.00	1,295.00	295.00

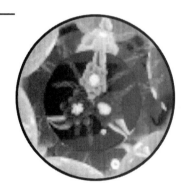

CT-1756
CHEVRONS

Designer: Stuart Cumming
Type: Weight — Spherical
Colour: See below
Edition: 1999
Status: Active
Series: Unlimited — Modern Design
Original Issue Price: £25.00, U.S. $79.50, Can. $100.00

Colourways	U.S. $	Can. $	U.K. £
1. Blue	79.50	100.00	25.00
2. Green	79.50	100.00	25.00
3. Pink	79.50	100.00	25.00

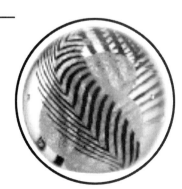

CT-1757
DASH

Designer:	Alastair MacIntosh
Type:	Weight — Teardrop
Edition:	1999
Status:	Active
Series:	Unlimited
Original Issue Price:	£30.00, U.S. $79.50, Can. $130.00

Name	U.S. $	Can. $	U.K. £
Dash	79.50	130.00	30.00

CT-1758
OZONE

Designer:	Alastair MacIntosh
Type:	Weight — Spherical
Colour:	See below
Edition:	1999
Status:	Active
Series:	Unlimited
Original Issue Price:	£30.00, U.S. $95.00, Can. $125.00

Colourways	U.S. $	Can. $	U.K. £
1. Amethyst	95.00	125.00	30.00
2. Cobalt	95.00	125.00	30.00
3. Kingfisher	95.00	125.00	30.00

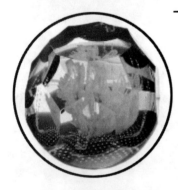

CT-1759
FROZEN IN TIME

Designer:	Philip Chaplain
Type:	Weight — Spherical
Edition:	1999 in a limited edition of 50
Status:	Fully subscribed
Series:	Premier Stockist/Premier Dealer Paperweight Collection
Original Issue Price:	£295.00, U.S. $895.00

Name	U.S. $	Can. $	U.K. £
Frozen in Time	900.00	1,350.00	300.00

CT-1760
GOTHIC SPLENDOUR

Designer:	Helen MacDonald
Type:	Weight — Teardrop
Edition:	1999 in a limited edition of 100
Status:	Active
Series:	Premier Stockist/Premier Dealer Paperweight Collection
Original Issue Price:	£225.00, U.S. $675.00

Name	U.S. $	Can. $	U.K. £
Gothic Splendour	675.00	—	225.00

CT-1761
INTREPID

Designer: Alastair MacIntosh
Type: Weight — Spherical
Edition: 1999 in a limited edition of 50
Status: Active
Series: Premier Stockist/Premier Dealer Paperweight Collection
Original Issue Price: £325.00, U.S. $975.00

Name	U.S. $	Can. $	U.K. £
Intrepid	975.00	—	325.00

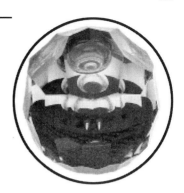

CT-1762
MIDNIGHT MYSTERY

Designer: Colin Terris
Type: Weight — Spherical
Edition: 1999 in a limited edition of 75
Status: Active
Series: Premier Stockist/Premier Dealer Paperweight Collection
Original Issue Price: £250.00, U.S. $775.00

Name	U.S. $	Can. $	U.K. £
Midnight Mystery	775.00	—	250.00

CT-1763
STATUS QUO

Designer: Alastair MacIntosh
Type: Weight — Domed
Edition: 1999 in a limited edition of 100
Status: Active
Series: Premier Stockist/Premier Dealer Paperweight Collection
Original Issue Price: £225.00, U.S. $675.00

Name	U.S. $	Can. $	U.K. £
Status Quo	675.00	—	225.00

CT-1764
MILLENNIUM 2000

Designer:	Helen MacDonald
Type:	Weight — Spherical
Colour:	See below
Edition:	1999
Status:	Active
Series:	Millennium Collection
Original Issue Price:	£40.00, U.S. $130.00

Colourways	U.S. $	Can. $	U.K. £
1. Cobalt	130.00	—	40.00
2. Heather	130.00	—	40.00
3. Emerald	130.00	—	40.00
4. Gold	130.00	—	40.00
5. Kingfisher	130.00	—	40.00

CT-1765
MILLENNIUM CARNIVAL

Designer:	Colin Terris
Type:	Weight — Spherical, magnum size
Cane:	2000
Edition:	1999
Status:	Active
Series:	Millennium Collection
Original Issue Price:	£60.00, U.S. $195.00

Name	U.S. $	Can. $	U.K. £
Millennium Carnival	195.00	—	60.00

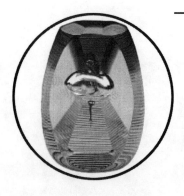

CT-1766
MILLENNIUM JEWEL

Designer:	Colin Terris
Type:	Weight — Domed, multifaceted
Edition:	1999 in a limited edition of 100
Status:	Fully subscribed
Series:	Millennium Collection
Original Issue Price:	£200.00, U.S. $650.00

Name	U.S. $	Can. $	U.K. £
Millennium Jewel	650.00	950.00	200.00

CT-1767
MILLENNIUM DANCER

Designer: Colin Terris
Type: Weight — Spherical
Edition: 1999 in a limited edition of 650
Status: Active
Series: Millennium Collection
Original Issue Price: £60.00, U.S. $175.00

Name	U.S. $	Can. $	U.K. £
Millennium Dancer	175.00	—	60.00

CT-1768
CAPITAL CELEBRATION EDINBURGH

Designer: W. Bain
Type: Weight — Spherical, engraved
Edition: 1999
Status: Active
Series: Millennium Collection
Original Issue Price: £37.00, U.S. $110.00

Name	U.S. $	Can. $	U.K. £
Capital Celebration Edinburgh	110.00	—	37.00

CT-1769
LONDON TIME

Designer: W. Bain
Type: Weight — Spherical, engraved
Edition: 1999
Status: Active
Series: Millennium Collection
Original Issue Price: £37.00, U.S. $110.00

Name	U.S. $	Can. $	U.K. £
London Time	110.00	—	37.00

CT-1770
MILLENNIUM LIBERTY

Designer: Colin Terris
Type: Weight — Domed
Edition: 1999 in a limited edition of 350
Status: Active
Series: Millennium Collection
Original Issue Price: U.S. $295.00

Name	U.S. $	Can. $	U.K. £
Millennium Liberty	295.00	—	—

Note: This paperweight is issued only in the U.S.

CT-1771
MILLENNIUM COUNTDOWN

Designer:	Colin Terris	
Type:	Weight — Spherical	
Edition:	1999 in a limited edition of 750	
Status:	Active	
Series:	Millennium Collection	
Original Issue Price:	£55.00, U.S. $175.00	

Name	*U.S. $*	*Can. $*	*U.K. £*
Millennium Countdown	175.00	—	55.00

CT-1772
MILLENNIUM GLOBE

Designer:	Colin Terris	
Type:	Weight — Spherical	
Colour:	See below	
Edition:	1999	
Status:	Active	
Series:	Millennium Collection	
Original Issue Price:	£45.00, U.S. $145.00	

Colourways	*U.S. $*	*Can. $*	*U.K. £*
1. Blue	145.00	—	45.00
2. Red	145.00	—	45.00

CT-1773
MILLENNIUM STARBURST

Designer:	Colin Terris	
Type:	Weight — Domed	
Edition:	1999 in a limited edition of 650	
Status:	Active	
Series:	Millennium Collection	
Original Issue Price:	£45.00, U.S. $240.00	

Name	*U.S. $*	*Can. $*	*U.K. £*
Millennium Starburst	240.00	—	45.00

CT-1774
MILLENNIUM PEBBLE

Designer:	Colin Terris	
Type:	Weight — Sculptural, miniature	
Edition:	1999	
Status:	Active	
Series:	Millennium Collection	
Original Issue Price:	£12.50, U.S. $39.50	

Name	*U.S. $*	*Can. $*	*U.K. £*
Millennium Pebble	39.50	—	12.50

CT-1775
MILLENNIUM TEDDY

Designer:	W. Bain
Type:	Weight — Spherical, medium-sized
Colour:	See below
Edition:	1999
Status:	Active
Series:	Millennium Collection

Original Issue Price:　£27.00, U.S. $87.50

Colourways	U.S. $	Can. $	U.K. £
1. Pink	87.50	—	27.00
2. Blue	87.50	—	27.00

CT-1776
MILLENNIUM DOVES

Designer:	Helen MacDonald
Type:	Weight — Spherical, medium-sized
Edition:	1999
Status:	Active
Series:	Millennium Collection

Original Issue Price:　£27.00, U.S. $87.50

Name	U.S. $	Can. $	U.K. £
Millennium Doves	87.50	—	27.00

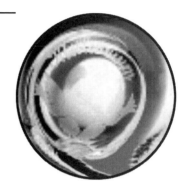

CT-1777
MILLENNIUM VOYAGER

Designer:	Colin Terris
Type:	Weight — Spherical, magnum size
Edition:	1999 in a limited edition of 250
Status:	Fully subscribed
Series:	Millennium Collection

Original Issue Price:　£150.00, U.S. $475.00

Name	U.S. $	Can. $	U.K. £
Millennium Voyager	475.00	700.00	150.00

CT-1778
MILLENNIUM FANTASY

Designer:	Colin Terris
Type:	Weight — Spherical
Cane:	2000
Edition:	1999 in a limited edition of 500
Status:	Active
Series:	Millennium Collection

Original Issue Price:　£90.00, U.S. $295.00

Name	U.S. $	Can. $	U.K. £
Millennium Fantasy	295.00	—	90.00

CT-1779
MILLENNIUM BLOSSOM

Designer:	Helen MacDonald	
Type:	Weight — Teardrop	
Edition:	1999 in a limited edition of 250	
Status:	Active	
Series:	Millennium Collection	
Original Issue Price:	£140.00, U.S. $450.00	

Name	U.S. $	Can. $	U.K. £
Millennium Blossom	450.00	—	140.00

CT-1780
MILLENNIUM SANDS OF TIME

Designer:	Colin Terris	
Type:	Weight — Hourglass	
Edition:	1999 in a limited edition of 200	
Status:	Fully subscribed	
Series:	Millennium Collection	
Original Issue Price:	£99.00, U.S. $295.00	

Name	U.S. $	Can. $	U.K. £
Millennium Sands of Time	300.00	450.00	100.00

CT-1781
MILLENNIUM FIESTA

Designer:	Colin Terris	
Type:	Weight — Domed	
Edition:	1999 in a limited edition of 650	
Status:	Active	
Series:	Millennium Collection	
Original Issue Price:	£75.00, U.S. $240.00	

Name	U.S. $	Can. $	U.K. £
Millennium Fiesta	240.00	—	75.00

CT-1782
MILLENNIUM AWAKENING

Designer: Helen MacDonald
Type: Weight — Spherical
Edition: 1999 in a limited edition of 750
Status: Active
Series: Millennium Collection
Original Issue Price: £70.00, U.S. $225.00

Name	U.S. $	Can. $	U.K. £
Millennium Awakening	225.00	—	70.00

CT-1783
MILLENNIUM VISION

Designer: Colin Terris
Type: Weight — Spherical with black glass foot
Edition: 1999
Status: Active
Series: Millennium Collection and the 1999 Collectors' Weight
Original Issue Price: £85.00, U.S. $225.00, Can. $350.00

Name	U.S. $	Can. $	U.K. £
Millennium Vision	225.00	350.00	85.00

TOPSY-TURVY

Shona Spittal shows us, step-by-step, how to create four spiraling silvery bubbles, each rising from its own individual colour thread from a sparkling crystalline base.

1 Laying down four colour pattern

2 Blocking a large gather of glass

3 Re-warming at the glory hole

4 Picking up the powdered glass colours

5 Paletting to shape (5 & 6).

6

7 Piercing a hole through each colour

8 Using compressed air to blow bubbles

9 Pulling out excess glass

10 Cutting-in and sealing off bubbles

11 Marvering to twist bubbles

12 Picking up sand for base

13 Cutting-in at the back of the paperweight

14 Applying the punty

15 Pulling out and cutting off the punty mark

16 The final shaping

COMMISSIONED WEIGHTS

ANTHONY JACKSON CHINA AND GLASSWARE
BLACKBURN, U.K.

AJ-001
THE ROCKET

Designer:	Caithness Engraving Studios
Type:	Weight — Spherical, engraved
Edition:	1980 in a limited edition of 1,000
Status:	Closed at No. 250
Original Issue Price:	£57.60

Name	U.S. $	Can. $	U.K. £
The Rocket	125.00	185.00	80.00

ART INSTITUTE OF CHICAGO
CHICAGO, U.S.

AI-001
ORCHID

Designer:	Allan Scott
Type:	Weight — Spherical
Edition:	1991 in a limited edition of 150
Status:	Fully subscribed

Original Issue Price: U.S. $595.00

Name	U.S. $	Can. $	U.K. £
Orchid	600.00	900.00	400.00

AI-002
WATERLILY IMPRESSIONS

Designer:	Colin Terris
Type:	Weight — Spherical
Edition:	1994 in a limited edition of 250
Status:	Fully subscribed

Original Issue Price: U.S. $295.00

Name	U.S. $	Can. $	U.K. £
Waterlily Impressions	295.00	450.00	200.00

AI-003
TRANQUIL FLIGHT

Designer:	Colin Terris
Type:	Weight — Spherical
Edition:	1998 in a limited edition of 75
Status:	Active

Original Issue Price: U.S. $310.00

Name	U.S. $	Can. $	U.K. £
Tranquil Flight	310.00	450.00	195.00

ARTISTIC TREASURES
RICHMOND, U.K.

AT-001
SOLAR FLOWER

Designer:	Colin Terris
Type:	Weight — Spherical
Edition:	1995 in a limited edition of 100
Status:	Closed
Original Issue Price:	£175.00

Name	U.S. $	Can. $	U.K. £
Solar Flower	275.00	400.00	175.00

ASHBOURNE HOUSE
ASHBOURNE, U.K.

AH-001
CANDLELIGHT

Designer:	Margot Thomson
Type:	Weight — Domed
Edition:	1995 in a limited edition of 75
Status:	Closed
Original Issue Price:	£95.00

Name	U.S. $	Can. $	U.K. £
Candlelight	325.00	450.00	200.00

AH-002
AMBIENCE

Designer:	Colin Terris
Type:	Weight — Spherical
Edition:	1996 in a limited edition of 75
Status:	Closed
Original Issue Price:	£115.00

Name	U.S. $	Can. $	U.K. £
Ambience	400.00	550.00	250.00

BERGSTROM-MAHLER MUSEUM
NEENAH, U.S.

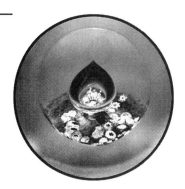

BM-001
MECCA

Designer: Colin Terris
Type: Weight — Spherical
Edition: 1989 in a limited edition of 100
Status: Fully subscribed
Original Issue Price: U.S. $195.00

Name	*U.S. $*	*Can. $*	*U.K. £*
Mecca	300.00	450.00	200.00

Note: This weight was commissioned to celebrate the 1989 PCA Convention
held in Nina, Wisconsin in 1980. (Paperweight Collectors Association)

CASHS OF IRELAND

CI-001
FUCHSIAS

Designer:	Margot Thomson
Type:	Weight — Spherical
Edition:	1990 in a limited edition of 250
Status:	Closed
Original Issue Price:	U.S. $169.00

Name	U.S. $	Can. $	U.K. £
Fuchsias	175.00	250.00	125.00

CI-002
HOLLY and BELLS

Designer:	Allan Scott
Type:	Weight — Spherical
Edition:	1991 in a limited edition of 150
Status:	Closed
Original Issue Price:	U.S. $159.00

Name	U.S. $	Can. $	U.K. £
Holly and Bells	175.00	250.00	125.00

CI-003
MINIATURE HEART

Designer:	Allan Scott
Type:	Weight — Spherical
Edition:	1991
Status:	Closed
Original Issue Price:	U.S. $59.00

Name	U.S. $	Can. $	U.K. £
Miniature Heart	75.00	125.00	50.00

CI-004
FORGET ME NOT

Designer:	Allan Scott
Type:	Weight — Spherical
Edition:	1994
Status:	Closed
Original Issue Price:	U.S. $49.00

Name	U.S. $	Can. $	U.K. £
Forget Me Not	50.00	75.00	35.00

CI-005
IRISH WILD FLOWERS

Designer:	Allan Scott
Type:	Weight — Spherical
Edition:	1997 in a limited edition of 500
Status:	Closed
Original Issue Price:	U.S. $139.00

Name	U.S. $	Can. $	U.K. £
Irish Wild Flowers	140.00	200.00	90.00

CI-006
IRISH SHAMROCK

Designer:	Allan Scott
Type:	Weight — Spherical
Edition:	1997
Status:	Closed
Original Issue Price:	U.S. $39.00

Name	U.S. $	Can. $	U.K. £
Irish Shamrock	40.00	60.00	25.00

CI-007
IRISH WILD FLOWER

Designer:	Allan Scott
Type:	Weight — Spherical
Edition:	1998 in a limited edition of 500
Status:	Closed
Original Issue Price:	U.S. $159.00

Name	U.S. $	Can. $	U.K. £
Irish Wild Flower	160.00	250.00	100.00

THE COCA-COLA COMPANY
ATLANTA, U.S.

CC-001
RIBBONS MEMORIES

Designer:	Helen MacDonald
Type:	Weight — Spherical
Edition:	1998 in a limited edition of 1,000
Status:	Active
Original Issue Price:	U.S. $99.50

Name	*U.S. $*	*Can. $*	*U.K. £*
Ribbons Memories	99.50	140.00	65.00

Note: The Coca-Cola weights are issued in the U.S. only.

CC-002
RIBBONS WINDOW

Designer:	Helen MacDonald
Type:	Weight — Spherical
Edition:	1998 in a limited edition of 1,000
Status:	Active
Original Issue Price:	U.S. $115.00

Name	*U.S. $*	*Can. $*	*U.K. £*
Ribbons Window	115.00	160.00	75.00

CC-003
EFFERVESCENT RIBBONS

Designer:	Helen MacDonald
Type:	Weight — Spherical
Edition:	1998 in a limited edition of 1,000
Status:	Active
Original Issue Price:	U.S. $89.50

Name	*U.S. $*	*Can. $*	*U.K. £*
Effervescent Ribbons	89.50	120.00	60.00

CC-004
ALWAYS…!

Designer: Helen MacDonald
Type: Weight — Spherical
Edition: 1998 in a limited edition of 750
Status: Active
Original Issue Price: U.S. $195.00

Name	*U.S. $*	*Can. $*	*U.K. £*
Always…!	195.00	275.00	125.00

CC-005
INNER SPACE

Designer: Helen MacDonald
Type: Weight — Spherical
Edition: 1998 in a limited edition of 750
Status: Active
Original Issue Price: U.S. $165.00

Name	*U.S. $*	*Can. $*	*U.K. £*
Inner Space	165.00	225.00	100.00

CC-006
BUBBLES 'N STRIPES

Designer: Helen MacDonald
Type: Weight — Spherical
Edition: 1998 in a limited edition of 750
Status: Active
Original Issue Price: U.S. $150.00

Name	*U.S. $*	*Can. $*	*U.K. £*
Bubbles 'n Stripes	150.00	200.00	95.00

CC-007
COOL CAP

Designer: Helen MacDonald
Type: Weight — Bottlecap
Edition: 1998 in a limited edition of 1,000
Status: Active
Original Issue Price: U.S. $95.00

Name	*U.S. $*	*Can. $*	*U.K. £*
Cool Cap	95.00	130.00	65.00

CC-008
THE REAL THING

Designer: Helen MacDonald
Type: Weight — Spherical
Edition: 1998 in a limited edition of 1,000
Status: Active
Original Issue Price: U.S. $115.00

Name	U.S. $	Can. $	U.K. £
The Real Thing	115.00	160.00	75.00

CC-009
ICE COLD

Designer: Helen MacDonald
Type: Weight — Spherical
Edition: 1998 in a limited edition of 100
Status: Active
Original Issue Price: U.S. $725.00

Name	U.S. $	Can. $	U.K. £
Ice Cold	725.00	1,050.00	475.00

CC-010
LIFE'S A BEAR...N-ICE!

Designer: Allan Scott
Type: Weight — Spherical
Edition: 1998 in a limited edition of 50
Status: Active
Original Issue Price: U.S. $895.00

Name	U.S. $	Can. $	U.K. £
Life's A Bear...N-ice!	895.00	1,250.00	575.00

CC-011
FOUNTAIN MEMORIES

Designer: Helen MacDonald
Type: Weight — Tumbler style
Edition: 1998 in a limited edition of 750
Status: Active
Original Issue Price: U.S. $185.00

Name	U.S. $	Can. $	U.K. £
Fountain Memories	185.00	250.00	125.00

DAVID SANDBACH
LLANDUDNO, U.K.

DS-001
WELSH DRAGON

Designer: Caithness Engraving Studios
Type: Weight — Spherical, engraved
Edition: 1981 in a limited edition of 100
Status: Fully subscribed
Series: Royal Wedding Collection
Original Issue Price: £36.00

Name	U.S. $	Can. $	U.K. £
Welsh Dragon	115.00	165.00	75.00

Note: This paperweight was issued to commemorate the wedding of Prince Charles and Lady Diana Spencer.

GOVIER'S OF SIDMOUTH
SIDMOUTH, U.K.

GS-001
UNICORN, DAWN

Designer:	Colin Terris
Type:	Weight — Domed
Edition:	1999 in a limited edition of 50
Status:	Open
Original Issue Price:	£295.00

Name	U.S. $	Can. $	U.K. £
Unicorn, Dawn	—	—	295.00

GS-002
UNICORN, TWILIGHT

Designer:	Colin Terris
Type:	Weight — Domed
Edition:	1999 in a limited edition of 50
Status:	Open
Original Issue Price:	£295.00

Name	U.S. $	Can. $	U.K. £
White Fugue	—	—	295.

GS-003
UNICORN, DUSK

Designer:	Colin Terris
Type:	Weight — Domed
Edition:	1999 in a limited edition of 50
Status:	Open
Original Issue Price:	£295.00

Name	U.S. $	Can. $	U.K. £
Unicorn, Dusk	—	—	295.00

GUMP'S
SAN FRANCISCO, U.S.

GU-001
WHITE FUGUE

Designer:	Colin Terris
Type:	Weight — Spherical
Edition:	1983 in a limited edition of 500
Status:	Fully subscribed
Original Issue Price:	U.S. $225.00

Name	U.S. $	Can. $	U.K. £
White Fugue	225.00	325.00	150.00

GU-002
TWIN HEARTS

Designer:	Colin Terris
Type:	Weight — Spherical
Edition:	1991
Status:	Closed
Original Issue Price:	U.S. $175.00

Name	U.S. $	Can. $	U.K. £
Twin Hearts	175.00	250.00	125.00

GU-003
ENTWINED HEARTS

Designer:	Colin Terris
Type:	Weight — Spherical
Edition:	1993
Status:	Closed
Original Issue Price:	U.S. $175.00

Name	U.S. $	Can. $	U.K. £
Entwined Hearts	175.00	250.00	125.00

GU-004
HEART OF HEARTS

Designer:	Colin Terris
Type:	Weight — Spherical
Edition:	1996
Status:	Closed
Original Issue Price:	U.S. $190.00

Name	U.S. $	Can. $	U.K. £
Heart of Hearts	190.00	275.00	125.00

GU-005
HEART and FLOWERS

Designer:	Colin Terris
Type:	Weight — Spherical
Edition:	1997 in a limited edition of 250
Status:	Closed
Original Issue Price:	U.S. $120.00

Name	U.S. $	Can. $	U.K. £
Heart and Flowers	120.00	175.00	75.00

HADLEIGH CHINA & CRYSTAL
ABINGDON, U.K.GU-001

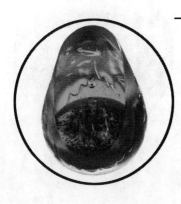

HC-001
LUNAR SEA

Designer:	Alastair MacIntosh and Helen MacDonald
Type:	Weight — Domed
Edition:	1992 in a limited edition of 100
Status:	Closed
Original Issue Price:	£200.00

Name	U.S. $	Can. $	U.K. £
Lunar Sea	475.00	675.00	300.00

HISTORIC SCOTLAND
EDINBURGH, U.K.

HS-001
HONOURS

Designer: Helen MacDonald
Type: Weight — Spherical
Edition: 1996
Status: Closed
Original Issue Price: £26.00

Name	U.S. $	Can. $	U.K. £
Honours	50.00	70.00	30.00

Note: The designs of weights HS-001, 002 and 003 are based on the Honours of Scotland (the Scottish crown jewels).

HS-002
HONOURS, FLEUR-DE-LYS

Designer: Helen MacDonald
Type: Weight — Spherical
Edition: 1996 in a limited edition of 750
Status: Closed
Original Issue Price: £65.00

Name	U.S. $	Can. $	U.K. £
Honours, Fleur-de-Lys	95.00	130.00	65.00

HS-003
HONOURS, ORB

Designer: Helen MacDonald
Type: Weight — Domed
Edition: 1996 in a limited edition of 50
Status: Closed
Original Issue Price: £225.00

Name	U.S. $	Can. $	U.K. £
Honours, Orb	550.00	775.00	350.00

IN THE SPIRIT MAIL ORDER
HANOVER, PENNSYLVANIA, U.S.

IS-001
ICHTHUS

Designer:	Helen MacDonald
Type:	Weight — Spherical
Edition:	1998
Status:	Active
Original Issue Price:	U.S. $98.00

Name	*U.S. $*	*Can. $*	*U.K. £*
Ichthus	98.00	150.00	65.00

LADS PORCELAIN AND GLASS
TORONTO, CANADA

LP-001
KING TUTENKHAMUN

Designer:	Jennie Robertson
Type:	Weight — Spherical, engraved
Edition:	1979 in a limited edition of 250
Status:	Closed at No. 120
Original Issue Price:	Can. $150.00

Name	*U.S. $*	*Can. $*	*U.K. £*
King Tutenkhamun	275.00	475.00	175.00

L. H. SELMAN LTD.
SANTA CRUZ, U.S.

LS-001
GARDEN POOL and DRAGONFLY

Designer: Colin Terris
Type: Weight — Spherical
Edition: 1995 in a limited edition of 50
Status: Fully subscribed
Original Issue Price: U.S. $450.00

Name	*U.S. $*	*Can. $*	*U.K. £*
Garden Pool and Dragonfly	550.00	850.00	375.00

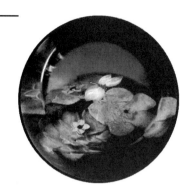

LS-002
HONEY BEE

Designer: Colin Terris
Type: Weight — Spherical
Edition: 1996 in a limited edition of 25
Status: Fully subscribed
Original Issue Price: U.S. $260.00

Name	*U.S. $*	*Can. $*	*U.K. £*
Honey Bee	350.00	525.00	250.00

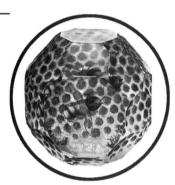

LS-003
FLYING PEGASUS

Designer: Colin Terris
Type: Weight — Spherical
Edition: 1997 in a limited edition of 500
Status: Active
Original Issue Price: U.S. $115.00

Name	*U.S. $*	*Can. $*	*U.K. £*
Flying Pegasus	115.00	175.00	75.00

LS-004
SILVER UNICORN

Designer:	Colin Terris
Type:	Weight — Spherical
Edition:	1997 in a limited edition of 500
Status:	Active
Original Issue Price:	U.S. $115.00

Name	U.S. $	Can. $	U.K. £
Silver Unicorn	115.00	175.00	75.00

LS-005
UNICORN DANCE

Designer:	Colin Terris and William Manson
Type:	Weight — Spherical
Edition:	1997 in a limited edition of 150
Status:	Active
Original Issue Price:	U.S. $315.00

Name	U.S. $	Can. $	U.K. £
Unicorn Dance	315.00	475.00	200.00

LS-006
SANTA'S TREE

Designer:	William Manson
Type:	Weight — Spherical
Edition:	1997 in a limited edition of 150
Status:	Active
Original Issue Price:	U.S. $315.00

Name	U.S. $	Can. $	U.K. £
Santa's Tree	315.00	475.00	200.00

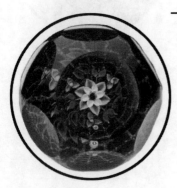

LS-007
SPIDER'S WEB

Designer:	Colin Terris and Allan Scott
Type:	Weight — Spherical
Edition:	1998 in a limited edition of 50
Status:	Active
Original Issue Price:	U.S. $465.00

Name	U.S. $	Can. $	U.K. £
Spider's Web	465.00	700.00	300.00

LS-008
BURGUNDY BOUQUET

Designer:	Colin Terris and Allan Scott
Type:	Weight — Spherical
Edition:	1998 in a limited edition of 50
Status:	Active
Original Issue Price:	U.S. $465.00

Name	U.S. $	Can. $	U.K. £
Burgundy Bouquet	465.00	700.00	300.00

LS-009
TEARDROP PETUNIA

Designer:	Colin Terris
Type:	Weight — Teardrop
Edition:	1998 in a limited edition of 250
Status:	Active
Original Issue Price:	U.S. $85.00

Name	U.S. $	Can. $	U.K. £
Teardrop Petunia	85.00	125.00	60.00

LS-010
MODESTY

Designer:	Helen MacDonald
Type:	Weight — Spherical
Edition:	1999 in a limited edition of 50
Status:	Active
Original Issue Price:	U.S. $395.00

Name	U.S. $	Can. $	U.K. £
Modesty	395.00	575.00	250.00

LS-011
ONE TRUE LOVE

Designer:	Helen MacDonald
Type:	Weight — Spherical
Edition:	1999 in a limited edition of 50
Status:	Active
Original Issue Price:	U.S. $395.00

Name	U.S. $	Can. $	U.K. £
One True Love	395.00	575.00	250.00

PETER DYER
SOUTHSEA, U.K.

PD-001
SILVER JUBILEE FLEET REVIEW

Designer:	Peter Dyer and Colin Terris
Type:	Weight — Spherical
Edition:	1977 in a limited edition of 100
Status:	Fully subscribed
Series:	HM Queen Elizabeth II Silver Jubilee Collection
Original Issue Price:	£75.00

Name	U.S. $	Can. $	U.K. £
Silver Jubilee Fleet Review	325.00	475.00	200.00

Note: This paperweight was issued to commemorate the 25th anniversary of the coronation of Queen Elizabeth II.

Photograph not available at press time

PD-002
MARY ROSE

Designer:	Helen MacDonald
Type:	Weight — Spherical, engraved
Edition:	1982 in a limited edition of 100
Status:	Fully subscribed
Original Issue Price:	£75.00

Name	U.S. $	Can. $	U.K. £
Mary Rose	200.00	300.00	125.00

PETER JONES CHINA
WAKEFIELD, U.K.

PJ-001
ARK ROYAL

Designer: Caithness Engraving Studios
Type: Weight — Spherical, engraved
Edition: 1980 in a limited edition of 500
Status: Closed at No. 263
Original Issue Price: £35.00

Name	U.S. $	Can. $	U.K. £
Ark Royal	165.00	225.00	100.00

PJ-002
YEAR OF THE VIKING

Designer: Gordon Hendry
Type: Weight — Spherical, engraved
Edition: 1980 in a limited edition of 500
Status: Closed at No. 325
Original Issue Price: £39.95

Name	U.S. $	Can. $	U.K. £
Year of the Viking	165.00	225.00	100.00

PJ-003
ROYAL CYPHER

Designer: Caithness Engraving Studios
Type: Weight — Spherical, engraved
Edition: 1981 in a limited edition of 500
Status: Closed at No. 200
Series: Royal Wedding Collection
Original Issue Price: £50.00

Name	U.S. $	Can. $	U.K. £
Royal Cypher	165.00	225.00	100.00

Note: This paperweight was issued to commemorate the wedding of Prince Charles and Lady Diana Spencer.

PJ-004
BATTLE OF BRITAIN

Designer:	Colin Terris
Type:	Weight — Spherical
Edition:	1990 in a limited edition of 2,000
Status:	Closed
Original Issue Price:	£29.50

Name	U.S. $	Can. $	U.K. £
Battle of Britain	50.00	70.00	30.00

Note: This paperweight was commissioned to commemorate the 50th anniversary of the Battle of Britain.

PJ-005
40TH ANNIVERSARY OF QEII ACCESSION

Designer:	Colin Terris
Type:	Weight — Spherical, engraved
Edition:	1992 in a limited edition of 2,000
Status:	Closed
Original Issue Price:	£35.00

Name	U.S. $	Can. $	U.K. £
40th Anniversary of QEII Accession	70.00	95.00	40.00

PJ-006
CHRISTOPHER COLUMBUS — 500TH ANNIVERSARY

Designer:	Colin Terris
Type:	Weight — Spherical
Edition:	1992 in a limited edition of 500
Status:	Closed
Original Issue Price:	£49.95

Name	U.S. $	Can. $	U.K. £
Christopher Columbus — 500th Anniversary	80.00	110.00	50.00

Note: This paperweight was commissioned to commemorate the 500th anniversary of Christopher Columbus's voyage of discovery.

PJ-007
RED ARROWS

Designer:	Alastair MacIntosh
Type:	Weight — Spherical
Edition:	1992 in a limited edition of 2,000
Status:	Active
Original Issue Price:	£39.95

Name	U.S. $	Can. $	U.K. £
Red Arrows	70.00	95.00	40.00

PJ-008
75TH ANNIVERSARY OF ROYAL AIR FORCE

Designer: Colin Terris
Type: Weight — Spherical
Edition: 1993 in a limited edition of 1,000
Status: Closed
Original Issue Price: £45.00

Name	U.S. $	Can. $	U.K. £
75th Anniversary of Royal Air Force	75.00	100.00	45.00

PJ-009
40TH ANNIVERSARY QEII CORONATION — COBALT BASE

Designer: Colin Terris
Type: Weight — Spherical, engraved
Edition: 1993 in a limited edition of 250
Status: Closed
Original Issue Price: £95.00

Name	U.S. $	Can. $	U.K. £
40th Anniversary, Cobalt Base	250.00	350.00	150.00

PJ-010
40TH ANNIVERSARY QEII CORONATION — RUBY BASE

Designer: Colin Terris
Type: Weight — Spherical, engraved
Edition: 1993 in a limited edition of 2,000
Status: Closed
Original Issue Price: £39.95

Name	U.S. $	Can. $	U.K. £
40th Anniversary, Ruby Base	70.00	95.00	40.00

PJ-011
40TH ANNIVERSARY QEII CORONATION — RUBY OVERLAY

Designer: Colin Terris
Type: Weight — Spherical
Edition: 1993 in a limited edition of 40
Status: Closed
Original Issue Price: £295.00

Name	U.S. $	Can. $	U.K. £
40th Anniversary, Ruby Overlay	475.00	675.00	300.00

PJ-012
THE CHANNEL TUNNEL

Designer: Margot Thomson
Type: Weight — Spherical
Edition: 1994 in a limited edition of 500
Status: Active
Original Issue Price: £69.95

Name	U.S. $	Can. $	U.K. £
The Channel Tunnel	100.00	150.00	70.00

Note: This paperweight was commissioned to commemorate the opening of the Channel Tunnel on May 6, 1994.

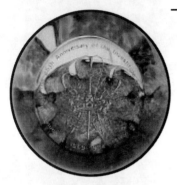

PJ-013
25TH ANNIVERSARY OF INVESTITURE OF PRINCE OF WALES

Designer: Colin Terris
Type: Weight — Spherical
Edition: 1994 in a limited edition of 500
Status: Closed
Original Issue Price: £39.95

Name	U.S. $	Can. $	U.K. £
25th Anniversary of Investiture of Prince of Wales	70.00	95.00	40.00

PJ-014
25TH ANNIVERSARY OF INVESTITURE OF PRINCE OF WALES — PRESTIGE EDITION

Designer: Colin Terris
Type: Weight — Spherical
Edition: 1994 in a limited edition of 100
Status: Closed
Original Issue Price: £195.00

Name	U.S. $	Can. $	U.K. £
25th Anniversary of Investiture of Prince of Wales — Prestige Edition	325.00	450.00	200.00

PJ-015
MOON LANDING

Designer: Colin Terris
Type: Weight — Spherical
Edition: 1994 in a limited edition of 250
Status: Closed
Original Issue Price: £75.00

Name	U.S. $	Can. $	U.K. £
Moon Landing	115.00	165.00	75.00

Note: This paperweight was commissioned to commemorate the 25th anniversary of humankind's first landing on the moon.

PJ-016
D-DAY LANDINGS

Designer: Alastair MacIntosh
Type: Weight — Spherical
Edition: 1994 in a limited edition of 750
Status: Closed
Original Issue Price: £59.95

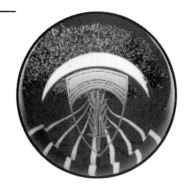

Name	U.S. $	Can. $	U.K. £
D-Day Landings	90.00	125.00	60.00

Note: This paperweight was commissioned to commemorate the 50th anniversary of D-Day.

PJ-017
CONCORDE

Designer: Colin Terris
Type: Weight — Spherical
Edition: 1994 in a limited edition of 250
Status: Closed
Original Issue Price: £39.95

Name	U.S. $	Can. $	U.K. £
Concorde	70.00	95.00	40.00

Note: This paperweight was commissioned to commemorate the 25th anniversary of the Concorde's first flight.

PJ-018
QEII VISIT TO RUSSIA

Designer: Colin Terris
Type: Weight — Spherical
Edition: 1994 in a limited edition of 250
Status: Closed
Original Issue Price: £49.95

Name	U.S. $	Can. $	U.K. £
QEII Visit to Russia	80.00	110.00	50.00

PJ-019
HMQM FAVOURITE FLOWERS

Designer: Colin Terris
Type: Weight — Spherical
Edition: 1995 in a limited edition of 95
Status: Closed
Original Issue Price: £195.00

Name	U.S. $	Can. $	U.K. £
HMQM Favourite Flowers	325.00	450.00	200.00

Note: This paperweight was commissioned to commemorate the Queen Mother's 95th birthday.

PJ-020
ELIZABETH OF GLAMIS PERFUME BOTTLE

Designer: Colin Terris
Type: Perfume bottle
Edition: 1995 in a limited edition of 95
Status: Closed
Original Issue Price: £245.00

Name	U.S. $	Can. $	U.K. £
Elizabeth of Glamis Perfume Bottle	400.00	550.00	250.00

Note: This perfume bottle was commissioned to commemorate the Queen Mother's 95th birthday.

PJ-021
HMQM COAT OF ARMS

Designer: Colin Terris
Type: Weight — Spherical, engraved
Edition: 1995 in a limited edition of 500
Status: Closed
Original Issue Price: £45.00

Name	U.S. $	Can. $	U.K. £
HMQM Coat of Arms	75.00	100.00	45.00

Note: This paperweight was commissioned to commemorate the Queen Mother's 95th birthday.

PJ-022
VICTORY

Designer: Colin Terris
Type: Weight — Spherical
Cane: E (Europe)
Edition: 1995 in a limited edition of 100
Status: Closed
Original Issue Price: £175.00

Name	U.S. $	Can. $	U.K. £
Victory	275.00	400.00	175.00

Note: This paperweight was issued to commemorate the 50th anniversary of VE Day (May 8, 1945).

PJ-023
WORLD PEACE

Designer: Colin Terris
Type: Weight — Spherical
Edition: 1995 in a limited edition of 250
Status: Closed
Original Issue Price: £95.00

Name	U.S. $	Can. $	U.K. £
World Peace	160.00	215.00	95.00

Note: This paperweight was issued to commemorate the 50th anniversary of VJ Day (August 15, 1945).

PJ-024
VICTORY IN JAPAN

Designer: Colin Terris
Type: Weight — Spherical
Cane: J (Japan)
Edition: 1995 in a limited edition of 100
Status: Closed
Original Issue Price: £175.00

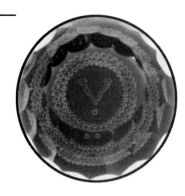

Name	U.S. $	Can. $	U.K. £
Victory in Japan	275.00	400.00	175.00

Note: This paperweight was issued to commemorate the 50th anniversary of the victory in Japan.

PJ-025
PEACE IN EUROPE

Designer: Colin Terris
Type: Weight — Spherical, engraved
Edition: 1995 in a limited edition of 500
Status: Closed
Original Issue Price: £49.95

Name	U.S. $	Can. $	U.K. £
Peace in Europe	80.00	110.00	50.00

Note: This paperweight was commissioned to commemorate the 50th anniversary of VE Day (May 8, 1945).

PJ-026
QUEEN ELIZABETH ROSE

Designer: Colin Terris
Type: Weight — Spherical
Edition: 1996 in a limited edition of 100
Status: Closed
Original Issue Price: £225.00

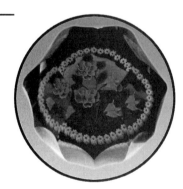

Name	U.S. $	Can. $	U.K. £
Queen Elizabeth Rose	400.00	550.00	250.00

Note: PJ-026 and 027 were issued to commemorate the 70th birthday of Queen Elizabeth II.

PJ-027
QUEEN ELIZABETH ROSE PERFUME BOTTLE

Designer: Colin Terris
Type: Perfume bottle
Edition: 1996 in a limited edition of 70
Status: Closed
Original Issue Price: £245.00

Name	U.S. $	Can. $	U.K. £
Queen Elizabeth Rose Perfume Bottle	400.00	550.00	250.00

PJ-028
EDINBURGH CASTLE

Designer: Colin Terris
Type: Weight — Spherical
Edition: 1996 in a limited edition of 250
Status: Active
Original Issue Price: £45.00

Name	U.S. $	Can. $	U.K. £
Edinburgh Castle	80.00	110.00	50.00

Note: PJ-028 and 029 were commissioned to celebrate the 75th birthday of the Duke of Edinburgh.

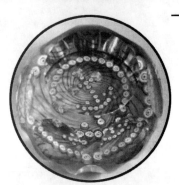

PJ-029
ANCHOR

Designer: Colin Terris
Type: Weight — Spherical
Edition: 1996 in a limited edition of 75
Status: Active
Original Issue Price: £150.00

Name	U.S. $	Can. $	U.K. £
Anchor	250.00	350.00	150.00

PJ-030
QUEEN VICTORIA DIAMOND JUBILEE CENTENARY

Designer: Colin Terris
Type: Weight — Spherical
Edition: 1997 in a limited edition of 250
Status: Active
Original Issue Price: £49.95

Name	U.S. $	Can. $	U.K. £
Queen Victoria Diamond Jubilee Centenary	80.00	110.00	50.00

PJ-031
FAREWELL BRITANNIA

Designer: Colin Terris
Type: Weight — Spherical
Edition: 1997 in a limited edition of 350
Status: Active
Original Issue Price: £49.95

Name	U.S. $	Can. $	U.K. £
Farewell Britannia	80.00	110.00	50.00

Note: This paperweight was issued to commemorate the decommissioning of the Royal Yacht *Britannia* on December 11, 1997.

PJ-032
END OF AN ERA

Designer:	Colin Terris		
Type:	Weight — Spherical		
Edition:	1997 in a limited edition of 500		
Status:	Active		
Original Issue Price:	£49.95		

Name	U.S. $	Can. $	U.K. £
End of an Era	80.00	110.00	50.00

Note: This paperweight was issued to commemorate the handover of Hong Kong to China on June 30, 1997.

PJ-033
TUTANKHAMUN

Designer:	Colin Terris		
Type:	Weight — Spherical		
Edition:	1997 in a limited edition of 250		
Status:	Active		
Original Issue Price:	£49.95		

Name	U.S. $	Can. $	U.K. £
Tutankhamun	80.00	110.00	50.00

Note: This paperweight was commissioned to commemorate the 75th anniversary of the discovery of King Tutankhamun's tomb.

PJ-034
ROYAL WEDDING ORCHID BOUQUET

Designer:	Allan Scott		
Type:	Weight — Spherical		
Edition:	1997 in a limited edition of 50		
Status:	Closed		
Original Issue Price:	£225.00		

Name	U.S. $	Can. $	U.K. £
Royal Wedding Orchid Bouquet	350.00	500.00	225.00

Note: PJ-034, 035 and 036 were commissioned to celebrate the golden wedding anniversary of Queen Elizabeth II and Prince Philip.

PJ-035
ROYAL WEDDING ORCHID BOUQUET PERFUME BOTTLE

Designer:	Allan Scott		
Type:	Perfume bottle		
Edition:	1997 in a limited edition of 50		
Status:	Closed		
Original Issue Price:	£250.00		

Name	U.S. $	Can. $	U.K. £
Royal Wedding Orchid Bouquet Perfume Bottle	400.00	550.00	250.00

PJ-036
WESTMINSTER ABBEY

Designer: Colin Terris
Type: Weight — Spherical, engraved
Edition: 1997 in a limited edition of 250
Status: Closed
Original Issue Price: £45.00

Name	U.S. $	Can. $	U.K. £
Westminster Abbey	75.00	100.00	45.00

PJ-037A
PINK ORCHID

Designer: William Manson
Type: Weight — Spherical
Edition: 1997 in a limited edition of 150
Status: Closed
Series: Tropical Orchids
Original Issue Price: £195.00/set

Name	U.S. $	Can. $	U.K. £
Pink Orchid	165.00	225.00	100.00

Note: PJ-037A and B were issued as a set.

PJ-037B
YELLOW ORCHID

Designer: William Manson
Type: Weight — Spherical
Edition: 1997 in a limited edition of 150
Status: Closed
Series: Tropical Orchids
Original Issue Price: £195.00/set

Name	U.S. $	Can. $	U.K. £
Yellow Orchid	165.00	225.00	100.00

PJ-038
HMQM 75TH TRIBUTE

Designer: Allan Scott
Type: Weight — Spherical
Edition: 1998 in a limited edition of 75
Status: Active
Original Issue Price: £195.00

Name	U.S. $	Can. $	U.K. £
HMQM 75th Tribute	300.00	425.00	195.00

Note: PJ-038, 039 and 040 were commissioned to commemorate the Queen Mother's 75 years of service to the United Kingdom.

PJ-039
HMQM 75TH TRIBUTE PERFUME BOTTLE

Designer: Colin Terris
Type: Perfume bottle
Edition: 1998 in a limited edition of 50
Status: Active
Original Issue Price: £220.00

Name	U.S. $	Can. $	U.K. £
HMQM 75th Tribute Perfume Bottle	.00	.00	220.00

PJ-040
HMQM 75TH TRIBUTE — GLAMIS ROSE

Designer: Colin Terris
Type: Weight — Spherical
Edition: 1998 in a limited edition of 250
Status: Active
Original Issue Price: £79.95

Name	U.S. $	Can. $	U.K. £
HMQM 75th Tribute — Glamis Rose	.00	.00	.00

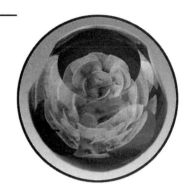

PJ-041
HRH PRINCE OF WALES 50TH BIRTHDAY — FIRST EDITION

Designer: Allan Scott
Type: Weight — Spherical
Edition: 1998 in a limited edition of 50
Status: Closed
Original Issue Price: £150.00

Name	U.S. $	Can. $	U.K. £
50th Birthday — First Edition	250.00	350.00	150.00

PJ-042
HRH PRINCE OF WALES 50TH BIRTHDAY — SECOND EDITION

Designer: Allan Scott
Type: Weight — Spherical
Edition: 1998 in a limited edition of 50
Status: Active
Original Issue Price: £150.00

Name	U.S. $	Can. $	U.K. £
50th Birthday — Second Edition	250.00	350.00	150.00

PJ-043
ROYAL WEDDING PRESTIGE PERFUME BOTTLE

Designer: Allan Scott
Type: Perfume bottle
Canes: E and S (Edward and Sophie)
Edition: 1999 in a limited edition of 50
Status: Active
Original Issue Price: £250.00

Name	U.S. $	Can. $	U.K. £
Royal Wedding Prestige Perfume Bottle	400.00	550.00	250.00

Note: PJ-043, 044 and 045 were commissioned to celebrate the wedding of Prince Edward and Sophie Rhys-Jones.

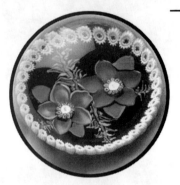

PJ-044
ROYAL WEDDING FLORAL BOUQUET

Designer: Melanie Stuart
Type: Weight — Spherical
Canes: E and S (Edward and Sophie)
Edition: 1999 in a limited edition of 100
Status: Active
Original Issue Price: £195.00

Name	U.S. $	Can. $	U.K. £
Royal Wedding Floral Bouquet	300.00	425.00	195.00

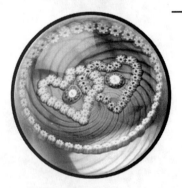

PJ-045
ROYAL WEDDING LUCKENBOOTH

Designer: Colin Terris
Type: Weight — Spherical
Canes: E and S (Edward and Sophie)
Edition: 1999 in a limited edition of 200
Status: Active
Original Issue Price: £75.00

Name	U.S. $	Can. $	U.K. £
Royal Wedding Luckenbooth	115.00	165.00	75.00

PJ-046
MILLENNIUM FLAME

Designer: Colin Terris
Type: Weight — Domed, dichroic
Edition: 1999 in a limited edition of 100
Status: Active
Original Issue Price: £140.00

Name	U.S. $	Can. $	U.K. £
Millennium Flame	200.00	290.00	140.00

PJ-047
MILLENNIUM CELEBRATION

Designer: Colin Terris
Type: Weight — Spherical
Edition: 1999 in a limited edition of 250
Status: Active
Original Issue Price: £85.00

Name	U.S. $	Can. $	U.K. £
Millennium Celebration	135.00	195.00	85.00

PJ-048
BIG BEN MILLENNIUM

Designer: Colin Terris
Type: Weight — Domed, prestige
Edition: 1999 in a limited edition of 200
Status: Active
Original Issue Price: £120.00

Name	U.S. $	Can. $	U.K. £
Big Ben Millennium	190.00	275.00	120.00

PJ-049
TOTAL ECLIPSE

Designer: Colin Terris
Type: Weight — Spherical
Edition: Limited edition of 500
Status: Active
Original Issue Price: £45.00

Name	U.S. $	Can. $	U.K. £
Total Eclipse	—	—	45.00

PJ-050
TOTAL ECLIPSE, PRESTIGE

Designer: Colin Terris
Type: Weight — Spherical
Edition: Limited edition of 200
Status: Active
Original Issue Price: £95.00

Name	U.S. $	Can. $	U.K. £
Total Eclipse, Prestige	—	—	95.00

PJ-051
30TH ANNIVERSARY CONCORDE

Designer:	Colin Terris	
Type:	Weight — Spherical	
Edition:	Limited edition of 500	
Status:	Active	
Original Issue Price:	£45.00	

Name	U.S. $	Can. $	U.K. £
30th Anniversary Concorde	—	—	45.00

PJ-052
30TH ANNIVERSARY CONCORDE, PRESTIGE

Designer:	Colin Terris	
Type:	Weight — Spherical	
Edition:	Linited edition of 100	
Status:	Active	
Original Issue Price:	£95.00	

Name	U.S. $	Can. $	U.K. £
30th Anniversary Concorde, Prestige	—	—	95.00

PJ-053
30TH ANNIVERSARY OF MOON LANDING

Designer:	Colin Terris	
Type:	Weight — Spherical	
Edition:	Limited edition of 300	
Status:	Active	
Original Issue Price:	£45.00	

Name	U.S. $	Can. $	U.K. £
30th Anniversary Of Moon Landing	—	—	45.00

PJ-054
30TH ANNIVERSARY OF MOON LANDING, PRESTIGE

Designer:	Colin Terris	
Type:	Weight — Spherical	
Edition:	Limited edition of 100	
Status:	Active	
Original Issue Price:	£125.00	

Name	U.S. $	Can. $	U.K. £
30th Anniversary of Moon Landing, Prestige	—	—	125.00

PJ-055
30TH ANNIVERSARY OF MOON LANDING, MAGNUM

Designer: Colin Terris
Type: Weight — Spherical
Edition: Limited edition of 30
Status: Active
Original Issue Price: £250.00

Name	U.S. $	Can. $	U.K. £
30th Anniversary of Moon Landing, Magnum	—	—	250.00

ROYAL SOCIETY FOR THE PROTECTION OF BIRDS
SANDY, U.K.

RS-001
PEREGRINE FALCON

Designer: Caithness Engraving Studios
Type: Weight — Spherical, engraved
Edition: 1978 in a limited edition of 200
Status: Fully subscribed
Original Issue Price: £66.00

Name	U.S. $	Can. $	U.K. £
Peregrine Falcon	250.00	350.00	150.00

RS-002
PUFFIN

Designer: Helen MacDonald
Type: Weight — Spherical, engraved
Edition: 1979 in a limited edition of 250
Status: Closed at No. 195
Original Issue Price: £75.00

Name	U.S. $	Can. $	U.K. £
Puffin	165.00	225.00	100.00

SCOTSMAN NEWSPAPERS
EDINBURGH, U.K.

SN-001
NORTH SEA

Designer: Colin Terris
Type: Weight — Spherical
Edition: 1976 in a limited edition of 1,000
Status: Fully subscribed
Original Issue Price: £20.00

Name	U.S. $	Can. $	U.K. £
North Sea	250.00	350.00	150.00

SMITHSONIAN INSTITUTION
WASHINGTON, D.C., U.S.

SI-001
HALLEY'S COMET

Designer: Colin Terris
Type: Weight — Spherical
Edition: 1985 in a limited edition of 500
Status: Fully subscribed
Original Issue Price: U.S. $90.00

Name	U.S. $	Can. $	U.K. £
Halley's Comet	200.00	300.00	125.00

Note: This paperweight was issued to commemorate the appearance of the comet.

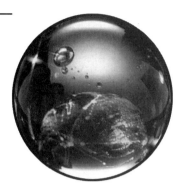

TOUCH OF CLASS
JACKSON, U.S.

TC-001
GRAND TETONS SUMMER

Designer: Alastair MacIntosh
Type: Weight — Domed
Edition: 1997 in a limited edition of 250
Status: Active
Original Issue Price: U.S. $275.00

Name	U.S. $	Can. $	U.K. £
Grand Tetons Summer	275.00	400.00	175.00

TC-002
GRAND TETONS WINTER

Designer: Alastair MacIntosh
Type: Weight — Domed
Edition: 1997 in a limited edition of 250
Status: Active
Original Issue Price: U.S. $275.00

Name	U.S. $	Can. $	U.K. £
Grand Tetons Winter	275.00	400.00	175.00

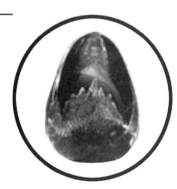

U.S. EXCLUSIVE WEIGHTS

US-001
MOUNT RUSHMORE

Designer:	Colin Terris
Type:	Weight — Spherical
Edition:	1987 in a limited edition of 500
Status:	Fully subscribed
Original Issue Price:	U.S. $250.00

Name	U.S. $	Can. $	U.K. £
Mount Rushmore	350.00	500.00	225.00

Note: Originally to be sold in the Mount Rushmore gift shop, this paperweight was commissioned to celebrate the 50th anniversary of the Mount Rushmore Memorial.

US-002
BLUE ANGELS

Designer:	Alastair MacIntosh
Type:	Weight — Teardrop
Edition:	1990 in a limited edition of 750
Status:	Closed
Original Issue Price:	U.S. $190.00

Name	U.S. $	Can. $	U.K. £
Blue Angels	225.00	325.00	150.00

US-003
DESERT STORM

Designer:	Colin Terris
Type:	Weight — Spherical
Edition:	1991 in a limited edition of 500
Status:	Closed
Original Issue Price:	U.S. $235.00

Name	U.S. $	Can. $	U.K. £
Desert Storm	300.00	450.00	200.00

US-004
MARIONETTE

Designer:	Colin Terris and William Manson		
Type:	Weight — Spherical		
Edition:	1996 in a limited edition of 50		
Status:	Closed		
Original Issue Price:	U.S. $850.00		

Name	U.S. $	Can. $	U.K. £
Marionette	850.00	1,250.00	550.00

US-005
MISTLETOE

Designer:	Helen MacDonald		
Type:	Weight — Teardrop		
Edition:	1996 in a limited edition of 350		
Status:	Active		
Original Issue Price:	U.S. $350.00		

Name	U.S. $	Can. $	U.K. £
Mistletoe	350.00	500.00	225.00

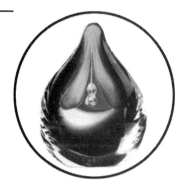

US-006
PIT STOP

Designer:	William Manson		
Type:	Weight — Spherical		
Edition:	1996 in a limited edition of 50		
Status:	Closed		
Original Issue Price:	U.S. $850.00		

Name	U.S. $	Can. $	U.K. £
Pit Stop	850.00	1,250.00	550.00

US-007
PRIMA DONNA

Designer:	Philip Chaplain		
Type:	Weight — Spherical		
Edition:	1997 in a limited edition of 250		
Status:	Active		
Original Issue Price:	U.S. $250.00		

Name	U.S. $	Can. $	U.K. £
Prima Donna	250.00	375.00	175.00

US-008
SHOAL MATES

Designer:	Charlotte Judd
Type:	Weight — Spherical
Edition:	1997
Status:	Active
Original Issue Price:	U.S. $100.00

Name	U.S. $	Can. $	U.K. £
Shoal Mates	100.00	150.00	75.00

US-009
STARS and STRIPES

Designer:	Helen MacDonald
Type:	Weight — Spherical
Edition:	1997
Status:	Active
Original Issue Price:	U.S. $100.00

Name	U.S. $	Can. $	U.K. £
Stars and Stripes	100.00	150.00	75.00

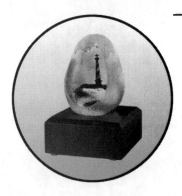

US-010
CAPE HATTERAS

Designer:	Philip Chaplain
Type:	Weight — Domed
Edition:	1998 in a limited edition of 200
Status:	Active
Original Issue Price:	U.S. $350.00

Name	U.S. $	Can. $	U.K. £
Cape Hatteras	350.00	500.00	225.00

YEAR OF THE CHILD NATIONAL CHARITY
SCOTTISH HEADQUARTERS
GLASGOW, U.K.

YC-001
YEAR OF THE CHILD

Designer:	Caithness Engraving Studios
Type:	Weight — Spherical, engraved
Edition:	1980 in a limited edition of 250
Status:	Closed at No. 80
Original Issue Price:	£30.00

Name	U.S. $	Can. $	U.K. £
Year of the Child	165.00	225.00	100.00

INDEX TO CAITHNESS PAPERWEIGHTS

C

H

I

J

K

L

M

N

Q

R

T

U

V

524

W

Y

Z